LONDON'S SECRET TUBES

LONDON'S SECRET TUBES

London's wartime citadels, subways and shelters uncovered

By Andrew Emmerson, Tony Beard
and members of Subterranea Britannica

Capital Transport

Dedicated to Jackie Thomas, whose keen and active encouragement got this book moving.

Updates

to this book and additional information will be posted on the Web at
www.subbrit.org.uk/LST

Other books by the authors

Tony Beard:
By Tube Beyond Edgware
Andrew Emmerson:
Electronic Classics
Old Telephones
Old Television
The Underground Pioneers

First published 2004
ISBN 1854 14 283 6
Published by Capital Transport Publishing,
P.O. Box 250, Harrow, Middlesex
www.capitaltransport.com
Printed by CS Graphics, Singapore

Contents

One of the enduring myths of London's secret subterranea is that cable tunnels provided handy short-cuts for civil servants walking between government buildings (Chapter 20). Security considerations alone would preclude this notion, not to mention the personal safety hazards from cable stanchions and other apparatus, bad air and getting lost! This view of a 7ft tunnel was taken under Newgate Street, looking towards the Faraday Citadel exchange near St Paul's cathedral.

[British Telecom]

Title page: If you want to get ahead, get a hat. Not a single head is uncovered in this shot of American aircraft production leaders ending a visit to the aircraft components factory at Ilford in October 1942. The escalator is most likely to be at the uncompleted tube station at Wanstead.

[Ministry of Aircraft Production press photo from the Mervyn Hall collection]

Preface

EVERYONE knows London's tubes. Travellers and non-users alike are familiar with the railway lines that burrow beneath the Capital, whilst some even know about the Post Office's own railway tube system, now mothballed, that used to shuttle mailbags between stations and sorting offices.

But there is another network of similar tunnels that far fewer have heard of. We call them London's secret tubes in this book, which for the first time describes all of these shadowy constructions, explaining their origins, construction and present status.

Built underground for strategic purposes between the 1930s and 1960s, these remarkable features include government citadels, public shelters and strategic communications facilities together with an extensive system of tunnels at deep level. Together they form an underground world that's entirely unknown to the public at large. This of course is no accident, considering the once highly secret nature of many of these projects.

Previous coverage has been largely speculative and written without complete access to official sources only recently declassified. Some articles were intended to promote particular political viewpoints. This new book takes a measured approach and offers only facts – and many more facts than have been published up to now. Without hyperbole or arrogance, it is the most comprehensive study on this subject to date.

This book cannot claim to be the last word, however. Some of the relevant source material is still secret, with files at the Public Record Office that will remain 'closed' (unavailable for examination) for two decades or more. And reflecting the amount of information available, some chapters are inevitably longer than others, leaving scope for further research. We shall be very pleased to receive material for inclusion in a future edition and on the book's update pages on the Internet.

The prime focus of this book is historical and concerns underground structures of the 20th century in the Greater London area that were built or used for maintaining public safety and the rule of central government, in war or the uneasy peace that followed war. Information readily available elsewhere has not been recycled here, so this book does not deal with civilian sheltering in pre-existing tube stations since another book by this publisher – *The Shelter of the Tubes* by John Gregg – is devoted to the subject. Nor does it cover Cold War bunkers, such as the one at Kelvedon Hatch, which can be found in another book, *Cold War Secret Nuclear Bunkers*, published by Leo Cooper.

All sources used in this book are in the public domain and no use whatsoever has been made of any secret or confidential information obtained from privileged sources. For obvious reasons too, no discussion is made of current security arrangements. Some previous books and articles have suffered from a preoccupation with conspiracy theories, making great play of supposed anomalies between official statements and perceived reality. As readers will discover, these 'inconsistencies' turn out to be supposition or misinterpretation.

Finally, no book on this subject can fail to acknowledge the work of previous researchers, notably Duncan Campbell, Nigel Pennick and the pioneer Peter Laurie, who with his book *Beneath The City Streets* set in motion a zeal for delving deep to expose subterranean secrets. We offer them each our profound respect.

Lastly, we cannot overemphasise the extent to which this book has been a major team effort, not just the work of a two-man-band. So our sincere gratitude goes out to all those who provided assistance, in particular the staff of the Science Museum, Redbridge Libraries, BAe Systems and of the British Telecom and London Transport archives together with the following individuals: the late Peter Bancroft, Ron Barnard, Eileen Bassett, John Batts, Roger Beckwith, Michael Bragg, Charles Brookson, Leonard Brown, Bob Burrell, Gordon Bussey, Nick Catford, Bob Clary, George Coney, Desmond Croome, Bob Darvill, Ian Dowling, Arthur Dungate, Dr James Fox, Steve Fox, Steve Graham, Norman Gunby, David Gunning, Mervyn Hall, Albany Harvey, Duncan Hawkins, David Hay, Roy Hayward, Samantha Heywood, Mike Horne, Alan A. Jackson, Jonathan James, Bob Jenner, David Jessop, Neil Johannessen, Richard Lamont, Geoff Leonard, John Liffen, Chris Lonsbrough, Nick McCamley, Dan McKenzie, Marc Maitland, Chris Mees, Roger Morgan, David Occomore, Nick Pedley, B.N. Reckitt, Peter Shorer, Pendar Sillwood, L.G. Smith, Roy Smith, Steve Thomason, Tony Thorndike, Adam Turner, Mike Tyrrell, Mary Veale, Keith Ward, Jim Whiting, Hywel Williams, Philip Wood, Trevor Wright and others (who know who they are!). Without their valuable contributions this book would have been a far poorer affair. Thanks are also due to the publishers and authors who allowed excerpts from their works to enhance this book and to the organisations that allowed copyright photographs to be reproduced.

The authors

Introduction

SOME people are able to navigate London's Underground railway system guided by no more than a tube map, whilst others need further help. The same applies to this book; seasoned delvers will dive straight in to find their chosen subjects but others will look for more support. This brief introduction maps out what's in this book, putting it into context with the political, social and economic events that led to the constructions described. Inevitably the book combines many elements of political, transport, civil engineering and communications history that do not fit tidily into single compartments. Imposing a strict chronological sequence on the events described

would not create meaningful history, only hopeless confusion. For this reason we have adopted a thematic approach, treating subjects as separate threads, although the story will make most sense if read in chapter order.

Historically the book spans the period from 1915 to around 1980, through two world wars and the Cold War period, embracing also the periods of inter-war depression and post-war austerity. During this extended period many bodies, government departments and ministries changed names and function, even if the underlying mechanism of government has changed relatively little. All the same, two bodies mentioned frequently in these

pages are no longer in existence. These are the Civil Defence organisation and the Royal Observer Corps, both of which performed vital functions during World War II and the Cold War period. As the underlying theme of this book concerns civil protection and both of these bodies are now largely forgotten, a word of explanation may be helpful to some readers.

The notion of civil defence came about in the late 1930s. Although war was considered virtually inevitable from 1938 onwards, its likely effect on the nation was by no means clear. The government was not ready to take any chances and its preparations for war included the creation of an integrated civil defence service (called Air Raid Precautions until 1941). It was feared that bombing would lead to immense casualties, overwhelming the country's capacity to continue. To maintain local functioning an official Civil Defence organisation was set up, with the country divided into a number of regions whose commissioners would take control if their region became isolated from central government in London by invasion or heavy bombing. More generally the commissioners acted as intermediary between the emergency services and other military and civilian organisations. Recognition that the Home Office, the responsible department, would need considerable strengthening also resulted in the creation of the Ministry of Home Security, to be responsible for all civil defence matters (fire and police services remained under the control of the Home Office). A summary of air raid precautions policy is given in Appendix 2.

The proven value of civil defence in war led to its retention after the end of hostilities into the Cold War era. With memories of the latter fading rapidly, many people are now unaware how terrifying its early period was, with an almost hysterical fear of unseen and unknown weapons of atomic mass destruction. Although these were never in fact deployed against this country, continued vigilance was necessary so long as the communist regimes of the Eastern Bloc remained in power. For this reason many Civil Defence activities continued through the 1950s and 1960s, albeit with successively decreasing support. Active Civil Defence ceased in 1968, although local authorities had a continuing obligation to maintain control centres. The function declined gradually down to the final end of the Cold War and following the collapse of the Warsaw Pact around 1990, the government declared planning activity for civil defence (and investment) unnecessary.

The other now forgotten body that performed a vital role during World War II was the Royal Observer Corps. Its role was to collect and co-ordinate information on enemy aircraft movements, then pass this immediately to the anti-aircraft operations rooms that controlled firing of gunnery. This role was maintained for a while during the Cold War period, after which its function became to monitor nuclear explosions when attack was imminent. The Corps was finally abolished in 1991, another consequence of the 'peace dividend'.

IMPORTANT NOTES:

¶ In this book the word 'citadel' is used in its specific World War II meaning, namely a building designed and constructed to be bombproof.

¶ Books, magazines and other sources referred to in the text are all listed at the end of the book, together with a list of abbreviations used.

¶ Finding illustrations of obscure subjects can be very difficult. In some case we were forced to use somewhat indistinct images but we feel the unique nature of those photographs provides adequate compensation.

¶ Government departments, commercial organisations and other bodies named in passing are identified and explained at the end of the book in Appendix 5. The same applies to terms, names and concepts that readers may find unfamiliar.

¶ Readers may find a street atlas of London a helpful companion for locating the various places mentioned here.

Refuge for Relics

The first 'alternative' use for tube tunnels

ALTHOUGH caves and cellars have been used over many centuries for storage, factors of convenience mean they are seldom the first choice of users. In time of war, with the risk of aerial bombardment, underground locations take on greater attraction. This was certainly the case during the First World War, when Londoners had to endure the brand new horror of air raids in 1915. The first serious attacks occurred in 1917, forcing the government to consider afresh its arrangements for protecting the royal family and national treasures. This was probably the first occasion on which man-made underground locations were selected as places of refuge and it is for this reason that our account starts here.

The most comprehensive account of the government's actions in this situation is given by Peter Bancroft in a talk entitled *The Tubes in Wartime*. Here he relates that in June 1917, the Director of the National Gallery, C. J. Holmes, approached the Underground Electric Railways Company (which at that time ran the majority of London's underground railways) with a view to finding secure accommodation for some of its paintings. The company subsequently offered the National Gallery the disused platform at Aldwych on the Piccadilly tube. With the backing of the Office of Works and the Treasury, the platform was sealed off and altered, also given an armed guard. A refrigerator drying system was installed and from September 1917 some 300 pictures, about one-tenth of the National Gallery's collection, were housed there. They remained there until December 1918.

Aldwych was an inspired choice for protected storage; the tunnel here is relatively deep (about 80 feet below ground) and thus one of the best protected parts of the London Underground system. The relatively small number of passengers using the line also made it possible to remove the eastern pair of tracks on the Aldwych branch without major disruption and this track was removed in August 1917 (and never reinstated).

Postal tube

Another convenient repository for national treasures was the uncompleted closed Post Office Railway, for which contracts were issued in 1914. This now closed electric narrow gauge (2ft) railway was intended to speed the transfer of letters and parcels between sorting and delivery offices in central London, a function that until recently it still fulfilled. The twin tracks were to run in a tube 70ft below the surface for six miles from Paddington station and Western District Office across to Liverpool Street station and the Eastern District Office (Whitechapel Road). Delays were encountered in its construction as a result of wartime conditions but by 1917 tunnelling by contractors John Mowlem & Co. was complete.

In December of that year the Office of Works called a meeting with galleries and museums to see what measures could be taken to protect additional treasures and records. Following a visit to the King Edward Building station it was arranged that the contractor should carry out work to adapt the tunnels for this new use. Peter Bancroft indicates this work started on 2nd April 1918, although L. C. Stanway in *Mails Under London* reports that these transfers were completed already in January 1918 (construction of the railway was delayed afterwards and the railway did not open until 1926).

According to Bancroft, the Tate Gallery, National Portrait Gallery and Public Record Office stored parts of their collections in the station tunnels at King Edward Building. The British Museum used the tunnels of the West Central District Office station at Holborn, and the Wallace Collection and apparently some of the King's paintings were kept at the Post Office Railway station at Paddington. The Victoria & Albert Museum declined the offer to use the Post Office Railway tunnels, preferring instead to use the nearby spare station tunnel at South Kensington, evidently shared with some cases of Buckingham Palace china. The superflous tunnel mentioned was the result of a plan to build an express route for relieving the District Line between Earl's Court and Mansion House. The scheme was abandoned but only after tunnelling had already begun construction at South Kensington.

At least one author has suggested that the Aldwych branch was considered as a shelter for the King, Cabinet or War Office but no evidence supporting this has come to our attention. In any case, the true risk of the Zeppelin raids came more from the panic they created and according to some sources they posed no threat to government or to property on any great scale.

Renewed anxiety

As the international situation deteriorated in 1938 museums once more looked to safeguarding their treasures in war and disused tube tunnels again figured in the authorities' plans. On 30th June 1938 London Transport granted the government a licence for "emergency storage of articles" at Dover Street for the London Museum (Lancaster House). It agreed to provide the same facilities at Brompton Road for the Victoria & Albert Museum but this consideration was overruled by interests of national security, as explained in Chapter 8.

In the same month, representatives of the British Museum, the Public Record Office and Office of Works made a joint inspection of the Aldwych branch, which led to an agreement that the museum and PRO would have joint custody of the tunnel for the duration of any coming war. Subsequently the British Museum, the Tate Gallery and the London Museum were allocated storage accommodation in disused passages at Piccadilly Circus station, probably those leading to the lifts that had been replaced by escalators when the station was rebuilt in 1928.

Only a small proportion of the museum's artefacts was destined for tube stations and others were dispersed to locations much further away in Wales and Northamptonshire, as Nick McCamley's book *Saving Britain's Art Treasures* details. Nonetheless on 2nd September the famous Elgin Marbles (or Parthenon Sculptures), weighing 100 tons, were transported in crates by low-loader lorry to the London Transport depot at Lillie Bridge, Kensington, and then transferred to railway wagons

for their final journey to Aldwych. Later part of the British Museum library and various oriental antiquities joined these treasures, and the public war memorial to the Machine Gun Corps was also housed in Aldwych station for safekeeping.

As time passed doubts arose over the safety and suitability of tube tunnels for storage, and in January 1941 Sir John Forsdyke of the British Museum informed the Office of Works that the tubes were not to be regarded as safe enough to house irreplaceable objects, and serious damage might occur if they received direct hits from bombs weighing 1,000lb or more. At Aldwych the museum's occupancy was not exclusive in any case. Following a fact-finding visit on 20th September 1940 by Lord Ashfield, chairman of London Transport, and Sir John Anderson, Minister of Home Security, part of the tunnel was handed over two days later to the local authority (Westminster City Council) for use as a public air raid shelter to relieve overcrowding at Holborn station. Spaces were provided in the station area and along 320 yards of running tunnel

Construction of the Post Office's own underground railway was delayed by the First World War but by early 1918 West Central District station was sufficiently complete to store valuables of the British Museum.

[British Museum]

towards Holborn for 2,500 people until the shelter closed in May 1945 (more information on civilian sheltering arrangements at Aldwych can be found in this publisher's book *The Shelter of the Tubes*).

Enforced removals

In March 1941 events took their own course; press publicity forced the Borough of Westminster (which operated the public air raid shelter in Aldwych station) to take over much of the museum's section of the tube in the eastern tunnel under Kingsway. Additionally it was discovered that partition walls erected for the air raid shelter were impeding the airflow around the museum artefacts, and to avoid risk of deterioration all British Museum library material was removed to safer storage at Skipton Castle in Yorkshire. The Elgin Marbles remained behind, however, as did the war memorial. The latter was hoisted to the surface again on 5th April 1946, the railway line and Aldwych station reopening on 1st July 1946.

The Elgin Marbles themselves enjoyed something of a charmed existence during this period. Although the millionaire art dealer Lord Duveen of Millbank had funded a new gallery for the Marbles in 1938, this was not completed before the outbreak of war. The monuments' storage underground was fortunate as the gallery built specially for them was badly damaged by enemy bombing and, of all the old Greek and Roman galleries on the ground floor of the museum, the old Elgin Room was the only serviceable accommodation. It was to here that the marbles

Above: Treasures of the British Museum were stored in a disused passage of Piccadilly Circus tube station during World War II.

[British Museum]

Right: Easy does it! Workmen lift British Museum exhibits up a staircase at Aldwych station, most likely in 1939.
A number of disused tube tunnels had been identified the previous year to provide safekeeping for valuables from London's chief museums.

[British Museum]

were returned, being retrieved from Aldwych station starting 25th November 1948 and attracting considerable press (and public) attention, as they were trundled on trucks through the passages of the station. It was only in 1962 that they were finally installed in the reconstructed Duveen Gallery.

Post-war decay

Aldwych station's suitability for art storage was not forgotten and during the 1950s, at the height of the Cold War, the Tate Gallery made enquiries about using either this station or Piccadilly Circus for sheltering valuable artworks in a nuclear war. In the public's mind, however, Aldwych gradually faded and following steadily declining passenger figures the branch and station saw their last passengers on 30th September 1994 (the station is retained for filming and training purposes).

Right: People are staring and not without reason, as priceless paintings are brought out of their Aladdin's Cave after nearly seven years of safekeeping in the bowels of Piccadilly Circus tube station. On 5th February 1946 the last paintings were returned to the Tate Gallery and London Museum. [The Times]

Below: 'Operation Elgin' is carried out – 100 tons of priceless Elgin marbles are moved from their wartime hideout in Aldwych tube station back to the British Museum, London. The year is 1948. [Hulton Archive]

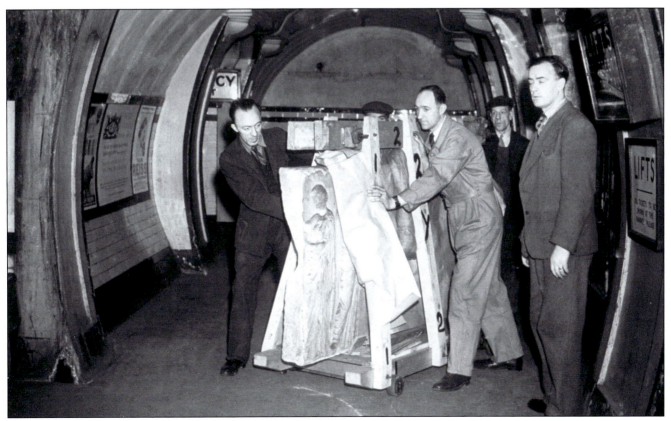

Express Relief

Aborted high-speed tube lines provide blueprint for wartime shelters

BY A quirk of fate, the construction, shape and location of London's wartime civilian deep shelters were determined almost entirely by developments of tube railway construction during two previous decades. This chapter explains how and why.

Back in the early 1920s public transport in London was struggling. Optimistic plans were made for constructing brand new tube lines, along with even more radical alternative solutions. Although economic realities prevented these projects from coming to fruition, one of them nevertheless helped determine the form of deep shelters in the following war, as we shall see.

Serious overcrowding on parts of the tube railway system led to the writing of a preliminary report for the Underground Railways Bill of 1924. This considered proposals for extensions to a number of existing lines as well as a new North and South tube. This official project was a deep level railway to run beneath the existing Bakerloo tracks between Elephant & Castle and Baker Street with extensions both to the north and south over existing surface suburban railways. From Elephant and Castle the line was to run in tube as far as Peckham on the South Eastern & Chatham Railway and then over that company's lines to Orpington via Nunhead, Crofton Park, Catford, Bellingham, Beckenham

run at deep level to Cricklewood with intermediate stations in the St John's Wood and West Hampstead areas. The alternative was a physical junction with the Metropolitan Railway at Baker Street and working over the company's lines to Amersham and Chesham. Nothing became of these plans, however.

Maverick monorail

'Machine Age' is one of the titles given to the inter-war period, when public imagination was fixated with modernity, automation, streamlining and speed. From this inspiration arose two radically different proposals for easing the lives of London commuters. First of these was the Kearney High Speed railway, the brainchild of engineer Chalmers Kearney whom we shall encounter again in Chapter 4.

His 'Gravity Tube Railway' was anything but conventional and used gravity to assist acceleration and deceleration. Trains would run from one summit to another along gradients of 1 in 7 for a total drop of about 120 feet. Stations would be near surface level (avoiding the need for lifts or escalators) with main running tunnels much lower, where speeds of 60mph would be attained. The streamlined single-car electric trains were to be suspended from a monorail, with a second guide rail below the train for stabilisation and current return. Claims were made for a great saving in electric current as well as mechanical wear and tear. Economy in construction would be achieved by building only a single tube, used by trains travelling in both directions with "positive safety being assured by turnouts at each station controlled by the train coming in the opposite direction".

Little wonder then that one learned journal commented, "It is somewhat difficult to see where the economy comes in of running

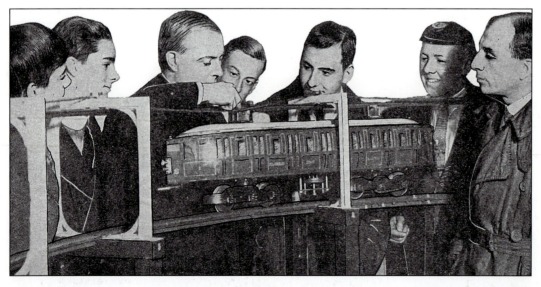

'Mr E. W. Kearney explains his wonder railway to a group of enthusiastic admirers,' says the caption to this promotional picture of 1930. Kearney had a gift for self-publicity.

Hill, Shortlands, Bromley South, Bickley and Orpington. This would tap a population of more than 200,000, it was stated.

Northwards from Elephant, the new tube would have new stations only at Waterloo, Charing Cross, Piccadilly Circus, Oxford Circus and Baker Street. Beyond here there were two options, one being to

down 150ft in order to run up the other side of the hollow but it cannot be denied that this switchbacking would provide much excitement for the public and, incidentally, some for the operators of the line." [*Junior Institution of Engineers' Journal*, 1912]

The maverick inventor's first plans to involve

London, announced in 1919, set out to provide two new tube railways, one connecting Crystal Palace with the Strand and the other linking Cricklewood with the Oval. Stations on Line 1 were Australia House, Strand (with subway connection to Temple and Aldwych Underground stations), North Lambeth (subway to Underground station), Oval (subway to Underground station), Brixton, Herne Hill and Crystal Palace (High Level). The second line was to start at the Oval, via Vauxhall (connection to main line railway), Victoria (subway to District Line), Hyde Park Corner (subway to Piccadilly Line), Marble Arch (subway to Central Line), Edgware Road (subway to Bakerloo Line), Maida Vale, Kilburn (connection to main line station), Brondesbury (for Metropolitan Line), ending at Cricklewood) for trams to Willesden Green, Edgware and Childs Hill. There was the possibility that this second line might be extended southwards to Camberwell Green and Peckham. None of this came to pass, any more than a more modest scheme the same a year, a ¾-mile shuttle beneath the Thames at Woolwich Arsenal connecting Beresford Square with the GER station at North Woolwich. Talks were held with the Ministry of Transport and a demonstration line was due to be constructed at Rottingdean but Kearney's funding failed to materialise.

Flying by train

Another novel rapid transit scheme of the inter-war period was the Bennie Railplane, also a suspended monorail system with a guide rail below. In Scotsman George Bennie's creation, however, the streamlined single carriage was to be driven by

engines and airscrews at either end, with predicted speeds of 120mph. At this velocity, it was claimed, a lifting action similar to that of an aeroplane came into play that diminished frictional losses by reducing pressure on the rails. Ball and roller bearing devices were also used to reduce friction to 5lb per ton of load, so that speeds of 120mph on the level would require just 120 horsepower of drive. The type of trestle construction envisaged was said

In 1938 the George Bennie Railplane appeared to be the ideal means of taking air passengers from central London to its airports in a reasonable time. Its six-minute journey time and frequent departures effectively provided the benefits of a central metropolitan airport.

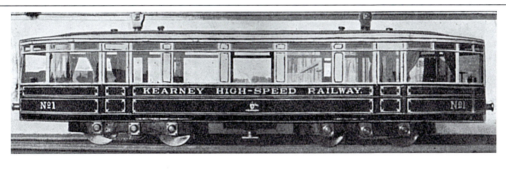

Because the Kearney High-Speed Railway never came to fruition, most illustrations of it in fact portray models. These photographs, although poorly reproduced, show the sole full-size carriage built. Subsequent designs were to have one door for every eight seats to facilitate rapid loading and unloading of passengers.

to reduce the cost of constructing the engineering works, which could span large stretches of water with ease and negotiate gradients more severe than on conventional railways.

Two double-track lines were proposed in the Capital, running out to airports from central London above existing railway lines for most of the way. The first would run from Holborn Viaduct to Croydon airport and the other from Paddington to Heston airport, with six-minute journey times claimed. According to its promoters the cost of constructing and operating a railplane route was significantly less than for conventional railways and would generate a profit with as few as three passengers aboard. Air journey time could also be saved by providing passport and customs examination on board the railplane. In the event, none of this came to pass, although a short demonstration line was built at Milngavie, north-west of Glasgow, in 1929 (it was demolished in 1941 to assist the scrap metal campaign).

This previously unpublished layout diagram of the Northern Line dates from October 1935 and shows the relief lines planned between Camden Town and Waterloo, and between Kennington and Balham. The pecked line route to Finsbury Park is a 'possible future development'. For clarity some stations on the City branch were not included.

MORDEN – EDGWARE LINE PROPOSALS 1935

GOLDERS GREEN
and EDGWARE

HIGHGATE and BARNET

FINSBURY PARK
for LNER

Chalk Farm

Kentish Town

Camden Town

Mornington Crescent

King's Cross

Euston

Warren Street

Goodge Street

TOTTENHAM CT RD

LEICESTER SQUARE

Strand

CHARING CROSS

WATERLOO

Borough

Elephant & Castle

KENNINGTON

Oval

Stockwell

Clapham North

CLAPHAM COMMON

Clapham South

BALHAM

Trinity Road

Tooting Broadway

Colliers Wood
South Wimbledon

MORDEN

— EXISTING DOUBLE-TRACK TUBE
— PROPOSED NEW DOUBLE-TRACK TUBE
- - - POSSIBLE FUTURE DEVELOPMENTS

Express Relief Lines

The problems that Kearney and Bennie sought to solve were very real, even if their planned high-speed railways were not. Measures almost as radical were taken to address London's transport troubles, beginning with the formation of the London Passenger Transport Board (LPTB, more generally called London Transport) in 1933. As the new body began to assess its responsibilities, considerable attention was paid to building faster trains and new tube lines that would modernise and improve public transport facilities in London.

These new trains were but one facet of a scheme generally tagged the '1935–40 New Works Programme'. The projects that were actually realised have been well documented, but some of the unfulfilled initiatives were never publicised and are thus less well known. One of these is the scheme to increase capacity on the heavily used Northern Line, which was then, as now, working to near capacity. A report by the General Manager (Railways) dated 17th October 1935 produced three separate solutions to address the growing traffic on the Morden line and the new traffic that would be generated from the High Barnet lines. The first two solutions, to accelerate or lengthen trains, need not detain here but the third does since it relates to new tunnels for relief lines. The text explains the capacity dilemma and how it could be solved.

When all the service possible is operated on the Highgate branch, 12 paths ['slots' for trains, per hour] remain north of Camden. South of Camden these paths exist via the City, where additional service is not wanted.

A relief line, if built, might form an express line parallel to the existing line from Camden Town to Charing Cross or Waterloo or beyond, omitting three or four stations. The ideal plan would be to construct island platforms at the express stations with the two northbound tracks at one platform and the two southbound at the other.

The above 12 trains being accepted on the express line for the relief of the High Barnet group, 28 additional trains would be required to complete the service. This could be done by constructing [another] new line, with possible 28 trains per hour, [from] Camden Town to Finsbury Park, in readiness for West End connection upon electrification of the L.N.E. (Great Northern) main line section, including Enfield Chase.

In regard to the southerly end of the Morden Line, relief is becoming necessary, and this can be obtained by breaking the Kennington loop and projecting the 26 trains per hour which now turn there onto a new track to Clapham Common, forming a junction there with the existing Morden Line. The new line would become a fast line between Kennington and Clapham Common (2¼ miles) or Balham (3¾ miles) and the junction at Balham would be arranged so that Morden Line trains may use the fast line.

The notion of building relief lines must have taken hold for in spring 1936 a team of four senior London Transport staff made a visit to New York with a remit 'to investigate and report upon the maximum capacity of train service which is being operated on the New York Subways, with a view to determining the maximum capacity of train service which it would be possible to operate upon the Board's system of railways'. The resulting document, entitled *Report on Maximum Capacity of Train Services – New York and London*, included examining the building of express relief lines as one method of increasing the capacity of existing Underground lines.

It's worth remembering that at the time we are discussing, London's tube lines were much shorter than today. Extending them out into the suburbs, as envisaged under the New Works programme, would cause capacity problems elsewhere, bringing in considerably more passengers than the existing central area stations could handle in the peak hour. Allowance had also to be made for normal expected growth in passenger traffic, meaning that altogether passenger numbers might grow up to 170 per cent of current maxima. The highest resulting growth

would be on the Central Line but that was only part of the predicament. The chief problem lay on the Camden Town–Charing Cross section of the Northern Line, which was "already fully taxed in the peak hours".

Additional capacity was clearly vital and the report identified three ways of providing this – providing longer trains and platforms, using faster trains (experiments were already in hand, as mentioned above) and building express relief lines. The section of the Central Line to be eased, it was suggested, was the 3½ miles between Marble Arch and Liverpool Street, with two additional tracks provided with stations only at Oxford Circus and Bank. The journey time between Marble Arch and Bank would be halved, from 12 minutes to six. For the Northern Line it was thought that the new relief line should run between Highgate Archway and Tottenham Court Road, with no intermediate stations. It would halve the journey time between those two stations by seven minutes (50 per cent)

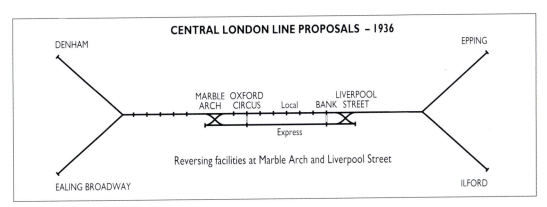

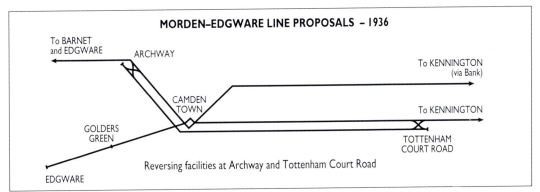

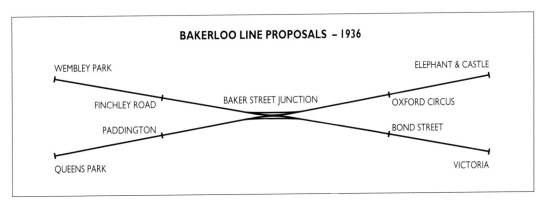

Following a study visit to New York in 1936, express relief schemes had been drawn up for three tube lines. The Bakerloo proposal anticipates the much later Jubilee Line.

and avoiding the existing route's detour to Euston station, it would take the straight line beneath Hampstead Road. For the Bakerloo Line, relief could be created by forming a junction immediately north of Baker Street and building a new line to Bond Street or Marble Arch and on to Victoria.

It is clear that ideas were still fluid at this stage and later plans for relieving the Northern Line considered a much longer bypass route starting at Golders Green or Finchley, passing Waterloo and Clapham and ending in areas unserved by the Southern Railway, such as Motspur Park and Chessington.

New tube lines set out in detail

Although none of these grandiose schemes came to fruition before war broke out in 1939, the notions behind them had a direct bearing on the choice of sites for the deep-level tube shelters built by the LPTB as agents of the Ministry of Home Security (their background and construction are described in Chapter 4).

At a meeting held at the Ministry of Transport on 16th November 1940 Lord Ashfield discussed the locations that London Transport favoured for the shelter tunnels. The Bakerloo Line extension to Camberwell had been added to the Board's expansion plans and the MoT's notes of that meeting give the most detailed survey of plans for construction of new lines, stating:

The extension from Elephant & Castle to Camberwell, much as the Board would prefer it, is impracticable owing to expense, bad ground and the necessity for construction under pressure.

In laying out the [shelter] scheme, careful consideration had been given to fitting it in to the Board's future plans, which envisage the quadrupling by express tubes of certain sections of

heavily used lines, e.g. the Northern and Central. The Board, however, could not be committed and no liability could be assumed for acquiring the works after the war. The proposals envisage high speed relief lines under existing running tunnels, to rise to interchange platform levels at the stations on either side:

(a) Central Line, between Bank and Holborn, passing St. Paul's and Chancery Lane.

(b) Northern Line, between Camden Town and Tottenham Court Road, passing under Mornington Crescent, Warren Street and Goodge Street. (Camden Town Junction will be reconstructed in the future to separate the two systems.)

(c) Northern Line, between Kennington and Balham, passing Oval, Stockwell, Clapham North, Clapham Common, and Clapham South.

Platform interchange would be effected by transposing the track and platform in the existing station tunnels at the new interchange stations. The Board considered that the facilities [at] the 10 existing stations named above . . . were adequate to deal with the refugee traffic at each.

The working shafts will not be a danger to the new tunnels as the latter would be approached by lateral tunnels and the shafts would be capped; their retention or blockage was a detail for future consideration, and they will be used, as necessary, for ventilation.

No difficulty is anticipated for finding sites for the 20 working shafts, having regard to the bomb damage to convenient buildings. It is anticipated that two working depots will be required, namely, in Hyde Park and Russell Square.

As the war progressed and blind optimism faded into a clearer perception of current reality, London Transport lost some of its enthusiasm for new high-speed railways. Its chairman, Lord Ashfield, argued the Board's position at a meeting held on 18th February 1942 at the Ministry of Home Security.

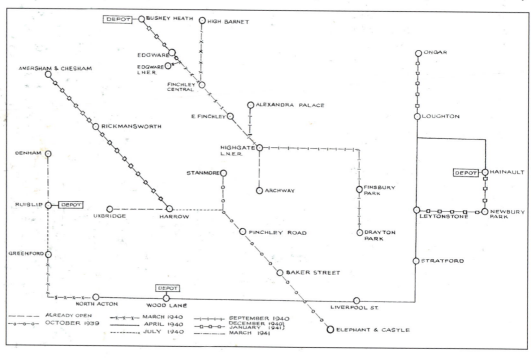

Under the title 'Follow The Job' London Transport printed this sketch diagram of the 1935–40 New Works targets in the September 1939 issue of its staff magazine. The completion dates shown were optimistic.

The notes of the meeting relate his attempt to disengage London Transport from any commitment to buy the tunnels, and the quandary that this placed on the Board.

The Ministry wished to provide deep shelter and had with the consent of the Board decided to site this below the Board's present railways as being the most advantageous plan. The Board could take no objection if it were proposed to abandon the works [later] and fill in the shafts. It was true that the Board had themselves proposed in the initial stages to take an option for two years but he could not conceive of the Board finding it possible to take over the tunnels within two years of the end of the war. If someone proposed to use the space under their railways now occupied by the tunnels they would feel obliged strongly to oppose such proposal on the ground that it would prevent a potential development of the Board's system. [On the other hand] after the war they could not undertake to lease the tunnels from the Ministry and maintain them.

Much to Ashfield's relief, the meeting concluded with an agreement in principle by the Ministry to offer the LPTB an option to purchase the tunnels at any time within five years of the end of hostilities. This was an expedient move, although in the event it was never taken up. The war years provided both incentive and opportunity to reconsider London's transport needs (and much more besides) on a far broader basis, culminating in the *County of London Plan*, commenced in 1943 and published in 1945. This document introduced far more radical plans for new railways in central London, with no mention of the two bypass lines planned before the war. Instead the overcrowded arteries were to be relieved by building brand-new lines along new alignments in fresh transport corridors. Bridges across the River Thames were to be eliminated in favour of new tunnels but these in the main would be for full-size trains and widespread expansion of the Underground as such was not in favour.

It is suggested that new deep-level lines totalling 14 miles should link the southern terminals and a north-south tunnel should link the northern terminals and the south-east and south-west systems. The northern stations should be linked by a new underground line providing interchange facilities for suburban traffic and the northern section of the existing Inner Circle should become part of a ring to distribute goods from the newly decentralised markets. There would also be an outer goods ring nearer the county boundary.

So said the report but its immediate influence was minimal,

for in 1944 a specialist body, the Railway (London Plan) Committee, was set up to investigate these proposals in greater detail. Several old schemes were dropped, a number of new routes were proposed, but as time went by and the realities of post-war austerity and funding cuts dawned, these grandiose schemes withered and died. Probably the last public reference to serious plans for re-using the deep shelter tunnels for rail purposes was in London Transport's annual report of 1945 but even this mention was half-hearted, stating that tunnels constructed during the war as deep level air raid shelters could be used for constructing new high-speed tube railways but that any tube construction was necessarily costly.

In 1946 the Ministry of War Transport decided that priority should be given to the easterly and westerly extensions of the Central Line together with electrification of the LNER company's Shenfield line. Construction was to go ahead as rapidly as the supply of labour would permit, whilst all other tube railway construction projects were to be deferred. In fact there was no further major investment in tube construction until the Victoria Line was built in the 1960s, turning into reality a post-war, not pre-war, project. Nonetheless, the possibility of re-using the tunnels for rail purposes was not ruled out privately for some years, as Chapter 12 recounts.

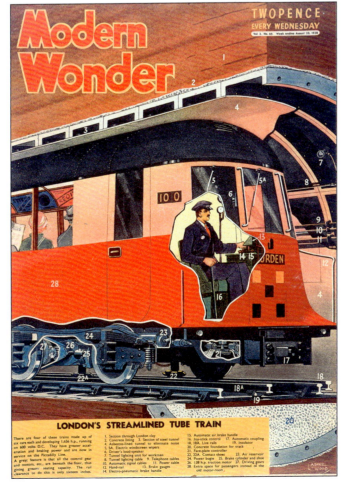

The widespread obsession with speed pervaded London Transport as well, with new streamlined trains and plans for express tube lines bypassing less important stations. Spectacular as it appeared in 1935, streamlining was not deemed to be a success and the express lines never came about.

(North) Westward-Ho!

Westminster's planned decampment: first underground, then to the suburbs – and further afield

ONE of the downsides of today's penchant for revisionist history is the now widely received notion that Britain entered war in 1939 with little preparation. This is entirely false of course and the likelihood of hostilities had been foreseen for several years. In fact from 1937 onwards public utilities, local authorities and national government embarked on air raid precautions and other exercises in preparation for a war that seemed inevitable. The Air Raid Precautions (A.R.P.) Act came into force on 1st January 1938 and the following autumn no fewer than 14 million copies of a booklet on protecting homes against air raids were printed for distribution to every householder in the country and shortly afterwards production began of Anderson shelters for personal protection. Nobody was unaware of the war clouds on the horizon.

A major element in the government's strategy was the evacuation of central government functions to protected sites outside central London, along with the creation of a hardened Central War Room and protected accommodation for the Cabinet in central London. This 'principle of dispersion' was recommended by the so-called Warren Fisher committee, set up in 1936 to determine the optimal location of government staff in the event of war. Research by the late Ken Valentine indicates that this five-man committee, chaired by Sir Warren Fisher (head of the Civil Service), reported early in 1937 with a suggestion that an alternative centre of government should be planned in the London area where Ministers and possibly Parliament could be relocated if Whitehall were to become unusable. After endorsement by the Cabinet in February 1937, this work was given in great secrecy to a new five-man sub-committee under Sir James Rae (Treasury), which had the task of turning these general proposals into a comprehensive scheme.

This resulted in two alternative schemes, one of which would accommodate not only civil servants but also Ministers and Parliament in London's northwest suburbs; if however, this nearby retreat were to prove insufficient, a further withdrawal should be made to prepared accommodation further out in the west of England at Corsham.

So secret were these contingency plans, declares Valentine, that when the Rae Report was circulated in December 1937 to the group of Ministers who comprised the Committee of Imperial Defence (C.I.D.) under the chairmanship of the Prime Minister, all the geographical locations were suppressed and replaced by a mass of serial code-numbers. At the C.I.D. meeting on 20th December each Minister had a list translating these numbers into locations but they had to hand the lists back to the C.I.D. secretary Sir Maurice Hankey at the end of the meeting. Only one copy of the full report with locations existed, kept personally by Hankey. Even the recently crowned King George VI, who received C.I.D. papers as a matter of routine, was not automatically sent this full report.

The worsening political situation in central Europe during 1938 meant these plans did not come to pass as anticipated. Instead these events forced efforts to be concentrated on an interim solution to be housed in the basement of the Office of Works at Storey's Gate, Whitehall, and such was the speed of construction that these new Cabinet War Rooms were ready for first occupation by the time of the Munich crisis of September 1938 (described in more detail in Chapter 7). As Samantha Heywood explains in her paper *Forts or Follies? Government Citadels of the Second World War*, policy on relocating the seat of government after Munich became confused. The Rae Committee was reconvened in November 1938 and favoured 'the partial retention of the North Western London scheme in . . . modified form' as 'it may well be the means of avoiding a removal of essential staffs to the provinces'.

As a result, three war rooms were built in the north-western suburbs in case bombing enforced the evacuation of Whitehall. The Cabinet and Chiefs of Staff were provided with a citadel in the Post Office Research Station at Dollis Hill; completed in June 1940, this was named Paddock and was described by Churchill in his memoirs as 'far from the light of day' and in his book *The Second*

These booklets, both issued in 1938, show that householders and public services were fully aware of what to do if air attacks came.

World War as having 'offices and bedrooms, wire and fortified telephone communications'.

Nearby was the Admiralty's alternative headquarters, located beneath their chart depot in Cricklewood (corner of 403/405 Edgware Road and Oxgate Lane), whilst the Air Ministry occupied the basement of a Stationery Office building located next to the Kodak works just west of the West Coast main railway line at Harrow, known as Station Z. The War Office chose for its standby headquarters the School of Military Music at Kneller Hall, near Twickenham. Although not protected securely enough to be bombproof, its location further outside London provided an element of safety.

Plans for evacuated government

In his book *Willesden at War – The Secret Citadels of WW2* the late Ken Valentine set out in more detail than ever published before how the House of Commons would occupy Willesden Technical College, how Dudden Hill and Gladstone Park schools were to accommodate the House of Lords and how other government departments were to be dispersed among other schools (it was assumed that all pupils would have been evacuated away from London). Neville's Court, a handsome block of flats close to the Post Office Research Station, was earmarked for housing Churchill, members of the War Cabinet and service chiefs. The bulk of the civil servants would be accommodated in neighbouring schools and colleges left empty by evacuation. Indeed, at one stage Willesden's schools were scheduled to accommodate some 1,400 civil servants, with Gibbons Road, Leopold Road and Furness Road schools taking about 700 from the external-affairs Departments, and Willesden County (Doyle Gardens) and Pound Lane about 500 from the Treasury and the Cabinet Office.

This was the initial thinking but recognition soon followed of the vulnerability of relocating the mechanism of government to the north-western suburbs. Already in January 1939 a decision was taken that if central London were to become uninhabitable, essential staff should be evacuated directly to the West of England and not initially to the suburbs. Work on the suburban war rooms was then given a lower priority but not abandoned. Indeed, the Post Office Telephone Branch War Diary for November 1938 states:

Important developments concerning large new installations for the Air Ministry at the Stationery Office, Harrow, and for the Admiralty at the Chart Factory, Cricklewood, occurred during the month. The telephone installation for the Air Ministry will include the provision of a private branch exchange comprising 11 CB No. 9 positions, about 15 exchange lines to Harrow and 15 to convenient out of area exchanges, and between 250 and 350 extensions. In addition, a number of circuits to Whitehall Exchange and the Air Ministry will be required, together with about 40 long-distance circuits. For telegraph purposes, approximately 16 teleprinters are to be installed, but 12 of these will be transferred from other Air Ministry sources.

The requirements at the Chart Factory had been under discussion in October and work had already commenced. A 7-position CB No. 9 private branch exchange is being installed, together with 10 exchange lines to Gladstone and 10 to Colindale Exchange, and up to 200 extensions. A number of subsidiary switchboards are also being provided. Communication with Whitehall and other Admiralty centres will be provided by means of private wires and many other circuits terminating at the Dollis Hill private branch exchange [presumably provided specifically for Paddock] will be extended to Cricklewood. In addition, 48 teleprinters will be installed.

Supreme concealment: although the government's headquarters of last resort was here, these unassuming surface buildings at Dollis Hill in north-west London would have given little clue to what lay below. Although now demolished to make way for new houses, the bunker survives below. The ventilation tower is prominent in this view, with traces of camouflage paint on the tower. [Imperial War Museum]

Confirmation of that statement comes from the recollections of a former telephonist, Mrs Monk, who states, "In 1939 I went for PBX training at Queen Anne's Mansions, and had just finished when war was declared. We were each allocated an office near enough to our home address to enable us to walk to work in the event of a breakdown of transport. I was sent to an Admiralty 'board [switchboard] which was housed temporarily at Dollis Hill Research Station. The office was eventually completed under the Admiralty Chart Factory at Cricklewood. We were allowed a few months at our home base, and then had to take our turn filling in elsewhere. I think I worked at most of the Ministries in Whitehall, and several elsewhere."

Provision on this scale indicates that the various services expected to make serious use of the new facilities. Another indication is found in document WO 205/7 (1942) at the PRO. This memo deals with the operation of communications facilities should it be necessary to evacuate Admiralty staff to the Insurance Party building in Cricklewood. It states there is a fully protected GPO position in Trafalgar Square tube station (located in a small square room behind a pair of double doors near the foot of the Bakerloo Line escalators), from which a direct and protected telephone circuit is provided to the Insurance Party building in Cricklewood and also gives numbers to call on Federal exchange [described later] and at the MI6 building in Broadway so that other departments would be alerted to this evacuation.

Although some writers have stated the government gave up any notions of evacuation to north-west London early on, official documents indicate otherwise. A 'most secret' meeting of the Committee on the Maintenance of the Machinery of Government under Rocket Bombardment (the 'Crossbow committee') on 17th December 1943 indicated divided opinions. The accommodation that had been reserved in schools formed 'a useful reserve' in the view of the Air Ministry, whereas the War Office considered theirs was never likely to be used. It was noted that the premises had no protected accommodation, only slit-trench shelters that were by now probably derelict, and that the Post Office was anxious to recover the switchboards and other telephone equipment that had been provided there. The outcome was each department could make its own decision whether to retain its rights or allow the Ministry of Works to add it to the general reserve. A note in the same file dated 4th May 1943 noted that the Air Ministry had given up its own use of the Station Z citadel by allocating it to RAF Transport Command. The Cricklewood premises were still earmarked by the Admiralty in case its main citadel was bombed.

Planning for Paddock

'Preliminary plans' for creating a purpose-built, totally bombproof war headquarters deep under the grounds of the Dollis Hill research station were first revealed on 14th October 1938 when three men who had worked together on the Whitehall Cabinet War Room project presented their plans at a meeting in the Office of Works in Storey's Gate. The Dollis Hill HQ would in general replicate the facilities of 'CWR1', including in particular a large map room with a usable wall surface of over a thousand square feet and a cabinet room with seating for thirty people, all housed in a sub-basement nearly forty feet below ground. The sub-basement would be protected by a roof of concrete five feet thick (probably in two layers with an intervening layer of sand as a shock-absorber) while over it would be a first basement considerably larger in area, protected by another concrete roof three feet thick. The entrance to this citadel would be concealed within a new three-storey building already planned by the Post Office to meet its own peacetime needs.

The ground floor of this building would be used for stores for the Post Office engineers' new experimental station. In peacetime the first and second floors would be used by the Post Office for lecture rooms, offices etc., but in wartime they would be adapted for use in quiet periods by a War Cabinet and its secretariat, by the Chiefs of Staff, the Joint Planning Committee, etc. During periods of air attack, however, there would be a general descent into the subterranean citadel. The cost of the war HQ was put at nearly £250,000.

According to Valentine this corrects the assertion that these plans were part of the Post Office's own emergency preparations; the GPO would not have needed a hugely expensive bombproof citadel, nor would the Treasury have allocated this department the necessary funds. He also notes the somewhat misleading statement in volume 2 of Winston Churchill's history of the Second World War (1949) that a reserve war room called Paddock had been prepared "near Hampstead" and the confusion caused by subsequent writers who repeated this statement, taken at face value, or tried to deduce that its name was derived from PAD or Passive Air Defence. In fact the name comes from a nearby street, Paddock Road.

Much nonsense has been written, probably unwittingly, about Paddock. To Churchill are attributed the words, "In wartime, truth is so precious that she should always be attended by a bodyguard of lies"; his reason for placing Paddock near Hampstead may have been deliberate obfuscation or perhaps merely failing memory. Either way it misled Peter Laurie to identify its location as the never-opened Northern Line tube station of North End (Bull and Bush). The notion that Nigel West's 1981 book *MI5* was the first to connect Paddock with Dollis Hill is also somewhat far of the mark. The staff who worked there used the place as a games room for lunchtime table tennis and 'Paddock Block' was shown on the ground plan printed in successive open day brochures of the establishment and in an article in the *IPOEE Journal* (October 1956, p. 238). Some writers also put Neville Court for Neville's Court,

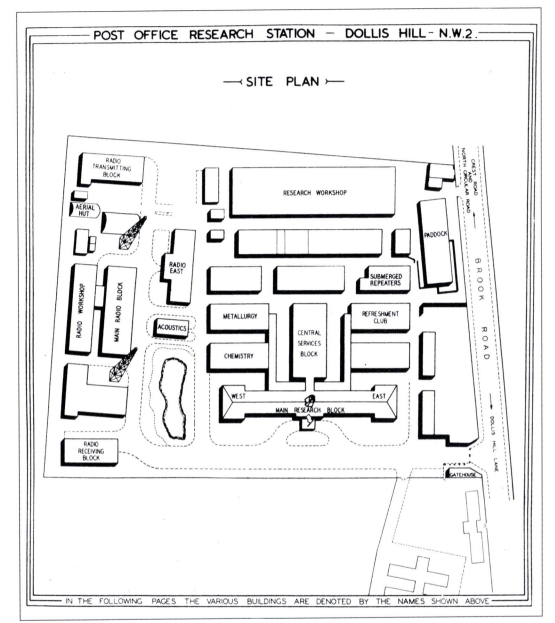

POST OFFICE RESEARCH STATION — DOLLIS HILL — N.W.2.

⟶ SITE PLAN ⟵

IN THE FOLLOWING PAGES THE VARIOUS BUILDINGS ARE DENOTED BY THE NAMES SHOWN ABOVE

Despite assertions made by other writers, the location of Paddock was never suppressed, as this ground plan from a Dollis Hill open day brochure of 1948 demonstrates. 'Paddock Block' is at the top right corner.

although here they are repeating Churchill's own mistake. However, Neville's Court is definitely not 'part of the Dollis Hill complex' as one writer puts it but a residential property (as mentioned above) 200 yards distant in Dollis Hill Lane.

The bunker takes shape

Construction work for the citadel started at the beginning of 1939 and involved earth-shifting on a massive scale. With creditable discretion, the thousands of tons of soil removed for the excavation of the Paddock bunker were carried away secretly, in bread vans it is stated, although this sight in itself must have attracted the unwanted curiosity of observant local residents. The land it was built on was marshy and required two pumps to prevent flooding during wartime; during subsequent periods of disuse the lowest storey did indeed become flooded.

The shape of the citadel as built was oblong, running parallel with Brook Road under the north-east corner of the research station's grounds. It was both longer and wider than the building erected on the surface and the first basement may have extended under the pavement of Brook Road. Reports of the structure's facilities speak of rooms built on two levels with walls of reinforced concrete 17 feet thick. The lowest storey was constructed 40 feet below ground and being designed to withstand the impact of a 500lb bomb, it was considered to be entirely bombproof.

Of the 22 rooms on the lower floor, the largest was the Map Room with rooms for the Cabinet and the Prime Minister next door. The upper storey was slightly larger in size than the floor below and contained the telephone exchange, ventilation plant and a small kitchen. Paddock was additionally provided with its own generators, a radio transmitter and receiver, all to serve a complex built to house 200 people. Previous writers have commented on the lack of lavatory facilities, alluding to scant regard for the comfort of the occupants (the nearest toilets were in the ground floor building above). They may have forgotten the forces of gravity, however; when accommodation is provided below sewer level the only way of removing the effluent is by pumping, a relatively complex and expensive assignment. Of the above-ground structure only one storey was built, possibly for economy since non-critical support staff could be accommodated in the research station's main building. All construction work was completed and ready for occupation in June 1940, at which time De Normann suggested to the deputy chairman of the Deputy Chiefs of Staff Committee, Col. Hastings Ismay, that a skeleton staff should be installed at Dollis Hill so that the cabinet could move in rapidly as soon as signs indicated the position in central London was "getting too hot". Whitehall officials generally were convinced that Dollis Hill would have to be used if Whitehall became uninhabitable; but Churchill had other ideas and refused even to think of leaving Whitehall.

Paddock in action

A note written in October 1940, shortly after the first War Cabinet meeting at Dollis Hill, and quoted by Valentine, describes daily life at Paddock. Government now occupied not only the 19 rooms of the basement and the 18 rooms of the sub-basement but also the ground floor with its 22 rooms and lavatories. These rooms were used predominantly for work while other workrooms were available in the main Post Office building. Staff could use the Post Office canteen for meals

and had living and sleeping accommodation in Neville's Court, where about thirty NCOs and men were quartered so as to allow a 24-hour guard over the whole complex to be maintained.

Security was extremely tight according to Geoff Cowell, a member of the 18th City of London Royal Fusiliers Home Guard whose primary task was the defence of the Research Station. In the *RSS Newsletter* he recalls:

> The regular army appeared on the scene at Dollis Hill for a short time when invasion seemed imminent shortly after Dunkirk. The Paddock Building, seemingly prepared for occupation by VIPs in case central London became untenable, was the object of an exercise which required occupation by regular troops for a day or so. Not being aware of this because of tight security, I was passing the Paddock in Home Guard uniform after a night's duty when a figure appeared on the roof and a rifle was pointed at me. "Don't come no nearer, mate, or you'll be shot!"
>
> "Bloody cheek," I thought. "Aren't we supposed to be on the same side?"

Paddock was a far cry from the comforts of Whitehall and on 22nd October 1940 Churchill stated: "The accommodation at Paddock is quite unsuited to the conditions which have arisen. The War Cabinet cannot work and live there for weeks on end, while leaving the greater part of their staffs less well provided for than they are now in Whitehall. Apart from the Citadel of Paddock there is no adequate accommodation or shelter and anyone living in Neville's Court would have to be running to and fro on every Jim Crow warning. Paddock should be treated as a last-resort Citadel."

This was confirmed in January 1941 when Churchill gave up his double-flat in Neville's Court and the armed guard, already reduced from a squad

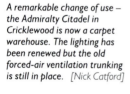

A remarkable change of use – the Admiralty Citadel in Cricklewood is now a carpet warehouse. The lighting has been renewed but the old forced-air ventilation trunking is still in place. [Nick Catford]

of 40 to one of 20, was about to be reduced further to half a dozen. Nonetheless five rooms at Paddock remained reserved for Churchill and his staff, seven for other War Cabinet Ministers, three for War Office chiefs, seven for Home Forces Advanced GHQ and ten for part of the War Cabinet secretariat and Joint Intelligence Committee, besides the map room, the Joint Planners' room and a room for the Dominions liaison officers. The War Cabinet room was, as at Downing Street, long and narrow, with the prime minister evidently seated half way along one side of a long table. In summer 1943 all such arrangements ceased.

Wasted effort?

One is left with a distinct impression that Paddock, conceived and constructed in haste, was not a great success. Valentine states that apart from two Cabinet meetings (3rd October 1940 and 10th March 1941), the Paddock facilities were never used, whilst Samantha Heywood of the Imperial War Museum declares that by the end of 1941 Churchill had branded it a "useless piece of folly" and ordered that it be re-allocated to another department. Most of its furniture, and the guards, were also re-allocated in 1943 to another alternative war room site, Anson (described in Chapter 7). Final closure came at the end of 1944. The Admiralty citadel in Oxgate Lane, Cricklewood (often known as the insurance party or I. P. building) did, however, see regular service and operated continuously until 1943. Like Paddock, its end came in 1944.

Paddock's facilities were not entirely wasted, however, and they played a vital role helping the war effort as part of the Post Office Research Station's little known involvement in acoustics. Among several interesting projects was one to devise special noise-cancelling microphones and headphones for use in tanks engaged in the battlefield. Deep below the research station in Paddock a special chamber with deafening sound effects was constructed to simulate a tank's interior. Recordings of a tank rumbling past a microphone were processed for playing continuously on a speaking clock machine. Similar machines were made for the Royal Air Force; these generated continuous background aircraft noise effects and spasmodic machine-gun fire for training radio operators and fighter pilots.

Further afield

In the wider scheme of things too, the evacuation of parliament to north-west London never took place at all, although the BBC did pay lip service to these plans. Throughout the war (and for a time afterwards), its publications unit occupied requisitioned premises at the Grammar School in Scarle Road, Wembley.

Although the upper levels of central government in the event remained in London to act as a 'nucleus', other functions were evacuated further and many government departments were moved out of London altogether under a dispersal scheme known as 'Yellow Move'. Two schemes had been drawn up before the outbreak of war, Black Move embracing the higher echelons of essential administration and Yellow Move for less essential staff. Following the fall of France considerations of national morale saw Black Move put in abeyance, with Churchill bitterly opposed to any "wholesale movement" of civil servants from the capital. It was reconsidered in 1943 when bombardment by V-weapons became a serious threat but once again deferred since by this time there was sufficient protected accommodation for key personnel in central London.

Yellow Move did, however, take place from September 1939 onwards. Civil servants were moved out to inland and seaside resorts where empty hotel accommodation was available; the Ministry of Supply went to Harrogate, for example, whilst the Ministry of Agriculture found a new home in Colwyn Bay. Ministry of Pensions staff found new quarters mainly in Blackpool, with a smaller outpost in Cheltenham. Vast numbers of service headquarters staff were evacuated too; in a highly co-ordinated scheme, the Admiralty moved to Bath ('Tennyson'), the War Office to Cheltenham and the Air Ministry to Gloucester, initially occupying colleges and hotels. Later semi-permanent hutments were built and the Victory issue of the *IPOEE Journal* (January 1946) records the telephone facilities provided in these establishments and some extensive installations in 'sites of exceptional importance', such as the Group centre exchange at Hawthorn (Wilts.) 80 feet underground.

Plans remained in place for a last ditch Black Move should London become unusable or threatened by invasion (also discussed in Chapter 7), although it never in fact became necessary. Under this plan – also known as the Government Department Evacuation (G.D.E.) scheme – the nucleus of central government would relocate to stately homes, hotels and other requisitioned accommodation in the West Midlands. Hutment sites were also erected and new telephone exchanges provide at key locations (practicalities of the elaborate mobilisation details by bus and train are described in *London Transport Carried On*). The Royal family would move to Madresfield Court near Great Malvern and the Prime Minister and entourage to Spetchley Hall near Worcester, whilst the War Cabinet would move to Hindlip House near Worcester and Parliament to Stratford-upon-Avon. The BBC had already established an emergency studio and control centre that remains to this day at Wood Norton, near Evesham.

The evacuation scheme was not put into full operation and the majority of the accommodation was occupied by armed service departments instead. The *IPOEE Journal* also states that the Air Ministry was set to move to Worcester (where the telephone exchange – and possibly the whole scheme – was codenamed 'Longfellow'), the War Office to Droitwich ('Chaucer') and the Admiralty to Malvern ('HMS Duke').

Bunker Mentality

The need to build deep-level shelters in World War II

ONE consequence of rearmament and the uneasy expectation of war in the mid-1930s was the Air Raid Precautions (A.R.P.) Act of 1937, which compelled local authorities to draw up plans for the safety of civilians in the event of air raids and gas attacks. Response to this legislation varied, but most authorities concentrated on the provision of gas masks and domestic shelters such as the Anderson Shelter. A number of communal street shelters looking like 'public conveniences' were built, on unused land or in some cases along the centre of residential streets and in some places communal underground shelters were provided as well. In the main, however, these large underground constructions were less favoured on the basis that a single incident could give rise to heavy casualties and perhaps more importantly, they were costly to construct (although grants from central government would fund 65–70 per cent of expenditure on approved projects).

To many this planning must have held an air of unreality, although press reports of the civil war that raged in Spain from 1936 to 1939 must have given an impression of the nature and horrors of modern aerial warfare. For security reasons and to avoid causing panic, many A.R.P. preparations were conducted in great secrecy. An example is the work of London Transport's 'Emergency Organization' committee of the period, whose documents are marked 'Confidential and strictly private – These minutes are on no account to be copied for circulation'. This committee investigated all parts of the underground system liable to flooding if bombs breached major water mains or the River Thames and caused movable floodgates to be built at strategic places to seal the tubes if this happened.

The Munich crisis of September 1938 gave added impetus to these concerns, with A.R.P. services being put on standby and trenches dug in some public parks. Newspapers carried articles on self-protection as well as advertisements for all manner of products with A.R.P. uses, whilst coloured picture cards, issued with cigarettes produced by the Imperial Tobacco Company all drove the message home. Prime Minister Chamberlain issued a public statement on 6th October 1938: "War to-day is a different thing, not only in degree but in kind, from what it used to be. When war starts to-day, in the very first hour, before any professional soldier or sailor or airman has been touched, it will strike the workman, the clerk, the man in the street or in the bus, his wife and children in their homes."

Two small boys make the descent to a world of greater safety 60ft beneath Borough High Street in the Southwark deep shelter. [Daily Mail]

Tube tunnels as shelters

London Transport commissioned a confidential survey of new tube lines not yet opened and suitable for shelter purposes. On 30th September 1938 the Emergency Organisation committee was advised that 12½ miles of tube tunnels were available for A.R.P. use forthwith and a further 3 miles could made available in about three weeks after the compressed air had been taken off. The lines in question were the Bakerloo Line extension being constructed between Baker Street and Finchley Road, the Northern Line from Highgate to East Finchley and the eastern extension of the Central Line. To gain access staircases would have to be constructed in working shafts between stations and in unfinished escalator tunnels; the depths involved varied between 40ft and 127ft and 16 staircases made of softwood and whitewashed to minimise fire risk would cost £5,000. In the event no immediate action was taken and fast work on completing the Bakerloo Line extension enabled it to open to traffic on 20th November 1939. The other new works succumbed to war conditions and the Central Line tunnels did indeed see use as shelters, as described in Chapter 7.

Government action initiated . . .

By January 1939 the situation had become extremely critical. Wing-Commander E. J. Hodsoll, Inspector-General of Air Raid Precautions for the Home Office, expressed the reality of the situation, conceding that although absolute immunity from air attack could not be guaranteed by any known defensive measures, the danger would be greatly reduced if everyone was properly warned, trained and protected beforehand.

Illustrated self-help guides to A.R.P. protection from the Stationery Office and other publishers went on sale everywhere. As war became ever more inevitable the Civil Defence Act was passed in July 1939, setting out extensive regulations about the running of air-raid shelters (it also covered utilities, the black-out of buildings, evacuation of children and pregnant women, as well as the treatment of casualties and control of diseases). The declaration of war followed soon after, on 3rd September 1939.

. . . and criticised

The government's provision for sheltering seemed inadequate to some observers and the call arose for purpose-built underground shelters. The politician Barbara Castle attacked the lack of an adequate shelter policy, citing the views of Professor J. B. S. Haldane, a communist sympathizer and eminent scientist. Her autobiography *Fighting All The Way* recalls how his first hand experience of fighting in the Spanish Civil War taught him that high explosive, not gas, would be the main threat. Aware of the deep psychological need of humans caught in bombardment to go underground, he urged the building of a network of deep tunnels under London to meet this need and give real protection.

At the same time a pressure group calling itself the A.R.P. Co-ordinating Committee put forward an elaborate scheme for deep shelters, encouraged in part by experience of bombing during the Spanish Civil War in which tunnels below the streets of Barcelona had provided good protection. But as Barbara Castle continues, the government did not want to know.

In 1939 Sir John Anderson, dismissing deep shelters as impractical, insisted that blast and splinter-proof protection was all that was needed and promised a vast extension of the steel shelters which took his name. These consisted of enlarged holes in the ground covered by a vault of thin steel. They had, of course, no lighting, no heating and no lavatories. People had to survive a winter night's bombardment in them as best they could. In fact, when the Blitz came, the people of London created their own deep shelters: the London Underground. Night after night, just before the sirens sounded, thousands trooped down in orderly fashion into the nearest Underground station, taking their bedding with them, flasks of hot tea, snacks, radios, packs of cards and magazines. People soon got their regular places and set up little troglodyte communities where they could relax. I joined them one night to see what it was like. It was not a way of life I wanted for myself but I could see what an important safety-valve it was. Without it, London life could not have carried on in the way it did.

A year later concerted campaigning caused the government to reconsider. The agitation by communists and the Far Left is the best remembered and these extracts from a pamphlet issued by the Leninist League of Great Britain in November 1940 illustrate the fervour that at least some people felt.

Has security gone? Is it possible now to imagine what a night of peace is like? London has shown the way. The masses of London have achieved a great victory over the ruling classes. The private interests decided that deep bombproof shelters were unnecessary and the London Passenger Transport Board ruled that the Underground was not to be used for deep shelter. But decrees and police persecution cannot withstand mass pressure. The Underground offered genuine protection from bombs and the workers of London sweeping all obstacles aside took over this protection. Officialdom, alarmed, gave way so that it can still act as the agent of the profit-making cement rings and big business. Only in ourselves can we, the masses, have full confidence. From among ourselves we can elect representatives to comprise our committees for the competent running of the shelters, of food rationing, of transport, of accommodation, of the building of deep bombproof shelters.

Questions in parliament

Leftwingers were also causing dissent elsewhere. Claud Cockburn, later a columnist in the satirical *Private Eye* magazine, upset MI5 by stating the government was employing hired thugs to suppress (presumably left-wing) platform committees in tube station shelters. The allegation was made in a publication he edited called *The Week*, which Home Office memos called 'a poisonous production' and 'a rag'.

More considered opinions were heard too. A Parliamentary Question by the pacifist MP Richard Stokes (Labour, Ipswich) on 9th October 1940 asked the Home Secretary if he was aware that deep bombproof shelters could be built for the entire six million population of London for £120 million, that such tunnels could be used for the relief of traffic congestion after the war and whether in view of the government's declared opinion that the war would continue for another three years, he would give instructions for this work to be put in hand forthwith. Stokes was chairman and managing director of the engineering company Ransomes & Rapier Ltd and could be assumed to be well informed on costings. He was curtly informed that the sum did not accord with the findings of the Hailey Conference that had reported on the problem in April 1939 but the minister would be pleased to receive the opinions of professional engineers. To which Mr Stokes replied he had provided this two years previously. Sir A. Lambert Ward then suggested the construction of these 'deep dugouts' would require material badly need for the manufacture of armaments, to which the MP Reginald (later Lord) Sorensen retorted, no doubt ironically, "Let the civilians die!" Mr Sorensen (Leyton West, Labour) returned to this subject of civilian sheltering many times more, as we shall see later.

Some commentators claim that the deep shelter programme that followed soon after this was a knee-jerk reaction by the government to this communist agitation. Regardless of whether the forces of the left can rightly claim the credit for this change of policy is irrelevant; the fact is that there was now a will to build bombproof shelters far underground.

Civic pride or ingenuity now led some boroughs to devise local schemes for deep shelters, although Southwark was the only place in London where these came to fruition (some failed attempts are also discussed). Funds for constructing shelters were provided by the Ministry of Home Security, which scrutinised local plans rigorously for their cost benefit and generally favoured its own broader solution, as described shortly.

Sheltering in tube stations

As already mentioned, opinion had run initially against the construction of elaborate underground shelters and in the same way, at the beginning of the war, the Minister for Home Security, Herbert Morrison, indicated the government's opposition against using the tube stations as public shelters. The stated reason was that children might fall on the tracks and be killed, although there were unspoken fears that people feeling safer below would stay there by day as well as by night. If people chose not to venture out during the day, workers would stop going to work and apathy would set in, leading to low morale all round. The author, critic and journalist G. W. Stonier summed it up rather nicely in his book *Shaving Through The Blitz*: 'The

Southwark's municipal deep shelter ran beneath Borough High Street virtually from London Bridge tube station to the next station at Borough. Entrances were built at the locations shown on this plan.

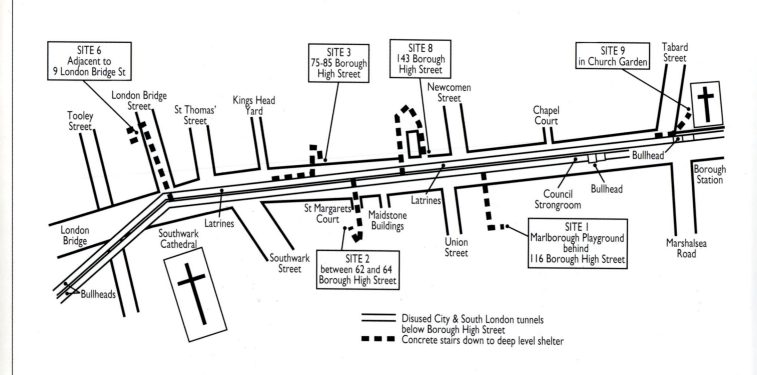

danger here is not bombs, or even burial or typhus, but of going native and not coming up again till after the war, when you will emerge with a large family and speaking another language.' Probably.

There were other, more practical reasons too. Tube stations had not been designed to provide a home for large numbers of people and being below the level of sewers, they were not by and large equipped with toilets or other sanitary facilities at platform level. Medical opinion had it that diseases would spread quickly when people crowd together, people with lower standards of hygiene would make things unpleasant for others and the rule of law might be difficult to maintain (all these predictions were subsequently fulfilled).

The 'blitz' bombing of London in 1940 caused a hasty reappraisal and this brief excerpt from the History of London website summarises events neatly.

> Londoners had different ideas. They were convinced that Mr Morrison's mind needed to be changed. On the evening of 8th September 1940, large crowds gathered outside Liverpool Street underground station, the East End Londoners' gateway to the underground system. The East Enders were determined that they were going to shelter that night in the safety of the Tube. At first the authorities refused to let them in but the crowds would not leave. Eventually the gates were opened and the people flowed in. Phil Piratin, a Stepney councillor, describes another such demonstration to force the government to change its mind and open the Tube for people to shelter, stating:
>
> *"Various implements such as crowbars happened to be available, and while the police stood on duty guarding the gates, they were quickly swept aside by the crowds, the crowbars were brought into action, and the people went down. That night tens of thousands sprawled on the Tube platforms. The next day Mr. Herbert Morrison, solemn as an owl, rose to make his world-shattering announcement; the government had reconsidered its opinion in the matter of the Tubes being used as shelters."*
>
> What Mr Morrison feared did not happen. Even when families found themselves bombed out of their own homes and they made a new home underground and daily life managed to continue very much as usual. The majority of people were determined that life should go on, that just 'getting on' in spite of everything that happened to them would help Britain win the war. The government 'got on' with the job of making the Tube a better place to shelter.

Southwark's saga

The deep tunnel air raid shelter in Southwark was an imaginative combination of new and existing assets, exploiting a disused tunnel for tube trains provided with new access points. It made use of the tunnels leading to the original terminus of the City & South London Railway at King William Street station. Opened in 1890, this station was abandoned just ten years later when what is now the Northern Line (City branch) was extended along a new route to Moorgate and other stations. This left high and dry a spur some 1,267 yards long that found no new use up to the outbreak of war in 1939. In an excellent monograph on the subject Peter Bancroft relates how already in 1936 an astute (or imaginative) report in *The Star* evening newspaper had suggested using the remains as a 'bomb-proof anti-aircraft tunnel' (among other things), a plan that was adopted by Southwark Borough Council in December 1939 after rejecting other proposals as more expensive.

Technical advice from Dr David Anderson of consulting civil engineers Mott, Hay and Anderson indicated the main work of conversion could be carried out in around three months for an estimated cost of £50,000, a plan of action that had been approved in principle by the Minister for Home Security. A large proportion of the cost would be covered by government grant, and London Transport agreed to rent the tunnel space to the council for £100 per annum. Construction work (by Kinnear Moodie & Co.) was authorised in January 1940 and the first entrance to the new shelter was opened by the mayor and mayoress of Southwark on 24th June 1940.

Photos and plans of the works are given in Peter Bancroft's booklet and these indicate that the section of tunnels used ran from the high water mark of the Thames at London Bridge south along Borough High Street to a point just north of St George's church (Tabard Street). Concrete bulkheads marked the two ends of the shelter. Out of the nine possible entrance places six were actually built at roadside points, with brick pillars and arches looking like miniature railway tunnel portals. New staircase tunnels were built from concrete segments and equipped with concrete staircases; these led to the original railway running tunnels, in which new concrete floors were provided. Toilets and a medical first aid post were provided and the walls white-washed. Bunk numbers were stencilled on these to indicate the places allocated to regular shelterers. Ventilation equipment was installed and a small strong room was constructed to house the council's valuables. The shelter closed on 7th May 1945.

Contemporary accounts of the facilities are by no means numerous, but this one by a Mr A. Gabe and first printed in Ben Wicks's book *Waiting For The All Clear*.

> The entrance was in the Borough High Street and was sandbagged, fairly wide and once inside, a gradual incline to a flight of wooden stairs. I think my mate and I counted 120. Dim electric lighting, terrible stench of dank, cold air and quite a few hundred people – men, women, babies in arms – but the air was so heavy that when the patient on the stretcher or a chair was carried to the top, one was covered in perspiration and really gasping for air. Of course, we were offered help and were only too glad to get it. They used to call it 'the deep shelter' and it really was.

When the bombing began in September 1940 thousands of people slept in this shelter nightly, with queues assembling already at 5pm even though nobody was admitted before 8pm. Christopher Jones's excellent book *Subterranean Southwark* cites a report in the *News Chronicle* of 4th September 1940 that describes the contrast between tired shelterers slumped between the ribs of the cast iron tunnels and alert individuals reading books and newspapers. 'Southwark has a new kind of inhabitant – the tunneller,' stated the article, noting the occupants' 'huge suitcases, bulging shopping baskets, old coats, parcels of food, bottles of milk and piles of old newspaper'. His book paints a vivid picture of life in the tunnel, the feeding arrangements, the disagreements when interlopers from other boroughs took up residence, all of which makes good reading.

A plan is born

Not all London boroughs had the expertise or incentive to develop their own deep shelter schemes and looked instead to central government for inspiration. In turn the Ministry of Home Security turned to the partnership of consulting engineers Mott, Hay and Anderson, recognised as expert in the field of tube tunnelling and retained as engineering consultants by the London Passenger Transport Board and other bodies. A report compiled by Dr David Anderson of the former organisation and commissioned by Herbert Morrison crystallised the options available for deep shelters. On 18th October 1940 he wrote that four ways of providing shelter were open, namely by driving tunnels into hills, by driving tunnels radiating out from existing deep-level tube railway stations, by constructing portions

This drawing shows how the deep shelters were built below existing tube stations. Although the surface shafthead portals are visible to those looking for them, passengers using the stations today are unaware that behind locked doors there are passageways to the lower level tunnels.

of tube railways that might be required by traffic in the future and by constructing comparatively shallow (semi-surface) shelters protected with alternate layers of earth and concrete.

Mr Morrison queried the possibility of deep shelters at sites not associated with existing or future tube railways and on the 22nd of the same month, Anderson replied that these too could take the form of tube railway-type tunnels or, at greater cost, involve the construction on open ground of 'what might be termed a multi-storied underground building'. The most economical option, he stressed, was a tunnel of about 16ft 6in diameter.

With the tube-type tunnels the clear favourite of the engineers, the ministry consulted London Transport as the authority with the greatest experience of – and interest in – tube tunnels. A meeting was held between Herbert Morrison and Lord Ashfield, chairman of the LPTB and the eventual decision went in favour of these deep tube shelters linked to existing Underground stations.

The position of the LPTB was that these tunnels were to be taken over for railway use after the war and their locations should facilitate subsequent use for building new express tube railways along north-south and east-west alignments, paralleling in part the existing Northern and Central Lines. This was with the idea that they could be linked up afterwards, and reflected Ashfield's ingenious strategy to get part of these lines built without direct cost to London Transport.

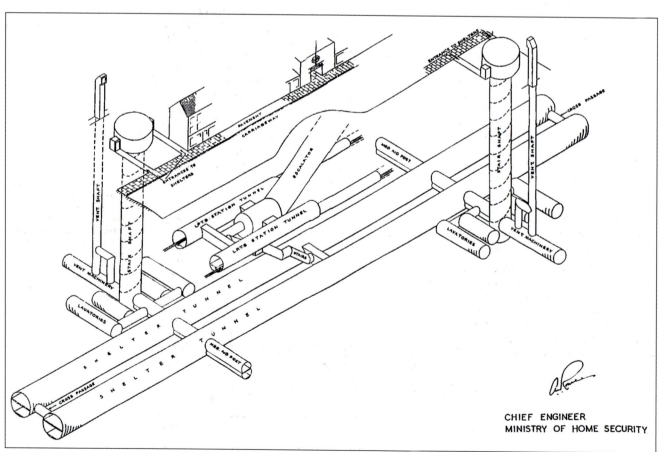

CHIEF ENGINEER
MINISTRY OF HOME SECURITY

The diameter envisaged for the express tubes planned before the war was 13ft 6in, designed to take standard-size tube train rolling stock; the larger diameter was to afford passage of air past the faster trains, reducing the problems of draughts to some extent. For shelter purposes this size of tube would have been restrictive (giving insufficient headroom for people standing when split into two levels) and from the outset the new deep-level tube shelters were planned to use tubes of 16ft 6in diameter as recommended by Dr Anderson. A few people have inferred from this that the tunnels were intended to take main-line size trains when put to subsequent rail use, but no evidence has been seen to support this hypothesis.

Firm plans materialise

A month later on 20th November 1940 Lord Ashfield set out concrete plans for the new shelters to representatives of the Ministry of Home Security, the Ministry of Transport, the consulting engineers and his own organisation. These envisaged twin parallel tube tunnels of 16ft 6in diameter and 400 yards long that would accommodate 9,600 persons in bunks. These new tubes would be placed below existing station tunnels at places where the deep-level express tubes would not stop (it would not be possible to re-use the shelter tubes for stations as the tunnel diameter was too small).

By this time a preliminary review had already been made to select the most suitable locations for the proposed shelters, of which there were ten:

North of the River Thames

St Paul's	*later abandoned*
Chancery Lane	*selected*
Mornington Crescent	*abandoned and Camden Town substituted*
Warren Street	*abandoned and Belsize Park substituted*
Goodge Street	*selected*

South of the River Thames

Oval	*started but abandoned later*
Stockwell	*selected*
Clapham North	*... selected*
Clapham Common ...	*selected*
Clapham South ...	*selected*

Further notes of this meeting reveal the names of some of the rejected locations. Leyton, Leytonstone and Wanstead were not deep enough, although there was good ground at Leyton [nevertheless public shelters and a factory were opened in tube tunnels here, as we shall see later in this book]. Bank to Bethnal Green was also suitable from a constructional point of view but it would have no value thereafter from the traffic aspect. These documents do not, however, reveal the reasons for selecting the particular sites nominated and for this we need to look to Home Office correspondence of 1951 in which the writer relates:

I have looked through the early papers and while it is clear that very careful consideration was given to the selection of sites, it is equally clear that the reasons for the final selections were never put on paper. Very many sites were considered and the field was gradually narrowed, mainly on technical grounds. For example Warren Street was considered as a site and rejected because of the nature of the subsoil in which the excavations would have taken place. The position is perhaps best summed up in a passage in the printed brochure about these shelters, which says "they have been constructed beneath existing stations so that access to them is easy, and they have been so arranged as to line and levels that they could be incorporated at a later date in a new system of tube tunnels, should further development of London's tube railways become necessary".

This is borne out by notes of a meeting held at the Ministry of Transport on 16th November 1940 when Lord Ashfield discussed the locations chosen and stated there was "no other plan that the Board knows by which such facilities could be provided on the North and South side of the river. It would be impracticable to make provision in the East End". A meeting at the Ministry of Home Security four days later underscored the idea that the shelters would serve the whole London area, not their immediate surroundings, and in support of this Lord Ashfield stated that London Transport would provide free transport for people travelling to the shelters.

Substitute scheme

A radically different proposition came from the remarkable mind of the Australian consulting civil engineer Chalmers Kearney (the first syllable of his name rhymed with *pear* as he was wont to state in his publications). Of these publications there were many, since from the time of the First World War onwards he had issued pamphlets, held public demonstrations and campaigned ceaselessly for his brainchild, the Kearney High Speed Railway. Between the wars it was impossible to find a book on engineering that did not describe his bizarre but fascinating concept of streamlined single-carriage

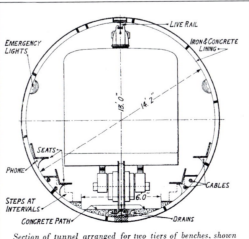

Two rows of seats would have been available to people sheltering in Kearney's tube tunnels, making the scheme superficially quite attractive. The recessed running and conductor rail would not have created an obstacle, whilst the overhead live rail would have been out of reach and hence no hazard.

Section of tunnel arranged for two tiers of benches, shown in relation to running position of a Kearney railcar

tube trains. Luxurious carriages would be suspended from an overhead monorail, running on frictionless bearings, with a matching but less substantial guide rail below the train for stabilisation. In this scheme the stations would be at street level behind shops and offices, with trains ascending and descending steep inclines to reach deep-level tubes.

For more than 20 years the irrepressible Mr Kearney and his associates had pushed to be allowed to build lines of this kind across London, provincial and colonial cities, but without success. An article published by the *Railway Gazette* in July 1939 made the intriguing proposal that tunnels of this kind could be built in London, to be used first as air raid shelters and be turned to rail use after the war was over. Well argued and provided with detailed drawings, it must have aroused some consideration and could have served as inspiration for the government's scheme of deep tube shelters that followed. The lack of any official recognition must have frustrated Kearney, for in September 1940 he petitioned the prime minister personally to consider his proposal, adding that he had access to capital in the USA worth up to £500,000 and could provide a valuable shelter in a very short time.

Unfortunately neither Churchill nor anybody else was prepared to take this eccentric character any more seriously than beforehand. Home Security ministry files reveal his proposal had been discussed *ad nauseam* and no adequate reasons had been advanced why this non-standard monorail system was preferable to ordinary railways. As a scheme for sheltering it had the considerable disadvantage that the stations and adjoining sections of tube were not at deep level and thus offered no protection, whilst although Kearney had argued that it was only the vested interests of London Transport that had hindered him from constructing his tubes, official papers make clear that no reliance could be placed on Mr Kearney's statements of finance. For this reason his offer was rejected in November 1940 by both the Transport and Home Security ministries.

Local initiatives

Southwark, mentioned earlier, was not the only London borough to take an independent line on defence against air attack. Finsbury for instance collaborated with the progressive architectural practice Tecton and produced a number of highly ambitious schemes that culminated in a text book that attracted such interest and acclaim in 1939 that it was also published in the USA two years later. The shelter design chosen was a circular underground affair designed as a spiral with a very shallow slope, approached from street level by ramps. Fully air-conditioned and provided with air locks, the idea was that these structures could be used as shelters for the duration of the war (for between 7,600 and 12,600 people according to size) and then as car parks when the hostilities were over. The street plan in Tecton's book *Planned A.R.P.* shows that locations were chosen for 14 of these ambitious underground shelters but nothing concrete came of it.

Acting on its own accord in similar vein the Metropolitan Borough of Islington submitted a detailed plan for deep shelters to the London Civil Defence Region headquarters on 6th November 1940. This proposed refuge in 12ft diameter tube tunnels at five locations, each connected to the surface by spiral staircases in two 18ft 6in diameter shafts and by inclined ways. The shelters would be adjacent to existing tube railway stations and would also have direct connections to the platforms of these stations. The locations were to be

Northern Line
Highgate [now Archway]
Tufnell Park

Piccadilly Line
Caledonian Road
Holloway Road
York Road [closed station]

Although this plan was carefully conceived and had the merit of having been prepared by Sir Harley Dalrymple-Hay, it failed to secure central government approval on the grounds that no additional resources were available. This the borough deplored on 13th December, noting that although Islington was the second largest borough in London and very densely built-up, the deep shelter proposals of central government all lay outside the borough. Notwithstanding, nothing more was heard of the proposals and all effort was placed in the central government scheme. Islington was not alone among the London boroughs complaining that their local shelter needs were overlooked and this illustrates an interesting conflict of opinions. The official line, established in joint meeting on 16th November, was that the deep tube shelters were to serve the whole of London, shelterers (or 'refugees' as they were originally termed) reaching deep cover by tube train, with "free transportation provided to enable refugees to reach their allotted places". This argument failed to convince Islington council, however, which was "of the opinion that proximity of access" was "most essential".

Some boroughs appear to have treated the Ministry of Home Security's announcements on deep shelters as a free-for-all. Hornsey's Town Clerk staked its claim on 28th December 1940, asserting that "deep shelters are desirable wherever possible", that "any deep shelter programme should be correlated to traffic needs after the war" and that "this district lends itself to a programme of deep shelter construction". After the ministry replied that local authorities had to produce evidence that tunnelling was necessary in their area and take the initiative putting forward proposals nothing more was heard.

Similar disappointment was felt in Greenwich, where the authority's proposals for deep shelters were rejected by the Ministry of Home Security, since they did not fit into the overall scheme for

London. Last and probably least worthy of mention was a proposal for an underground car park that could be used as an air raid shelter in wartime. This was seen – in model form – on the Movietone cinema newsreel in February 1939. The so-called Auger method was a means of parking cars mechanically underground in the trench shelters proposed for construction under London squares.

The scheme adopted

Returning to Lord Ashfield's memorandum, this stated that the total cost would not be less than £1.5 million (a significant underestimate as it turned out) and work could start immediately. It was proposed to allot two locations to each of five contractors selected by the LPTB and that the Board, as agents for the Minister of Home Security, would undertake supervision of the work in conjunction with the consulting engineers. The contractors chosen were Balfour Beatty [Belsize Park and Goodge Street], Charles Brand [Clapham Common and Clapham South], John Cochrane [Chancery Lane and St Paul's], Kinnear Moodie and Nuttall [Clapham North and Stockwell]. Finally Lord Ashfield emphasised that the scheme was designed to harmonise with possible future tube railway developments and it had already been agreed that were these developments to take place, an equitable agreement between the Government and the Board would follow; but it was to be understood that the Board were in no way committed to these developments.

Each tube was designed to have two decks, fully equipped with bunks, medical posts, kitchens and sanitation. The initial intention was that each installation should accommodate 9,600 people as mentioned but this figure was subsequently reduced to 8,000 in order to provide improved living standards. The shelters had entrances from street level as well as access from the platform level of their 'parent' tube stations, but use of the latter connections was always refused by London Transport. From the street entrances both lifts and stairs were provided, but the lifts were not for general public use. The reason for this decision was simple, as Dr David Anderson of consultants Mott, Hay and Anderson explained in a report to the Ministry of Home Security. "Lifts are expensive and deal with only a limited number of people at a time." This assertion was borne out by later studies that showed that 8,000 persons per hour could negotiate stairs whereas lifts could carry only 1,000 in the same period.

Construction begins; further options are examined

No time was wasted and work began on 27th November 1940. Optimistically it was hoped to have the first shelters ready by the following summer, although in the event there were great difficulties in obtaining labour and material. Originally it was believed that the first shelter would be complete by July 1941, but miscalculations and the difficulties

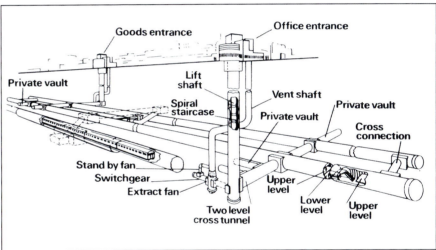

just mentioned resulted in significant delays, by which time the major bombing was over. With the blitz abated, the Government had second thoughts. To quote Jackson and Croome in their book *Rails Through The Clay*, "the old bogey of 'deep level mentality' was brought out of the cupboard by those who opposed the lavish expenditure of money and labour on this project, and in the middle of 1941 a select committee on national expenditure recommended that no further deep shelters be built, but those started should be completed". This followed some difficulties settling the terms of a formal agreement between the government and London Transport over the latter's basis of acquisition. The Board's original proposal was that in return for arranging the construction of the tunnels, it should have an option unlimited in time to acquire them after the war at such reasonable price as should be agreed, or else as settled by arbitration. The Treasury felt this was too generous an arrangement and one resolution was that London Transport should pay the aggregate of

Top: This view of the south entrance of Belsize Park shelter in Haverstock Hill shows how little the structures blended into their surroundings. The overhanging air intakes and the lack of windows also gave the buildings a stark, forbidding aspect.

[The National Archives]

Above: Diagrammatic view of the deep level shelter at Belsize Park, after conversion to a security vault. Other shelters were largely similar.

[Security Archives Ltd.]

The austere construction of the shafthead buildings at deep shelters meant they did not weather well, as this 1956 photo of Clapham Common (north entrance) illustrates all too well.

[The National Archives]

the amount saved by incorporating these tunnels in its system or a sum taking account of the traffic value of the new works.

At this time no firm decision had been reached on precisely which sites should be used for the ten new shelter tunnels and two that figured in early plans were later abandoned. One of these was Leicester Square, of which a Home Security briefing memo of 20th March 1941 states: "In a few days the question of Leicester Square station may need to be settled. Personally I consider this an ideal site for the purpose." The principal officer involved replied: "I agree that the proposal to use Leicester Square station is a good one and should be proceeded with unless either there are technical objections or any additional expense is involved." A marginal note adds: "Even if additional expense is involved it would be useful to have an enhanced Leicester Square station." These plans came to naught, however, as a follow-up dated 31st March clarifies: "It has not been found practicable to proceed with a proposal for Leicester Square. Belsize Park has been suggested as an alternative and with Mr Scott's approval it is proposed to . . . arrange for trial borings to be made."

Another option revolved around the continuing construction works of the Central Line extension east of Liverpool Street, where running tunnels were already complete. It is clear from ministry files that an extra shelter at Bethnal Green was on the list, and notes of a visit to sites dated 20th February 1941 state at Bethnal Green "boring is continuing but there are signs of serious water trouble – am awaiting report as to whether this is just a pocket of water or a constant flow". Flooding was already recognised as a hazard here; Desmond Croome's history of the Central Line notes that permission had been given for the incomplete station at Bethnal Green to be used as a public shelter for the first three nights of heavy bombing in 1940 (it had been adapted for shelter use by the LPTB at government expense and leased to the local

authority according to O'Brien's *Civil Defence*) but was then closed by London Transport because of the danger of flooding.

Memos regarding this new problem continued on 20th February:

This station, as you know, is not a working station and access would have had to be from the street, down the spiral staircase. Dr Anderson said he was looking for a site nearer the others but of course it would not connect with any station though it would be in part of any tube extension plan.

. . . and on 26th February:

Dr Anderson telephoned. Two borings at Bethnal Green show water and indicate that this site is unsatisfactory. He has found another site halfway between Liverpool Street and Bethnal Green where he proposes to sink boreholes. Talking over the matter with Mr Halcrow, Dr Anderson suggested to him that it might be [as] well if he (Mr Halcrow) investigated possibilities on other lines, e.g. on the Piccadilly at York Road, etc.

The site at Bethnal Green was indeed abandoned and the two new boreholes mentioned were constructed during March and April, being carried out "in view of the general uncertainty regarding the tenth station" of the express tube scheme. The tenth station was eventually settled as St Paul's but by the time of the next progress statement (27th May) no final decision had been taken, for reason to be revealed shortly. At Chancery Lane a public air raid shelter for 120 people had been opened in the basement under the disused booking office, and this had to be closed to allow construction of the deep shelter to begin. Agreement for this was given by the Borough of Holborn on 23rd November 1940.

Practicalities

At the construction sites chosen, abandoned buildings and derelict spaces were selected for shafts where possible. Goodge Street involved the partial loss of a public park at Whitfield Gardens but occupied property was requisitioned only where necessary. Nevertheless numerous complexities arose regarding the acquisition of property that might be required in connection with their construction. In order to simplify the acquisition of sites, the Minister of Home Security delegated to the London Passenger Transport Board his functions under Defence Regulation 51 enabling it to take possession of certain premises (spoil dumping sites were negotiated separately with the London County Council). There was, of course, a procedure to be followed in situations where the Regulation was enforced whereby notices would be issued to the occupier of the premises and where practicable, the owner of the buildings and land to be requisitioned. Unfortunately it soon became apparent that the provisions contained within the Regulation only took into account structures on or over land and a certain number of amendments were necessary to cover constructions beneath. Even then further adjustment was necessary in order to meet the requirements of the Defence Regulation Act.

Much consideration had been given in the selection of sites in order to hasten construction. Areas with poor subsoil were disregarded, those comprising London clay offering better conditions for tunnelling. David Anderson, in his initial report, had carefully thought about construction methods and conjectured that in normal circumstances the use of a tunnelling shield doubled the speed of progress when compared with excavation by hand. However, there was normally a four-month delay whilst a shield was transferred to site and erected in a special chamber below ground.

Calculations and theories

Anderson erroneously stated that due to completion of the Board's 1935–1940 New Works Programme, there were about 40 to 50 shields in existence that had been used for constructing tunnels with a diameter of twelve feet. Most of the programme to which Anderson referred had been postponed soon after the declaration of war in September 1939. In fact two shields were still *in situ* beneath Elstree Hill, which obviously did not feature in Anderson's calculations. With speed being the overriding factor in the construction of the shelters, hand tunnelling was accepted as the only viable option. The amount of progress using this method was given as 45ft per week for 12ft diameter tunnels and 28ft per week for those of 16ft, based on three shifts of eight hours per day.

The location of the shelters, as originally proposed, was designed to serve the whole of the tube system from which those seeking refuge would be drawn. From almost the outset different conditions were being considered under which the installations would be made available, free transport being proposed in order that persons could reach their allocated places. The Board confidently stated that it was unaware of any other plan by which such facilities could be offered north and south of the river, recording that it was impracticable for provision to be made in the East End.

Almost out of context here was mention of the extension of the Bakerloo line from Elephant & Castle to Camberwell, which, much as the Board would have preferred it, was outside the construction criteria of the shelters, due to the poor state of the ground. If work were to commence, tunnelling under pressure would be the only option greatly adding to the cost. It can only be assumed that from this statement, the Board had looked towards using part of the extension to Camberwell to increase the shelter network. (In the event a short section of the extension tunnel was built along Camberwell Road in 1939/40.)

Work begins

On 20th February 1941, soon after construction work had commenced, came the first of many inspection visits to determine what progress was being made, the ensuing report describing the adopted construction method.

Following site clearance, the initial work involved the sinking of two shafts, the base of each providing access to a cross passage excavated at right angles beneath the existing railway. From the cross passage and paralleling the tube line, four working faces would be established, two in each direction, from which would be driven the twin shelter tunnels. The shafts were 200yd apart and the shelter tunnels were driven 100yd in both directions from the bottom of each shaft, making two parallel shelter tunnels 400yd long.

Traditional construction methods were employed in the sinking of shafts, the depths of which varied from site to site. A ring with a cylindrical height of 20 inches was inserted as excavation continued and in normal circumstances, it was found possible to install two rings during every shift of twelve hours. Two shifts of 12 hours duration were worked once excavation of the shelter tunnels began, the depth of the shafts varying between 60 and 75 rings.

To gain experience of laying and fitting out the tunnels, London Transport was at the same time erecting on Clapham Common a full-scale model of a section of tube, complete with bunks and ventilation (this was inspected by the Ministers of Home Security and of Health). Also during February 1941, London Transport concluded negotiations for the purchase of 80 second-hand lorries at a cost of £34,000 (£425 each) then considered inexpensive when compared with the level to which prices had risen. The lorries would then remain the property of the Ministry of Home Security and hired to the contractors, their most important use being the removal of spoil from the extensive tunnelling operations and the transfer of tunnel lining segments.

In view of the excessive expense of hiring additional vehicles, a further purchase of 50 lorries was approved by the Treasury in May 1941, the price of each having then risen to £500. It remains on record that each of the second batch of used lorries was in need of reconditioning, although the actual nature of the work required is unknown, their daily maintenance, servicing, housing and staffing falling to the LPTB.

Spoil tactics

Naturally, the next important consideration was to identify suitable spoil dumping sites. Negotiations were entered into with the Ministry of Works and Buildings to use Regent's Park for sites north of the river, which proved successful following the LPTB's agreement to assume accountability for damage repair that involved the cost of removing topsoil followed by its replacement and reseeding at a new level. Some of the spoil was used to raise an area of grassland in the park by several feet to provide additional cricket pitches on ground previously unsuitable. The park was also used for the storage of cast iron tunnel lining segments and the majority of the lorry fleet was allocated here.

Spoil dumping south of the river required a greater number of sites. It was estimated that excavations would produce some 200,000 cubic yards of spoil and the London County Council gave its approval for approximately half of this amount to be dumped on Clapham Common. This figure was later raised to 125,000 cubic yards, the height of the dump rising 20 feet in consequence. Following the cessation of hostilities, the Board undertook to make good any LCC open space so utilised.

A site in Nightingale Lane was soon identified for the deposit of a further 20,000 cubic yards of spoil. The proximity of this location to the Clapham South site was sufficient to allow the use of a gantry for spoil transfer, thus alleviating the need for lorries. Similar circumstances existed at a site comprising three bomb-damaged houses in Clapham Road, where a further 20,000 cubic yards of spoil could be dumped using a gantry above the Clapham North site, but there were allotments here and the Ministry of Agriculture agreed to give relocation expenses of £5 to each of their occupiers.

The establishing of a further spoil dump in Kennington Park was considered but rejected when it was suggested that unrecovered bodies of air raid victims might be found in the vicinity. Further frustration was experienced following the abandonment of a plan to relocate the dump in the grounds of a convent, the area having been requisitioned by the Ministry of Agriculture to provide replacement allotments for those who had vacated land in Clapham Road. The Ministry of Home Security came under pressure to secure the use of an additional dumping site, but further intense negotiation surprisingly resulted in the release of the aforementioned convent grounds and an increase in the area available on Clapham Common.

Progress reported

Of the sites inspected on 20th February, that at Chancery Lane was the most advanced, where one shaft was complete, having been accelerated by the use of a redundant lift shaft previously providing access to the station from the former entrance at the corner of Fulwood Place and High Holborn. As a result it had only been necessary to excavate an additional 30ft to achieve the required depth. The cross passage at this location was also complete and a start had been made on the shelter tunnels to which it gave access. A start on the second shaft located in Furnival Street was also noted at the time of the survey.

Of the remaining sites north of the river (discounting those unbuilt at St Paul's and Bethnal Green) the shafts at Goodge Street had been dug to depths of nineteen and seventeen rings and arrangements were in hand for the introduction of night work. The Camden Town workings provided some cause for concern where poor supervision had resulted in shaft depths of just seven and five rings. As previously arranged, all north London sites were using Regent's Park as a spoil dump.

In south London, Clapham North had progressed to an extent whereby one shaft was complete and a start made upon its associated cross passage, whilst the second vertical excavation had reached two thirds of its required depth. At the Clapham Common site, a similar circumstance existed to that at Chancery Lane, where a former lift access had facilitated the swift completion of one shaft, the second having reached a depth of six rings. At Clapham South one shaft was down some 53ft but work had yet to commence on the other.

All that could be perceived at Stockwell was the erection of a gantry above the location of one shaft only and some initial borings at the other, the delay in obtaining both sites being given as the primary cause. At Oval one shaft had reached 40 rings and a gantry erected for the second.

Materials and methods

The most important components used in the construction of the shelters were the cast iron segments for lining the excavations and in order to expedite their availability a special contract had been raised. In addition to those of new manufacture, identical segments produced for shelters in Middlesbrough were to be made available. Discussions with the Treasury Solicitor on 13th February 1941 had ascertained that there was no question regarding ownership, a 100 per cent Government grant having been made available for their fabrication. But in order to ascertain the total cost of the Capital's deep shelters, Middlesbrough's second-hand segments would be charged to the project as if new. By the time of the following week's inspection, some urgency was being voiced by the contractors regarding the acquisition of the cast iron linings from the Yorkshire town. In early April the segments were reported as still *in situ* and reservations were being raised regarding their eventual release.

Despite the uncertainty, 6,052 cast iron segments from Middlesbrough were shipped south during July and August 1941, 4,381 being delivered to Balfour Beatty at Regent's Park, the balance of 1,671 going straight to Charles Brand at the Clapham Common site. A special rate for the transfer was arranged with the LNER, although there appeared some confusion in the amounts actually consigned, a situation not resolved until the following November.

The South London sites were the subject of further observation on 19th March and by comparison with the initial inspection, the state of progress can be determined.

At Clapham South both shafts were now complete. Approximately half of the cross passage at the base of one shaft had been dug and from this a shelter tunnel had been commenced; a start had been made on the second cross passage. At Clapham Common both shafts were almost complete.

Those inspecting progress at Clapham North were provided with a visualisation of a deep level shelter installation. At the base of one shaft the cross passage was complete with an offshoot for the installation of kitchen facilities. The twin tunnels branching from the cross passage were being excavated in both directions, the longest being 50ft.

The existence of water mains in the area had had some effect on the progress of the second shaft. The higher of the two mains was in the process of being diverted. The lower, incapable of similar modification, was being encased in a concrete slab that would cover the first 15 to 20ft of the shaft, where it would present no risk of flooding in the event of a direct hit.

Stockwell still lagged behind in the overall construction programme, although one shaft was almost complete. The second shaft, having reached only six feet in depth was to be lined with concrete, using a process that was less expensive and only recently introduced.

In conclusion the report anticipated an acceleration of the work at all sites, current calculations then placing a time limit of seventeen weeks on the completion of the shelter tunnels, whilst noting that these had only just commenced at Clapham South, Clapham North and Chancery Lane.

Progress to date

A document headed *Home Office Tunnel Shelters* provides progress achieved at all locations on 27th May 1941. By this date shafts at all sites had been finished with the exception of Belsize Park (Oval was still included in the list and reference was made to a tenth site yet to be selected to replace that at St Paul's).

Varying degrees of success were demonstrated with the horizontal tunnelling operations, the 12ft cross passages having reached various lengths as had the twin 16ft 6in main shelter tunnels as follows:

Clapham South	615ft
Clapham North	530ft
Chancery Lane	365ft
Goodge Street	240ft
Clapham Common	75ft
Oval	45ft
Stockwell	None
Belsize Park	None
Camden Town	None

Time was still considered as being of the essence, in order for the deep level shelters to be ready for occupation as soon as humanly possible.

By June 1942 Clapham South had reached final fitting out stage, whilst Clapham Common and North, Chancery Lane and Camden Town were largely finished. Goodge Street and Stockwell were part finished, with tunnels only at Belsize Park. Four months later, on 21st October Clapham South and North had been handed over, Stockwell, Goodge Street, Chancery Lane and Clapham Common would be ready by the end of the month, whilst half of Camden Town was already in use and the rest would be by mid-December. Half of Belsize Park would be ready by end-November, the rest by January 1943.

Costing and finances

Lord Ashfield's original contention that the work would not cost less than £1.5 million was borne out in the event. Assessing the actual cost of the deep shelters is easier said than done, however, as a Mr R. Chatterton of the Home Office explained to G. L. Galway of the Ministry of Works on 27th April 1951.

> As regards the cost of the particular shelters, this is … not straightforward since certain items of cost, such as consultants' fees, disinfection stations, loudspeaker and alarm installations, and profit on the fleet of lorries used for transport of spoil, have never been allocated among individual stations. The total cost of the eight completed shelters and the abandoned Oval shaft was £2,779,179, which gives an average of about £340,000 for each completed shelter. The cost of adaptation for other purposes of certain shelters which were never used by the public is not included.

In actual fact these figures may well be wrong, if an internal London Transport briefing is correct. An un-named official writing on 8th July 1949 stated the cost had already exceeded £3 million by 1942 and since he had been the sole assistant assigned to these works during their construction, his knowledge was first-hand. Regardless of this, assuming full occupation (which of course never happened) it is plain that the cost of the shelters worked out to at least £35 per head, well over twice the original estimate.

The cast-iron segments making up the deep shelters are clear in this 1941 construction view.

[Hulton Archive]

A Home from Home?

The shelters are finally inhabited

The unease that the air raid siren created was nothing to the dread instilled by the sound of approaching V weapons. It was this terror that finally moved the government to open the deep shelters in 1944.

WHEN the deep shelters were first conceived the Battle of Britain was already past its zenith. Regular daylight attacks on London (popularly termed 'The Blitz', from the German *Blitzkrieg* or lightning war) were replaced by an almost continuous nightly bombardment. The effect of both strategies had resulted in a sizeable proportion of the civilian population seeking a troglodyte existence courtesy of the London Underground.

As the construction of the deep shelters neared completion, a noticeable change had already occurred in the attacks suffered by London at the hands of the Luftwaffe. The major raid on the night of 10/11th May 1941 was followed by a conspicuous decrease in the enemy's bomber offensive against the capital, no doubt in anticipation of Hitler's plan to attack Russia, along a broad front, which began on 23rd June. Had the shelters been included amongst the Air Raid Precaution initiatives of 1938, their value during the Blitz would have been exceptional in the extreme. Unfortunately their need had been established not in perception but in consequence of aerial attack.

To bunk or not to bunk

Under normal circumstances the method of equipping the tube shelters might have been left in the hands of the original designer but a dispute between the Ministries of Home Security and of Health over the use of the shelters called into question the basis of how bunks should be installed. An MoHS report dated 30th May 1941 explains how this 'difference of opinion' arose and was resolved.

It followed the erection (in late February 1941) of a full-scale section of shelter on Clapham Common by London Transport. The innocent purpose of this was to assist the MoHS in approving the bunking layout. During the subsequent visit of Herbert Morrison, the Minister for Home Security, he expressed an opinion that 25 per cent of the space should remain without bunks and suggested that his opposite number at the Ministry of Health, Ernest Brown, should be given opportunity to comment.

Unfortunately Brown disliked the whole deep level shelter concept and insisted that ample free space should be provided from the point of view of morale and public health. He stressed that 50 per cent of the accommodation should be left unbunked (although he would accept a minimum figure of 25 per cent) and in the outcome it was generally agreed that Morrison's figure was the more acceptable and would provide a refuge for approximately 8,000 persons. Had Brown's plan been adopted accommodation would have been reduced to 4,800 with bunks situated on one side of the shelter tunnels.

Endorsement for Morrison's suggestion came following a visit to the Clapham model by S. F. Wilkinson, a senior member of staff from the Ministry of Health, who envisaged bunks forming a cross pattern along one side of the shelter tunnels and positioned longitudinally along the other.

Conflicting views

It was apparent that the Ministers of Home Security and Health held conflicting conceptions; the Ministry of Home Security advocating that the deep level shelters should be swiftly commissioned upon completion. The Ministry of Health took the view that the new installations should be held as a 'hidden reserve', recording this conviction in a letter to the Ministry of Home Security on 25th March 1941. In support of its initial opposition, the Ministry of Health placed emphasis on the importance of issuing no publicity regarding the construction of the shelters, which might give the public some notion that they would soon be available. In confirming a report on the conclusions reached at a meeting with both ministries represented, S. F. Wilkinson requested an additional paragraph be added encapsulating the Ministry of Health's line of thinking:

The Ministry of Health on the other hand, consider that, whatever may have been the original conception, concentrations for hours at a stretch of 10,000 (or even 7,500) people are bound to give rise to such serious risks of health that the shelters should be regarded as hidden reserves to be brought into (regular) use only in emergencies.

This statement infuriated Ellen Wilkinson, Parliamentary Secretary at the Ministry of Home Security, who was moved to add in a personal footnote to the report:

It is idle to talk of 'no publicity' and 'hidden reserves' in view of the enormous publicity these tubes have already had. People in nearly as great numbers as the tubes in far less safety and hygiene conditions sleep in our shelters without any epidemics so far. In any case, all this was discussed and agreed with the Ministry of Health under MacDonald. It is surely too late in the day for the Ministry of Health to upset our main scheme now (which was) fully agreed beforehand with them.

In attempting to give an accurate record of recent discussions, S. F. Wilkinson suggested to his opposite number at the Ministry of Home Security that he incorporate a line to emphasise that the fundamental difference of opinion regarding users of the shelters could only be resolved by the Ministers. However, as this was the general opinion of those present, its inclusion was deemed unnecessary.

A more positive step from recent meetings was approval of the proposal to leave 25 per cent of the space in each shelter without bunks upon which all layout plans were subsequently based. However, there was a general consensus that, should the need occur, this space could be used for unbunked occupation.

A committee is the solution

Yet another obstacle could have emerged at this point when it suggested that the Treasury's reaction to this modification might be unduly rigid. Feelings ran high within the Ministry of Home Security and contact was soon made with Sir George Gater, the Permanent Secretary, setting out all recent discussions and placing emphasis on the aversions of the Ministry of Health. Gater's assistance was to prove exceptional and he asked for a report on the new bunking arrangements that he would ensure met with the acceptance of the Treasury. He added that the health ministry's prejudices regarding the opening of the shelters pointed to the establishing of a committee that would advise upon their use.

A committee was soon established under the chairmanship of Ellen Wilkinson, initially to consider a proposal that the shelters be used for essential workers. Both the Ministries of Labour and Health were represented, although preliminary discussions had not included the latter. Debate centred upon the practicability of the deep shelters being allocated to essential factories and, in consequence, the facilities required in the event of such an occupation.

In response the Ministry of Labour swiftly supplied a list of factories the output from which was considered of greatest importance to the war effort. Discussion was then deferred when the committee agreed to consult with the Ministries of Supply and Aircraft Production in order to secure the highest selection of eligible factories. The initiative prompted consideration being given to providing whole family accommodation should all members elect to remain in London but without any suitable refuge. If this option were considered viable, then catering facilities beyond the visualised supply of tea and cakes would be essential.

Food and drink

The supply of food within the deep level shelters initiated a dialogue with the Ministry of Food, whose views were sought in connection with the type of occupancy currently being promoted by the committee. In situations where the shelters were given over to the general public there was a possibility of a joint catering facility being deployed in connection with the associated station. However, the use of shelters by essential workers dictated the provision of a more substantial repast, morning and night for which the Ministry of Food would act only in an advisory capacity.

Approaches were therefore made to the London County Council as provider of Londoners' meal services and the London Passenger Transport Board. Whilst neither body was equipped to handle immediately the expected high demand, both were prepared to establish new organisations specifically for the purpose.

The thorny problem of those eligible for admission into the new shelters continued throughout the latter half of 1941 whilst work to complete them provided employment for many. A meeting convened under the auspices of the Ministry of Home Security in November 1941, contemplated a selection scheme for shelterers, under the following criteria:
1. That those admitted should not have already been provided with a satisfactory shelter;
2. That preference be given to those engaged in vital war work.

The Ministry's proposals met with stiff opposition from the Commissioners for the London Civil Defence Region, who collectively recorded that the new shelters should be available to all those who applied for admission. Their use in the first instance should be to reduce the occupation of the more popular facilities and thus form part of the capital's public shelter scheme.

The Ministry indicated that it was prepared to waive its second criterion, the administration of which was dependent upon assistance being provided by the Ministry of Labour (whose co-operation was considered unlikely). But the availability of the shelters to all would require the sanction of the Treasury, from which opposition was expected. Ultimately it was resolved that places should be restricted to persons resident in the

County of London and the County Borough of West Ham who had not been provided with a table (Morrison) shelter, accommodation in a usable Anderson shelter or a surface shelter of domestic or communal classification.

The spiritual needs of shelterers were another consideration. In November 1942 Sir George Wilkinson of the New Tube Shelters committee asked the Minister for Home Security whether religious services could be held in the shelters. The latter held no objection in principle, provided these were confined to 'the generally recognised sects and denominations' and that services ended sufficiently early not to interfere with sleeping arrangements'.

Red tape

A ticketing system would therefore be introduced and managed by the relevant local authority, those seeking admission being required to sign a declaration avowing that none of the aforementioned shelter types was available to them. Also required of applicants would be particulars of any ticket held for a public shelter or one of London Transport's tube stations. Local authorities would then be required to verify the provided particulars for each applicant and forward these to a management committee, which, subject to its discretion, would issue the appropriate tickets. Any permit subsequently issued for another form of shelter would require the surrender of the deep level shelter ticket. These regulations proved that there was no shortage of red tape even when the safety of the public was under consideration.

In order to contain expenditure on staffing the new facilities, only those sections of shelter would be taken into use to cater for those granted admission. Reserve accommodation for approximately 500 persons would be maintained at each location and provided with the appropriate number of bunks. This contingency provision was designed for utilisation at night for those made homeless from rest centres in surrounding areas for whom protected sleeping was considered essential.

Moreover, such facility would be but brief until the homeless could be re-housed, although for psychological reasons it was considered undesirable to segregate homeless persons or subject them to any special treatment. The temporary nature of the accommodation provided for the homeless addressed an instruction of the Ministry of Health that denied the establishing of rest centres within the shelters or any form of permanent residence.

Change of plan

Apart from verifying the applications of those who sought the solace of the shelters, the management committee was requested to contain expenditure by giving some thought to modifying the construction programme, recent estimates showing an unacceptable increase in the cost of the scheme. Thus it was decided to abandon the second half of the site at Oval; the construction at all sites of separate entrances from tube station platforms; any

operations which had not reached an advanced stage and the junction tunnel connecting Clapham Common and Clapham North shelters. This last deletion is of interest. Once savings on the whole scheme had been identified following the abandonment of St Paul's and Oval sites, a plan was submitted to extend the main shelter tunnels by the addition of a further 100ft at the end of each; their original length increasing from 1,200ft to 1,400ft in consequence. At the same time it was noted that the ends of the shelter tunnels at Clapham North were only 650ft from those at Clapham Common and it was therefore planned to connect both (it appears this scheme was not carried out).

On 15th December 1942, members of the London Civil Defence Region met to discuss the formation of a shelter management organisation and criteria for its operation. At its conclusion, the opinions formed were conveyed to the Ministry of Home Security with a request that it formally sanction the proposals, the statement of intent being –

> that the position of the Committee should equate, as far as possible, with that of a local authority in its relation to the Regional Commissioners. Funding to be provided from a source nominated by the Ministry.

Thus the committee would be provided with its own bank account and capable of disbursements within a specific framework. This action suited the Commissioners, as alternatively they would be required to assume accountability for all expenditure. Second –

> that the Committee should be established as a legal entity being formed into a joint stock company limited by guarantee.

Other instances of this initiative had been successful when adopted by other Government departments. That the committee should be correctly constituted was also considered crucial especially when, in the case of necessity, the Company would shoulder liability for any action brought against it, thus negating any action brought against individual members. Sanction would also be sought from the Board of Trade to allow the omission of Limited from the Company's title. Third –

> that the whole of the Committee's administrative staff be engaged and remunerated by the Regional Commissioners.

However, the committee would engage junior staff responsible for the day-to-day management of the shelters, this category comprising wardens, cleaning and maintenance staff. Rates of pay were to be agreed with the Commissioners, as would the appointments of staff members of higher category such as Shelter Manager. Last –

> that the Regional Commissioners be empowered to deal with requests of a minor nature raised by the Committee; and

> that rules for operation and occupancy of the shelters be drawn up and submitted to the Ministry of Home Security's Legal Branch.

The Commissioners had also considered the most appropriate method for providing publicity in order that all applications for admission to the shelters were channelled through the committee. With the benefit of hindsight, it is interesting to observe the initial proposals for allowing access. This was detailed in a submission on Christmas Eve 1941, wherein the Commissioners recorded that, although the committee would be empowered to limit admission into any particular shelter from a specific locality or localities, it would be a serious oversight not to invite applications from persons in the area indicated by the Ministers in their first directive to the committee. This area included the whole of the Metropolitan boroughs, the City of London and the County Borough of West Ham.

The Commissioners were also of the opinion that, by immediately seeking applications from the aforementioned area, the committee would be capable of commencing an early appraisal process for all shelters. In support of this initiative the Commissioners were aware that Clapham South and Clapham North would be the first to open, and in consequence some hurried processing might be required in order to issue tickets in a reasonable time. It was therefore proposed to release a short statement in the London evening, local and national newspapers that would announce the anticipated opening of the new shelters and invite applications from those eligible. The notice for the press would be drafted for study by the Ministry of Home Security, local authorities being issued with explanatory circulars.

Another committee

At first glance, the proposals for opening the shelters were straightforward in the extreme. What could not be foreseen was the months of delay and debate that lay ahead.

Thus it came to pass that the London Tube Shelter Management Committee spawned in January 1942 the New Tube Shelters Committee, established as a company, limited by guarantee (i.e. without a share capital). The main object of the new establishment was, predictably, to manage all eight deep level shelters subject to instruction and other direction from the Ministries of Home Security and Health through the Regional Commissioners of the London Civil Defence Region. Also included within its remit was the acquisition of property or any rights and privileges necessary or convenient in the execution or promotion of the Company's objects that required the approval of the London Regional Commissioners.

The membership of the committee comprised Sir George Henry Wilkinson, Miss Violet Markham, Margaret Haig (Viscountess Rhondda), Mr I. J. Hayward (LCC) and Mr J. P. Thomas (late of the LPTB). The Ministers of both government departments jointly appointed Sir George as the committee's chairman and later co-opted the following officers:

Manager	Mr F. B. Copeman (*late Shelter Manager, City of Westminster*)
Medical Adviser	Major General F. G. Fitzgerald (*then currently Medical Adviser to the Regional Commissioners*)
Technical Adviser	Mr A. G. P. Thatcher (*Regional Architect, Ministry of Home Security*)
Secretary	Mr L. W. Medhurst, (*Assistant Principal, Ministry of Health, London Region*)

Fred Copeman, it may be mentioned, had joined the International Brigades on the outbreak of the Spanish Civil War and after returning wounded to England was elected to the Executive Committee of the Communist Party. Disillusioned in 1938 by the level of inequality in the Soviet Union, he ceased to be a member of the Communist Party. He worked closely with Herbert Morrison and in November 1945 was awarded the Order of the British Empire (OBE). After the war he worked as a foreman at the Ford Motor Company in Dagenham.

Among the committee's first actions was to give some thought to the recruitment of wardens, all of whom were part-time, unpaid volunteers. At Clapham South and Stockwell the wardens had been recruited from the general public but at the six remaining sites, business organisations had agreed to recruit voluntary wardens from among their staff. The establishments involved were:

Belsize Park	Cable and Wireless Ltd
Camden Town	Carreras Ltd, then from November 1944, Lloyds of London
Chancery Lane	The Prudential Assurance Company
Clapham Common	London Telecommunications Region (GPO)
Clapham North	Boots Pure Drug Company
Goodge Street	Lloyds of London

Recruiting started in February 1943 and the war history of Lloyd's of London relates how that organisation's contingent was fully trained in less than two months. Six voluntary wardens were on duty each night in every deep level shelter, one member of each team having been trained in the operation of the electrical switchroom. When finally the installations were brought into use, it was calculated that the number of wardens would be increased to eight and a number of marshals recruited from the shelterers.

In addition to the warden service, the committee made arrangements for catering, dividing the deep shelter network between two persons with responsibility for the four north and the four south of the Thames. Staffing would be voluntary and, with occupation by essential workers off the agenda, catering could concentrate on the supply of tea and cakes.

Masterly report

In April 1942, the New Shelter Committee issued a masterly document at the behest of the Regional Commissioners who called for a comprehensive report on the installations within its charge. Fortunately for the historian, it provides a clear outline and method of construction below ground that had no doubt been the subject of revision as tunnelling continued and agreement was reached on the layout for bunking. Each shelter had been built mainly to similar specification as mentioned earlier, although the two main parallel shelter tunnels in some instances reached 1,300ft, having been 1,200ft in the original plan. The twin tunnels were divided into an upper and lower deck and were linked at five points by cross passages at equal distances, along their length, with two situated at the extremities resulting in sixteen sections of approximately 325ft in every shelter. Each of the sixteen sections was bunked for an average of 500 persons, but no similar facilities were provided in the cross passages that gave access to lavatories, medical aid posts, control rooms and switchrooms. As a result the 8,000-person capacity per shelter could be provided as originally envisaged during the planning stages.

Each shelter was built with five entrances plus staircases from the tube station platforms giving access to the cross passage at the centre of the shelter. Spiral staircases led from the cross passages at the extremities to the protective caps provided at street level both provided with a small lift. Although the lifts were provided for delivering supplies, they were eventually brought into use for expectant mothers and those of a disabled or infirm constitution (lifts required attendants and studies showed that only 1,000 people per hour could be carried by lift, compared to 8,000 using stairs).

All mod cons

Mechanical ventilation was provided at all sites, as was a sewage ejector plant, a necessary expedient due to construction being beneath the existing sewer systems. As a result of their cylindrical design some attention had been given to the greatest possible freedom for traffic circulation. A system of folding bunks was therefore devised that incorporated the approved layout as set out in the sample section of shelter tunnel erected on Clapham Common, with transverse bunks occupying one side and longitudinal bunks the other. The former comprised double three tier bunks, their solid headboards forming alcoves that contained six bunk spaces. The centre bunk of each tier could be used as a seat, the upper bunk becoming its backrest when lowered. The longitudinal bunks were also in three tiers, but provided five bunk spaces on the upper floor using two double-width bunks and four bunk spaces on the lower floor. This style of bunking

could also be folded back against the tunnel lining to give continuous seating along its length and a gangway six feet wide.

Eight canteens were incorporated into the plan of each shelter where emergency reserves of food were held, sufficient for three night occupations should outside suppliers be incapable of providing provisions.

Access control

Each section of the shelters could be partitioned off from those adjoining by using a light wire-mesh barrier, allowing a partial occupation. Therefore as the shelters were opened following an alert, two sections would be brought into immediate use. The system devised decreed the end of one shelter tunnel, nearest the control room would be the first to receive members of the public, and one cap entrance opened together with access from the adjoining tube station. As demand increased, further sections of tunnel would be made available until half the shelter was full, at which point the second cap entrance would be opened. Some concern had been voiced that within the new shelters a general flow through the whole of the installation would occur by those admitted, but as all would be in the possession of tickets to allocated places and each site comprised sixteen separate units every effort had been made to contain this practice.

The committee had also studied the number of staff members required to operate the facilities in order to determine costs, the amounts varying from £1,729 per annum whilst closed to £8,902 per annum when open. However, there was a possibility the upper figure might increase should it be necessary for all eight shelters to open simultaneously when additional personnel would be required, some employees having been given responsibility at more than one installation. The committee also requested that the post of Shelter Superintendent be subject to an increase in salary, at its discretion, to £300 per annum from the existing £4 3s 6d per week (approx. £217 per annum) in view of the greater responsibility laid on this particular class of employee.

Deplorable habit

The first complete shelter was ready for occupation in March 1942 and the others were finished later in that year. At this point Mr J. P. Thomas, London Transport's representative on the New Tube Shelters committee convened by the Ministry of Home security, urged the government to open the shelters to relieve the strain on the tube stations and the obstruction both caused to passengers and to the operation of the Underground railways. Although he never deviated from this viewpoint, it was not one shared by the rest of the committee. The minister himself was "anxious to prevent the growth of a deep shelter habit and he did not think it was any credit to the community that people could be seen using the Tube station shelters in present conditions. He would prefer to see these shelters cleared."

So run the minutes of a meeting held 20th November 1942. Their conclusion stated that in the absence of indication of raiding on a substantial scale the New Tube Shelters were to be kept in reserve, not to be opened until pressure on other public shelter accommodation in London made this necessary. So far as shelters in existing tube stations were concerned, they would be regarded as full when the bunking capacity of 19,000 was fully occupied (which never in fact happened). Finally, responsibility for determining the point at which the new shelters should be taken in use rested with the Regional Commissioners for Civil Defence.

That the deep shelters were an expensive and valuable asset was always kept in mind, and it was no doubt notions of good stewardship and expediency that led the committee to make part of the Goodge Street shelter available for General Eisenhower's headquarters towards the end of 1942. Afterwards Chancery Lane was adapted for government use, as described later in this book.

Trial run

Another challenge for the committee came in November 1942 with a request for billeting troops coming to London on leave. This was considered impossible to refuse, on condition that numbers were limited to 1,000 men, physically separated from remaining shelter accommodation and entering by a shaft entrance, not through station platforms. Chancery Lane was the site recommended, to open on 5th December 1942 although in fact it was in use already from 28th November. Public resentment was anticipated to which the writer of a Home Office minute noted stoically, "the answer would of course be that the troops were using the shelter as sleeping accommodation, not as shelter, but I doubt whether this would avail to quell the clamour which might well arise."

Realisation now dawned that the exercise would be a good means of gaining practical experience of shelter management, and on 28th December it was agreed to open Stockwell to soldiers too (first used on 23rd January). Next National Fire Service personnel were allowed to benefit, with men allowed into Clapham North and women into Goodge Street from 12th May 1943. A decision in October 1943 allowed Stockwell to be converted to a hostel for American troops (later used for British and Colonial servicemen as well) and sections of four others (Belsize Park, Camden Town, Clapham North and Clapham South) were used to billet British servicemen on leave. Finally Goodge Street housed female members of all three branches of the forces, directed there from various hostels, YWCA establishments and so on. The difficulty of finding accommodation in London led to Goodge Street later being opened also to dependants and children of servicemen as well as civilian women.

The freshly painted sign in this official view of the Clapham South deep shelter compound indicates it was taken almost certainly in July 1944, just before public opening. Notable are the ventilation system outlets (removed a decade later from all shelters to improve their visual appearance) and the substantial heap where all spoil dug during the construction of the southern shelters was dumped.

[Popperfoto]

To improve orientation in a subterranean world where all corridors looked the same, they were given memorable names. This rare picture shows a junction of passageways, named after scientists, at Goodge Street deep shelter. It was 'adopted' in February 1943 by Lloyd's of London, whose staff provided volunteer wardens for the shelter. This photo shows an inspection visit, probably by directors; the nearest sign gives directions to Lavatories and the exit to Whitfield Gardens (still standing opposite the Heal's and Habitat furniture store in Tottenham Court Road).

Pressures for opening

These military uses were maintained throughout 1943 despite agitation that the shelters should be opened for their proper purpose. Typical of this campaigning is a letter dated 25th November 1943 from J. P. Thomas, London Transport's officer in charge of tube shelters, to Herbert Morrison, the Minister of Home Security. He writes:

I hope that you will forgive me once again for raising the question of the opening of one or two of the New Tube Shelters. I do this in view of the chaos reported in the papers out of the experience of the attacks upon Berlin. It is not impossible to believe that the same may happen here, and it would be our duty to be prepared to give effect to all the protective means that we have.

I feel that a shelter could be opened on either side of the Thames without more than passing publicity. Shelterers at Camden Town and Stockwell would be told by the local wardens to go down to the deep shelter to relieve the platforms for the heavy traffic now running. Gradually the surrounding stations would be told. This is a sufficient reason to give them, but is not the real one, which is to save some terrible accident through overcrowding of stations arising from the new technique of raiding, whilst ironically the New Tube Shelters are unused and have never yet been put to practical test. If only a nucleus of the public knew how to get to these obscure places, which will be difficult to reach under crowded raiding conditions, the public would become used to the movement and would shepherd others there at a time when crowds through fear become awkward. The shelter staff themselves, insofar as I know, have never had any practical experience of the mentality peculiar to the sheltering public. Shelterers may be more difficult to handle than during the blitz of 1940/41, as the raids may be more terrifying. The warden staff has been cut by 75 per cent. The railway staff has lost some of its best men. Women have taken their places and have never yet seen a shelter crowded or know anything about shelterers in the mass. The odds are against us and I do not look for the relatively smooth running again. [Most] damaging of all is the fact that none of these new shelters are due to be

opened within 24 hours of some terrible raid occurring, and then only with the authority of some person not necessarily upon the spot.

If his letter was alarmist, then the papers prepared for the Minister's reply are equally alarming.

I should think that Mr Thomas knows nothing about Crossbow. We have no reason to suppose the German air force can deliver an attack of anything like the same magnitude as the RAF has delivered on Berlin or Hamburg. Mr T. is arguing on a premise we don't accept. Under present arrangements the Regional Commissioners can order the opening of these deep tube shelters when the situation makes it necessary. I hope that the fear of reprisals is not making the public so jittery that the Regional Commissioners will feel bound to recommend the use of the deep shelters.

Crossbow creates a different problem which, according to the latest reports, is not likely to materialise before February. But the Newsam Committee recommends that the Ministry of War Transport should take the LPTB into consultation now in making plans for closing certain ordinary tube stations to prevent overcrowding. The Deep Shelters may not be available to the public. The deep shelters are in any case unsuitable for the speedy reception of frightened crowds, whether approached via the ordinary tube system or from the street. If once the deep shelters have been made available for the public, we can never put them back to use for the other purpose contemplated.

[Crossbow German V-weapon threat – see Appendix 5.]

In the event Mr Thomas received a very brief reply of thanks, stating that the Minister would bear in mind his thoughts but no action was needed at present. A note from the Minister's office to the Regional Commissioners revealed a continued resistance to open the shelters.

My dear Hutchinson,

I enclose a copy of correspondence with Mr. J. P. Thomas, from which you will see that he has either got a bad attack of the jitters or sees in the possibility of reprisals for heavy raids on Berlin an opportunity for renewing his campaign for the opening of the Deep Tube Shelters. In view of the suggestions he makes in his latest letter . . . we should be glad to know whether the Regional Commissioners have any observations as to the form which any further reply to Mr. Thomas should take.

Yours sincerely,
A. J. Edmunds

The reply from HQ London Civil Defence Region was equally dismissive of Mr Thomas's good intentions.

My dear Edmunds,

In reply to your letter of 4th December I do not see that it is possible to send any further effective reply to Mr J. P. Thomas without giving some sort of indication of the Government's views of the likelihood of heavy raids. I should have thought it best not to continue the correspondence, especially in view of the discussions now going on in connection with 'Crossbow', but I have no strong views provided that nothing is said to suggest that the Regional Commissioners would be willing to contemplate opening the shelters during the progress of a raid.

Yours sincerely,

A. S. Hutchinson.

No further reply was sent to London Transport after this.

News leaks out

Speculation over the existence of the deep level shelters provoked interest from the Press despite measures taken to enforce censorship. Louise Morgan, a *News Chronicle* reporter, gained access to the Camden Town and Belsize Park shelters soon after their completion, which she uniquely reported upon in the newspaper's edition for 31st August 1942.

Under the banner headline *London's Hush-Hush Shelters are the Last Word in Luxury – Bomb, Gas, Water and Fool Proof*, Miss Morgan revealed that the sites she visited were ready for use. She also divulged that two further shelters only needed their entrances finished to bring them to a state of readiness, with the remainder scheduled for completion by winter. Describing the location of the final four shelters as lying between Balham Hill and South Lambeth the intrepid reporter had also discovered that two other sites in Kennington had been abandoned 'because of water'.

In a statement that could be considered written in order to stimulate unrest, Miss Morgan announced she understood that none of the new installations would be open until a large-scale air raid on the Capital had occurred. Alternatively she reported this doctrine could change once arrangements regarding day to day management had been agreed between the Home Office, London County Council and local authorities.

Waxing lyrical about the subterranean white cities with their painted walls, miniature hospitals, shops, restaurants, inquiry and washing stations to be found at depths of up to 300ft below ground, our reporter turned budding interior designer continued:

> Lighting is by attractively covered lamps streamlined against the tunnel roof, the effect being remarkably like sunlight. The air is alive and just the right temperature for comfort. This is because each shelter has an air conditioning plant. Special entrance and exit pavilions are being built with two staircases, one either side of an emergency lift. These look rather like futuristic mosques, with a slender air tower at the back.

The piece concluded with some accommodation statistics and the eventual conversion of the shelters to provide an express railway tunnel beneath the existing Underground line, upon cessation of hostilities.

Negative reaction

The reaction in Whitehall was spontaneous, with an inquiry being launched in order to establish how the

Nearly two years before the shelters were finally opened this view of Clapham South was taken in September 1942. The facilities were nearing completion at that time and the mobile apparatus is described as an air purifier.
[London's Transport Museum]

News Chronicle's 'silly story' had been allowed to happen. However, ministerial reaction was not swift enough to prevent a further 'scoop' in the following day's edition in which a photograph was published of a dormitory in the Camden Town shelter. The caption writer picked up key phrases from Miss Morgan's article, continuing to emphasise the unavailability of the new shelters to the public.

Following this disclosure, there was concern that Sir Herbert Williams (a pro-establishment Conservative MP) would be displeased, especially if the wartime censor had not been involved. Miss Morgan's infiltration of the shelters consequently became the subject of investigation.

In view of the *News Chronicle's* revelations moves were soon made to allow the press to visit one of the completed shelters. On 9th September 1942, the Controller of Press and Censorship at the Ministry of Information sent a letter to each newspaper editor setting out ground rules for handling stories relating to new deep level shelters.

Emphasis was placed upon there being no possibility, in view of the lack of manpower, for extending this type of shelter to other locations in the London area or, to any appreciable extent, elsewhere in the country. Such clarification in any ensuing press articles was deemed important, as the public might gain an impression that significant enlargement had been made to national shelter resources. This could lead to the misconception that the new resources gave a substantially added measure of protection for the protection of the civil population in the event of heavy air attack. In the event of a really heavy bombardment this could give rise to an uncontrollable rush for places in the new shelters, with an absolute lowering of morale when it soon became apparent that only comparatively small numbers could be accommodated.

HOME OFFICE
NEW TUBE SHELTERS
STOCKWELL

SHELTERS
KENT   REYNOLDS
LAWRENCE   TURNER

ENTRANCE
BY
TICKET

SHELTERS
ARMITAGE ETTY
BLAKE   FLAXM

This strangely cropped view of the Stockwell shelter at its opening in July 1944 indicates that admission was by ticket only. [After The Battle]

For emergency use only

In an attempt to deflect any hostility arising from the recent revelations in the press, the Ministry of Home Security had bandied about the notion that only an emergency would cause the new havens to open their doors. Mr D. Medhurst, Secretary of the Deep Shelter Committee took up the points raised by the MoHS in support of this rationale, requesting guidance regarding the actual events that would constitute an emergency, this being the sole purpose for which they had been constructed.

Medhurst therefore listed the arrangements for opening the shelters, then currently in place and formulated by his committee. At the time each shelter, with the exception of Belsize Park, had a skeleton paid staff provided, comprising one superintendent, one full-time warden and one switchroom attendant. Although the warden and switchroom attendant were employed on a daytime basis, they would be available for night duty as the need arose and sufficient in number should the shelters be opened with little notice.

Further considerations for the staffing of the shelters included establishing a register of persons willing to undertake full-time paid work in the event of an emergency, hopefully having undergone some initial training. Twelve wardens were considered necessary for each site, five voluntary wardens being required for duty each night. The same number of voluntary wardens was deemed essential in the period leading up to full opening, an arrangement that was already in place at Clapham South and Chancery Lane. Other voluntary wardens would be recruited from the ranks of the shelterers themselves during times of occupation.

It was also anticipated that voluntary organisations would operate the canteen facilities and there was every expectation that these would function, even on the first night. Lavatory attendants would be appointed from amongst the shelterers and paid a night rate of 5s for men and 3s 6d for women. Medical and nursing staff would also be available.

Despite provoking much comment and discussion, the thorny problem of prior selection of persons to occupy the shelters was abandoned on the ground that any of the installations might be required in an emergency. In such an instance, which could involve the transfer of shelterers from overcrowded tube stations or other public provision, it was deemed impossible for anyone to be refused admission. A temporary ticketing procedure was nevertheless planned, although persons securing admission by this method would not be permitted to leave bedding in the shelter. This stringent ruling was necessary owing to the impending issue of permanent tickets to those who required regular accommodation.

The decision that the deep level shelters would be opened following commencement of the enemy's flying bomb campaign against the Capital was transmitted to newspaper editors in a private and confidential letter that also stressed no undue prominence be given to this action. By ignoring such a request, it was reasoned that any feature on the shelters in prevailing circumstances would hearten the enemy when there was a need to encourage optimism among would-be shelterers.

Statistical information also provided for editors at this time placed London's night population at

6,750,000 for which a total shelter accommodation of 7,250,000 was available. This seemingly inflated figure actually included domestic and trench shelters, 4,000,000 places being bunked.

Further deliberation

In fact this was not the first time that civil servants had agonised on how to test the eligibility of those wishing to use the shelters. Early on they debated whether the shelters be opened on a 'first come, first served' basis or if there should be a prior selection of occupants. If the former, how could ineligible people be 'weeded out' later and if the latter, was it right to treat preferentially those whose work was deemed vital to the war effort? The Commissioners decided in October 1941 that there should be ample provision for all who wished to spend the night in a public shelter but none should be encouraged to use it. The following month this doctrine was refined to restrict deep shelter accommodation to residents of the administrative county of London and the county borough of West Ham who had not been provided with indoor table or Anderson shelters or with domestic or communal surface shelters. Right of entry could be determined by ticket, supplied on application by the local authority. Some accommodation would also be reserved for homeless persons. A year later, a document of November 1942 noted with regret that no precise definition had yet been made of what constituted an emergency or overcrowding.

Decisions such as these were taken at a high level, generally by the civil defence committee of the War Cabinet or between the various ministries involved, and included some quite delicate issues. For instance, when deciding eligibility for admission to the deep shelters, the senior regional commissioner for London raised the problem of providing accommodation for women friends of members of the Forces who found themselves stranded in London overnight. It was decided that he should discuss this with representatives of the Ministries of Health and Home Security and then, if necessary, report back to the committee.

The major loss of life in Bethnal Green tube station in March 1943 (described in Chapter 7) brought a new focus to deliberations and two months later in May debate still continued over the basis for finally opening the deep shelters to the public. Concerns were raised that no practical exercise had been undertaken to test the means for ensuring the orderly admission of the public or for giving proper attention to the health and comfort of shelterers. Moreover, the shortage of labour made recruiting and training suitable staff at short notice effectively impossible. It was therefore vital to 'test the system' under calm conditions and not during the inevitable confusion of heavy raiding.

Serious disagreement

The New Tube Shelters management committee had previously made extremely clear their desire to partially open Camden Town and Stockwell shelters; persons already sheltering in the tube stations at those locations should be transferred compulsorily, allowing also members of the public who intended to shelter there regularly. They also argued that permanent tickets should be issued, giving entitlement to bedding. Another proposal from the New Tube Shelters Committee was to open additional deep shelters subsequently if the public used the first two and if this would relieve crowding on tube stations. The LPTB supported this idea, as it would allow shelterers to vacate bunks in operational tube stations, where they were causing no little inconvenience. On several occasions the committee threatened to resign, such was the divergence of opinion.

Below: This is Clapham South – deep shelter, not tube station – but given the design and construction, the similarity was hardly surprising and must have provided reassuring first impressions for shelterers. [After The Battle]

Bottom: Another view of Clapham South, showing the entrance to a sleeping area, with its bunks arranged to hinge upwards.

[After The Battle]

The white paint, unshaded lighting and unclad tunnel rings give a stark impression and combined with the lack of handrails, must have been disconcerting for many shelterers. All wardens, seen here at Clapham South, were volunteers.

[Imperial War Museum]

The government still ruled against opening the shelters, however. "To open the shelters now when it is two years since London had a serious raid would hardly fail to produce an impression that the Government expects raids on a more intensive scale," ran the argument of the Regional Commissioners for Civil Defence and this the Home Secretary and the Minister of Home Security endorsed. Herbert Morrison's memorandum to the War Cabinet on 26th February 1944 explained: "The spreading of the deep shelter mentality is a thing to be avoided. I recommend therefore that the deep shelters should not be opened to the public and request authority to issue a statement to the effect that the shelters may be needed for essential operational purposes in connection with the forthcoming offensive."

Accordingly the deep shelters would remain closed to the public, with a monthly review on whether the position had changed.

Open at last

Whilst the doors of the shelters remained closed to the public, several of them did indeed find other 'essential' occupants, as described in the next chapters. Part of Goodge Street was used as headquarters for General Eisenhower and later two others – Chancery Lane and Clapham Common – were adapted for use by government departments at a cost of £30,000 and £25,000 respectively. This was 'for a nucleus of essential government staffs to use as working and sleeping accommodation during a possible period of heavy air attack', although O'Brien states in *Civil Defence* that a section of one (Clapham Common) was used nightly as a hostel for American troops. Before the end of 1943 sections

of the 'public' shelters were used by British troops at weekends (three of these were Camden Town, Clapham South and Stockwell). As 1944 unfolded the number of soldiers requiring accommodation declined as a result of Army leave being cancelled from April onwards; in May 1944 for instance the Camden Town and Stockwell deep shelters alone were open and then only at weekends.

Around this time, however, the air attack warmed up anew and on 13th June the V1 assault began, to be followed on 8th September by the V2 rockets, which then came over intermittently until 27th March 1945. The arrival of the flying bombs finally moved the Government to open the shelters to the public. Stockwell was available from 9th July 1944, Clapham North from 13th July, Camden Town from 16th July, Clapham South from 19th July and Belsize Park from 23rd July. The other three remained in Government use. Regular shelterers at nearby tube stations and homeless people were given admission tickets, but demand was not high and by September some of the spaces available were made available to troops on leave.

Welcome news

When the shelters did finally open to the public, media reaction was extremely positive, almost ecstatic. Coverage in newspapers and cinema newsreels meant the whole country got to see these new wonders. Press agencies were now invited to take photographs (official pre-opening shots had already been taken for record purposes) and these saw quite widespread use, sometimes cropped by the censor to avoid revealing exact locations. Press descriptions of the shelters also give imprecise localities.

Pathé featured the shelters in a feature called *Front Line London* whilst British Movietone News called its piece *Shelter In Style*, with an upbeat commentary praising the feeding arrangements, sickbay and ventilation. The film itself shows satisfied shelterers, cheerful singsongs and the 'lights out and goodnight' announcement in an almost holiday camp-like atmosphere. The heady enthusiasm crossed the Atlantic too, with a Paramount newsreel gushing: "Five new and deeper shelters started in the early days of the 'Blitz' have been finished in London's most crowded sections to protect 40,000 of the city's population from the new menace of the robot bombs. Canteens are provided and medical service is assured 24 hours a day."

Organisational issues

When first handed over for use the shelters were managed on a day-to-day basis by the New Tube Shelter Committee, based at the London Civil Defence Region headquarters at 60 Princes Gate, South Kensington. In August 1943 or February 1944 (records give conflicting dates), preparatory to opening the shelters to the public, the committee was disbanded and all management of the shelters vested in the Regional Commissioners, who for this purpose were to be regarded as having the powers and responsibilities of a local authority.

Although the New Tube Shelter Committee was no more, the administration of its finances continued to give great concern to its new managers, the Regional Commissioners. Monthly expenditure by the NTSC had been in the region of £1,300, but now some thought was being given to allow some of the installations use by the military, there was an anticipated income of 1s per person per night for an occupation that could number around 2,500.

Day-to-day operation of the deep level shelters was devolved to London Transport along with the relevant local authority, with assistance from local volunteers. To handle the flow of shelterers admission tickets were printed along the same lines as for people sheltering in normal tube stations and special consideration was given to providing each subterranean city with a sense of identity. It was realised the sheer size and similarity of the shelters might lead to confusion and difficulty locating a particular place and to avert this, staircases were given distinctive colour coding (e.g. red and blue). Separate accommodation areas were named alphabetically after admirals, artists and so on (this last decision had been taken in December 1941, reversing a previous decision to use names of towns and ships).

Each of the sixteen sections within each shelter was allocated an individual name, with direction signs produced in the standard Johnston alphabet unique to London Transport. The names selected were an education in themselves, with each set of sixteen starting with a different letter of the alphabet, which might just be remembered, should the name itself be forgotten.

Clapham South was bestowed with the names of British naval commanders, the person responsible for their compilation finding an example to fill the first sixteen letters of the alphabet. Clapham Common boasted engineers whilst Clapham North displayed famous poets and authors. Stockwell's hall of fame recalled painters and architects; Chancery Lane, British leaders; Goodge Street, scientists; Camden Town, military and naval commanders; and Belsize Park, explorers. There was no truth in the rumour that the inventor of the water closet's name was to be used to indicate the location of the lavatories at Clapham Common and in any case the letter C had been allocated to Crompton. A list of all names is given in Appendix 1.

Entries and exits

Physical access to the shelters was a vexed issue and led to a lot of fevered memo writing in early 1942.

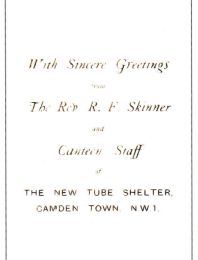

Below: **As this Christmas card shows, the wartime greetings shared by shelterers were as spartan as the accommodation down below.**
[Alan A. Jackson]

Bottom: **Close quarters were the order of the day if 8,000 people were to sleep in each shelter. Folding bunks were used to maximise occupancy in tunnels provided with upper and lower 'decks'. This is the lower floor and Civil Defence light rescue worker Robert Hunt of Kennington walks the floor as a volunteer warden on 21st July 1944. His armband states he is a 'New Tube Shelters Warden'.**
[Imperial War Museum]

With Sincere Greetings
from
The Rev R. F. Skinner
and
Canteen Staff
of
THE NEW TUBE SHELTER,
CAMDEN TOWN. N.W.1.

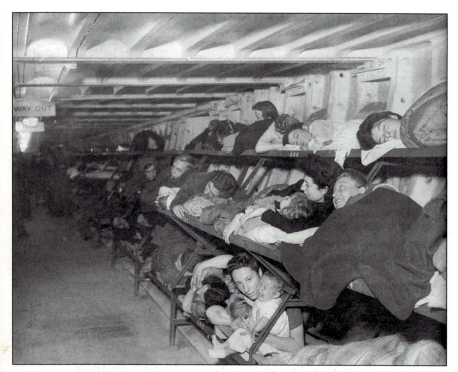

Above: It was a full house at Clapham South when this photograph was taken on 20th July 1944 but three months later the numbers sleeping underground had declined to the extent that some shelters could be closed. Total closure came in May 1945, by which time some shelters had no inhabitants at all. [The Times]

Above right: The 'shelter cities' (as the press dubbed them) were well provided for with amenities. Canteens provided light refreshments, as seen here at Clapham South, the cakes and sandwiches prepared by London Transport and delivered by trains called 'refreshment specials' in the transit case seen in the foreground.

[Imperial War Museum]

Entrances were provided by two routes – from street level by way of spiral staircases and lifts and from platform level of the associated tube stations. From the street, shelterers could reach their safe haven either by the direct stairs (as already stated, the lifts were not for general use) or by the normal station entrance and route to the platforms, then via the connecting passageways and electrically controlled gates to the shelters. Alternatively they could arrive by train. It was felt that during normal conditions the dedicated entrances would suffice but that during air raids, people should be able to reach cover through the main station entrance route as well. In any event, it was felt that without firm control it would be impossible to avoid incidents between passengers and shelterers 'with undesirable repercussions'. The LPTB should therefore have absolute control over the doors at the shelter entrance, but this control was to be exercised 'with due regard to the interests of the shelterers' and in close co-operation with the shelter staff.

That was the original plan but soon afterwards it was determined that all access should be via the dedicated staircases from street level and that the gates at platform level would be opened only "in the event of an overwhelming crowd filling the tube station concerned", and then only on the authority of the Regional Commissioners. The rule was relaxed latterly at Clapham South, where shelterers were allowed to leave direct to catch their trains in the early morning.

Storm in a teacup

Everyone must eat to live and this includes tube shelterers. In May 1941 the New Tube Shelter Committee consulted the Ministry of Food on the type of catering appropriate. They concluded jointly that if the deep shelters were given over to the general public, then light refreshments would be all that was required. If the accommodation were to be reserved for essential workers, however, something more substantial would be needed night and morning. "Though it has never been suggested that full meals should be available, it has been stressed that tea and cakes are insufficient. The Ministry of Food have special dishes prepared for such purposes, and would assist and advise on the method of feeding. The suggestions include soup, sausage rolls, cocoa and new dishes made up of unrationed foods," states the report.

By the time the shelters opened it was clear that refreshments alone would be sufficient and the Committee had firm ideas on how they would be served: "The food service will be operated from the canteens direct, food and drinks being sold across the counter, no peripatetic food selling is contemplated. No cooking is to be done in the canteens nor full meals supplied. Light refreshments bought ready made such as cakes, buns, pies, etc. are to be provided. Hot drinks, tea, cocoa and soup are to be made in the canteen."

The hazards arising from this ostensibly straightforward operation are highlighted in some droll correspondence of September 1944 that reads now like a Whitehall farce. Mr Smart of the Ministry of Food alerts Mr Walls of the Wartime Meals Division of a true storm in a teacup . . .

Dear Walls,

A rather awkward situation has developed in connection with the prices being charged for cups of tea in the deep tube shelters as opposed to those charged by the LPTB on the platforms.

Briefly the situation is this. Copeman, manager of the deep tube shelters, states that one of the voluntary helpers in the deep tubes has written to his M.P. (Mr Morrison, Minister of Home Security) stating that 2d for a cup of tea is excessive, and the price should be 1d. On the basis of 200 cups to the pound after paying from tea, sugar and milk, the profit is fantastic, particularly as the deep tubes are manned by voluntary helpers. Copeman is quite prepared to continue charging 2d but feels he will have difficulty answering the question.

It was suggested at a meeting held here today that the profits could go to providing additional amenities for the 10,000 people still using the deep tubes.

Unfortunately they charged the soldiers only a penny and even at that price made a good profit, solely on account of the fact that they had no overheads such as wages. When Copeman later raised the price to 2d per cup more or less to conform with the LPTB prices this formed the subject of the present protest.

As you know, although the LPTB charge 2d per cup, they have accumulated considerable overall losses and the LPTB strongly deprecate the idea of having to reduce their prices. With their existing staff overheads they have to serve a large number of beverages before they can break even. With their shelter trade falling away rapidly owing to the quiet period their losses are decreasing yet they are afraid to reduce their staff in case of further incidents occurring and the difficulty of obtaining further staff once the existing staff has left them.

The situation as it has been left at the moment is that Copeman will explain that if the prices of cups of tea in the deep tubes are reduced to 1d, these will be operating unfairly against many concerns where labour has to be paid for. What the outcome will be I do not quite know but I think you should be aware of what is going on.

Yours sincerely,
R. A. Smart.

Practicalities

Tunnels used as shelters were divided into eight bays of 1,000 bunks and each bay was provided with its own canteen. Electrical water boilers and food heating equipment were provided, along with a small storeroom for the use of caterers. Catering personnel were recruited from voluntary organisations, with the Women's Co-operative Guild staffing canteens in the four tunnels south of the river and the Methodist Mission, Whitfield Central Mission and two clergymen handling duties in the four northern tunnels; these volunteer staffs were already 'in post' when the shelters were used by troops alone and continued after the public was admitted. Food supplies were provided by the War Office for troops and by the Ministry of Food after the shelters opened to the public.

Overall direction was under the control of the New Tube Shelters Committee, based in the London Civil Defence Region bunker in Exhibition Road, South Kensington. Day-to-day operations of the eight shelters was administered by a manager (Mr Copeman) based at a compound in 4/6 Balham Hill SW12, next to the south entrance of the Clapham South shelter. Tickets were printed here and distributed to the various controlling boroughs for issue to shelterers. Specimens of these tickets, 3 x 4½ inches in size, are in the PRO file HO 200/0, which also notes in July 1944 that tickets would be allocated to all London boroughs except Bethnal Green and Southwark, which had their own shelters. Tickets were to be issued and allocated to people without adequate shelter, especially those who had recently lost their homes. Several boroughs reported having exceeded the numbers of places provided, Lambeth reporting a substantial waiting list of homeless families in August 1944. A small number of additional tickets were sent but in the main, boroughs were invited to 'weed out existing ticket holders'.

Family parties were allowed to remain together in groups and initially they erected curtains, allowing them to withdraw, so to speak, to the privacy of their 'own home'. The privilege of curtains was soon withdrawn, however, on account of fire risk. At times things got out of hand, as on 23rd August 1944 when several rowdy families turned up at the Camden Town shelter without tickets at 11pm. The volunteer staff, mainly young women, could not turn them away and had to call for police assistance.

How cheerful shelterers felt about their lot is a matter for conjecture; it probably varied according to their individual temperament. Those with spiritual needs were well cared for by local clergy, although this did not prevent a few inhabitants harbouring fears of immorality. One Member of Parliament was obliged to forward the following

Happy families! The original caption for this picture states that wherever possible families are kept together in the shelters, even though a few people feared it might encourage immorality among unmarried couples. This is the upper floor and the residents are making up their bunks for the night.

[Imperial War Museum]

letter to the Home Office (the spelling and grammar are unaltered).

THE NATIONAL UNION OF GENERAL AND MUNICIPAL WORKERS

Southern District.
Nine Elms Branch,
Secretary: F. Reed,
44, Binfield Road,
Stockwell, S.W.4.
July 16th, 1944.

Dear Sir,

I should esteem it a great favour if you would help to remedy of some of my branch members who complain of the system of the New Tubes Shelters. They have asked me to write you to see if you could get in touch with the Heads of these Shelters. (As they have been Bombed or Blasted out), they have had to take to these Shelters. Their complaint is that all Married Familes should live together in one part of the Shelter and all Women wether Married or not to be in another part, and all Men, wether Married or not should be seperated altogether, I have had it quoted to me that in some parts of the Stockwell Shelter there is only one man a Stranger at that sleeping beside 5 Bunks of Women surely this dont seem right also others over or underneath Womens Bunks, I have also been told that some of the unmarried Men and Women have got next to one and other purposely; at the same time my members speak highly of the other Systems of the Shelter and the Officials and think if the complaint as quoted as above could be remedied the shelter would be much better for it.

Yours Fraternally,
(Sgd.) F. Reed.

Having been constructed by London Transport, it was natural that the shelters' signage should also conform to the standard design used on the Underground. This example is Clapham South. The alphabet, unique to LT, was designed in 1916. The photo dates from about 1942 and the chap wheeling the casualty stretcher is wearing a standard Civil Defence ARP boilersuit. [Hulton]

The reply probably gave Mr Reed little satisfaction, stating that no contemplation had been given to introducing separate 'married quarters' and any systematic scheme of segregation would raise considerable practical difficulties. No such scheme had been found necessary in the ordinary tube station shelters nor in any of the large dormitory shelters in London.

Graceful decline

By summer 1944 five tube shelters were in use: Belsize Park, Camden Town, Stockwell, Clapham North and Clapham South. Declining numbers made it prudent to close Belsize Park and Clapham North as well as parts of the remaining two shelters on Saturday 21st October 1944; official records note that the process went smoothly and without the need for police interference. In the closing months of the war Camden Town became the busiest of the deep shelters, with 4,000 regular inhabitants plus 1,000 troops on Saturday nights. But this was not to last, and by the beginning of May 1945 occupancy had dropped to a handful. The nightly figures tell their own story.

Aldwych	12
Bethnal Green	nil
British Museum	nil
Gainsborough	nil
Liverpool Street	already closed
Southwark	nil
Stratford	1
Westdown	16

Apart from possible use of Aldwych by the LCC to house evacuees for two months, it was evident that the shelters had no further role and closure of the deep shelters in central London took place on Monday 7th May. Shelters in tube stations closed at the same time and arrangements for patrolling all these by the Metropolitan Police also ceased then.

Just before the shelters closed for good, the Ministry of Home Security had been making further plans for the expected return of evacuees following the end of the European war (which eventually came on 8th May 1945). In April it noted that deep shelters were open at Camden Town, Clapham South and Stockwell; at very short notice Belsize Park and Clapham North could be opened as well. This space was to be reserved for people normally resident in the County of London returning from evacuation in unorganised groups and without adequate sleeping accommodation. Rest Centres would issue admission tickets, although it was noted that it was "obviously undesirable that public shelters should be used for sleeping purposes for any lengthy periods". In fact the contingency never arose.

The final public use of a deep shelter occurred over the weekend 11th–14th May, when Air Training Cadets coming to London for the Hyde Park Review made a camp of the Camden Town shelter. Wardens from Lloyd's assisted in the welfare arrangements and on 17th May carried out their very last duties 'down below'.

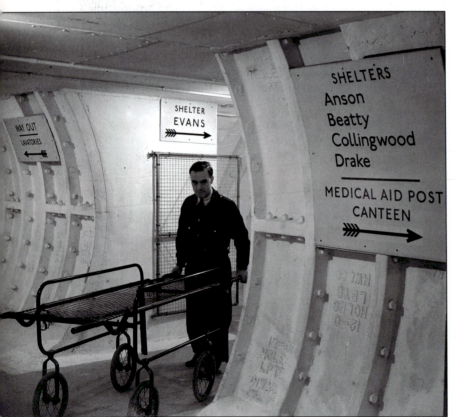

Were the shelters justified?

From a functional and technical viewpoint the New Tube Shelters were a spectacular success; at the time they provided secure accommodation for Londoners at risk from air raids and for more than half a century since they have served several other purposes without incident or failure other than the Goodge Street fire of 1956 (covered later). That said, despite all the fervent agitation for bombproof shelter accommodation back in 1940, the deep shelters were never fully occupied. The highest recorded nightly population was 12,297 on 24th July 1944, about one third of total capacity. On 21st October, two of the shelters were closed and nightly use fell until by January 1945 only about 25,000 people were using the tube stations and deep shelters. The last air-raid warning of the war was sounded on 28th March 1945 and the war in Europe ended on 8th May, but even at this stage the authorities were concerned the shelters might be put to the test once more. The Ministry of Health anticipated 'hordes of homeless people' making 'an unorganised return from the evacuation centres to London' and requested the Home Office to increase the equipped accommodation in the New Tube Shelters by 20,000. This was done although subsequent events proved it unnecessary.

A report written on VE Day (8th May 1945) by the London Transport official in charge of shelters, J. P. Thomas, provides a summary of the numbers using deep shelters throughout the war, to which he added, "The innate and irrepressible humour of the Cockney never forsook him. When there was anything cheerful to be found the Cockney was the first to find and give expression to it. This helped to sustain morale. He was grateful to the last to those who showed interest in his creature concerns."

To assist the public find cover, the above-ground location of air raid shelters was marked by these distinctive black and white signs. Paid for by Home Office grant, they were designed to be visible at a distance of 100ft, although black out regulations meant their illumination was a mere 15-watt bulb. The letter style has more than a superficial resemblance to the Johnston alphabet but this is coincidental.

style also known as Odeonesque. Although the shaft heads were erected close to tube stations, no attempt was made to blend in or make them match visually. If a parallel was sought in railway architecture, their exuberant style, including the sweeping rounded corners and stratified horizontal detailing, render them closer to the concrete structures on the Chessington line of the Southern Railway than to the more sober and cubic style favoured by London Transport, but in reality the resemblance is not great. Their architectural merit has been recognised at least by the borough of Wandsworth, which has accorded Grade II listed status to the shaft head buildings of Clapham South in Balham Hill, London SW12.

DORMITORY USE OF TUBE SHELTERS 1940–1945

	New Deep Shelters (from 9th July 1944)	Liverpool Street Bethnal Green Aldwych
1940 Sept. to Dec.	...	1,372,275
1941 ...	...	1,600,278
1942 ...	...	505,422
1943 ...	...	792,688
1944 ...	1,304,733	1,493,572
1945 ...	515,366	316,572
TOTAL ...	**1,820,099**	**6,080,807**

First raid – 7th September 1940;
Last missiles – 28th March 1945

Physical features

At this distance in time the surface buildings are for most people the only clue to the shelters' existence. Most now look derelict and their twin entrances do little to distinguish them from public conveniences, even if their dimensions are somewhat bulkier. Their architecture is, however, distinctive, with frontages that were once quite stylish in the 'cinema'

Pass enabling entry to Goodge Street shelter, reproduced actual size.

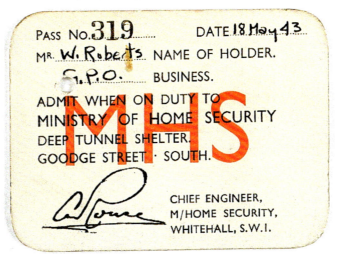

On Active Service

Changed plans for the deep shelters

As already mentioned, the government was not in a rush to open the deep shelters to the public after their construction. Instead more pressing uses were found for them to create troop shelters (as mentioned in the previous chapter) and citadel accommodation for vital service departments.

Goodge Street

It was in early 1942 that American forces arrived in Britain, followed in June by Major General Dwight D. Eisenhower, who had been appointed to command U.S. forces in Europe. A number of headquarters were established for the European theatre of war, ETOUSA, and one of the earliest was the communications centre created by the Signal Corps in July 1942 at 20 Grosvenor Square. The building suffered from inadequate protection, however, and the Americans asked for a more substantial building. What they were offered and accepted was the 'nearly bombproof' annexe of Selfridge's department store at Duke and Somerset Streets, safe against anything but a direct hit. Serving both army and navy communications centres from December 1942, it was 'a sizeable steel and concrete structure blessed with deep basements running 45ft down'. From a communications point of view this was well equipped, with a large telephone switchboard (PMBX) parented on MAYfair exchange, having 108 operator positions and 400 exchange lines. It was in this building's basement that the apparatus of Sigsaly (described in Chapter 10) used for encrypting and decrypting Churchill's conversations with Roosevelt was later installed.

The strategic importance and vulnerability of the facility were recognised and for additional security, work began on an auxiliary and bombproof signal centre to be completed in early 1943. For this the British government offered the Americans the southern part of the previously unused deep shelter at Goodge Street, known as Goodge Street South. In March 1943 the British GPO and US 3118th Signal Service Battalion completed installation of a fully-equipped emergency headquarters in the shelter, which, unlike the Selfridge's site, had the benefit of protected cable outlets through the deep tubes to the British service ministries and headquarters and also to the outskirts of London. Army and Navy message centres were here along with an emergency telephone switchboard, radio terminals and a British code room.

HQ, Base Command of ETOUSA occupied only half of the accommodation at Goodge Street (converted at a cost of £100,000). The other half, known as Goodge Street North, performed a similar function for the signal centre of Chief of Staff Supreme Allied Command (COSSAC), later Supreme Headquarters, Allied Expeditionary Force (SHAEF), converted at a cost of £80,000. A small staff of the War Office shared this accommodation. It was not, however, the occupants' first choice, as Brigadier L. H. Harris explains in his book *Signal Venture*.

> Wherever it was decided to establish SHAEF it was essential to have protected signal accommodation for the termination of control communications, including those which would eventually be working to the forces overseas. This necessarily had to remain permanently in the centre of London, where it was accessible via deep cables from the Service Ministries and all important headquarters in the U.K. who would require communication to the Continent. The anticipated V-weapon attack and the fact that trunk communications centred on London put protected accommodation at a premium, and it was disappointing that the heavily concreted and fully equipped Rotundas near Horseferry Road, which we had occupied for a while in 1942 and had been regarded as available, were now found to be required by the Air Ministry. We had therefore to build yet another signal installation and emergency headquarters in the only accommodation available; the vacant part of the Goodge Street accommodation adjacent to ETOUSA.

Official U.S. war historians allege a degree of obfuscation by the Air Ministry and the wartime narrative, prepared by The Historical Sub-Section, Office of Secretary, General Staff, Supreme Headquarters, Allied Expeditionary Force in May 1944, states bluntly:

> The South Rotunda, which had originally been fitted up as an anti-invasion base, was well protected in both these respects, and was connected to the various ministries by the Whitehall Tunnel. It was, however, too small for COSSAC's needs, and there was considerable haggling with the Air Ministry, which, while not actually wanting to occupy it, desired to maintain a lien on it for use in an emergency, such as a possible intensive rocket bombardment of London.

A word of explanation may be helpful here. In April 1943 the previously informal British-United States collaboration in the European theatre of war was strengthened by the establishment in London of a formal planning headquarters called Chief of Staff Supreme Allied Command, or COSSAC. In February 1944 this headquarters was replaced by the final inter-allied headquarters for the theatre – Supreme Headquarters Allied Expeditionary Forces (SHAEF), under which the elaborate activities of planning, supply, training, and military-diplomatic consultation for the forthcoming invasion of Europe went forward. General Dwight D. Eisenhower was Supreme Allied Commander of SHAEF and, from January 1944, also the commanding general of ETOUSA, but the staff organisations of each group were distinct.

Eisenhower made great use of these Goodge Street headquarters, a fact reflected in its commercial name today as the Eisenhower Centre. At this time it was equipped with a substantial mixture of radio and line communications, the latter including both telephone and teleprinter circuits. Direct telephone circuits from a 16-position switchboard ran to all military communication centres in the country (and in France following the invasion and liberation of that country), as well as the civil trunk telephone network. Brigadier Harris mentions that about a dozen senior officers at SHAEF were provided with additional telephones connected to a small 'Red' switchboard that provided instantaneous service to 21 Army Group, Air Headquarters, U.S. theatre headquarters, the

Service ministries and to the War Cabinet. In addition to the priority values of this separate switchboard it was useful that it left no doubt in the event of a breakdown or a move as to which circuits should receive priority of restoration or provision.

The British Goodge Street signal centre was equipped with around 20 direct (point-to-point) teleprinter circuits and another 40 terminating on a 70-line teleprinter switchboard. These were connected to subordinate and associated army headquarters, and also to various static centres on the (British) Defence Teleprinter Network. Radio communication links, connected from the radio room to remote transmitter/receiver stations, included the use of existing War Office, Air Ministry and Admiralty circuits to Algiers and Post Office channels to Washington. Four of the telephone switchboard positions were modified to control cross-Channel VHF radio circuits. Additional radio teletype circuits were opened to Allied force headquarters in Algiers and Caserta,

The telephone switchboard at Eisenhower's underground command centre looks a picture of tranquillity here but doubtless became frenetic under pressure.

[Public Record Office]

and all was made ready for direct communication with the force headquarters that would presently be landing in France. After the Allied expeditionary force had been established in France, Goodge Street was connected via a network of long-distance circuits totalling several thousand to static military exchanges in the theatre of war, including all the main towns from Marseilles to Antwerp and Eindhoven and from Nancy to Rennes and Cherbourg, as well as scores of switchboards at the mobile headquarters of the Supreme Command.

As already mentioned, signal operations at Goodge Street and other SHAEF locations in Europe were in the hands of the 3118th Signal Service Group of the U.S. Army and the British 5th Headquarters Signals Regiment. A memoir of the U.S. group's activities states that as the largest Signal Service Group in the Army, the unit was activated on 15th November 1943 as a Battalion. The first contingent arrived in the UK on 14th December 1943 and operated communications in London, Rotunda Signal Centre and SHAEF headquarters at Bushy Park. This unit conceived, installed, operated and maintained both a private telephone and private radio network, known respectively as the 'Redline Switchboard' and 'Redline Net' for the Supreme Commander to his Army Groups, Chiefs of Staff, and all echelons of SHAEF. With just eight men, in 29 days and working seven days a week, the unit installed for SHAEF (by implication at Goodge Street) a 14-position (1,400-line) manual switchboard – an installation that would be inconceivable in the United States in less than three months. In 20 months of operation the unit handled 5,250,000 tactical and administrative messages by wire and radio, totalling more than 700,000,000 groups. An

average of 10,000 long distance telephone calls and 30,000 local calls were handled daily through the exchanges operated by this unit. This would total 24 million for the 20-month period, or 28 calls per minute, a level of traffic that might be compared to the traffic generated by a city of 45,000 in the United States.

Working conditions at Goodge Street

For those working under these conditions life must have been strenuous to say the least. Ralph Scott of the US Signal Corps spent six months in London from October 1945 and soon discovered the relaxing properties of a pint of British beer. He states:

Upon arrival, I was put in charge of a radio station, with four other radio men. It was located in a tunnel, 185ft below the streets of London's West End. The tunnel had a barred gate at one end that once would have permitted access to the London subway system. There were two armed Military Police guards in a concrete building on a side street. An elevator took us down to the tunnel. It had been built by the British back when the Germans were bombing London every night. They had turned it over to General Eisenhower and it was all set up to be his alternate headquarters in the event he got 'bombed out' of SHAEF Headquarters. There were telephones on desks, and beds for 2,000 people along the tunnel walls. A Signal Corps unit had telephone equipment down there, which allowed the US Army to make phone calls to America. Our little radio station was in a 'net' with stations in Verdun and Paris, France.

We sent them stories of the 8th Air Force bombing raids for publication in the Paris edition of the *Stars & Stripes* newspaper (for American troops) and they sent us articles for publication in the London edition about 9th Air Force actions.

Original floor plan for Goodge Street deep shelter as converted to communications centre.

[Public Record Office]

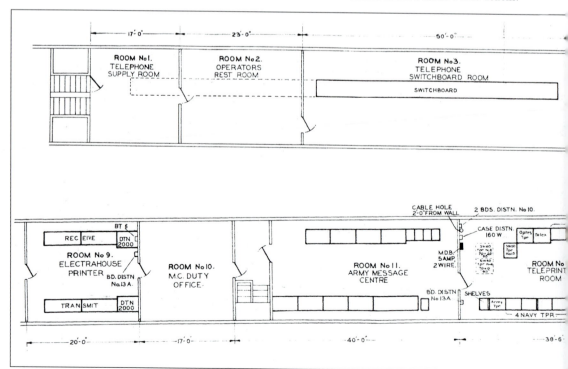

Creature comforts for staff in the Goodge Street signal centre were not forgotten. This somewhat lifeless photo nonetheless offers an impression of the almost surreal ambience provided for personnel at deep level.
[Public Record Office]

We slept down there and took our meals with a Military Police unit a block away.

My first night in London found me walking along on a sidewalk in total darkness. They didn't have any lights lit, and the normal London fog and smoke made it impossible to see much. I could hear someone walking in front of me when suddenly the air raid sirens started to wail. I had been instructed that in such a case, one went into a bomb shelter.

operator working as part of the British contingent of SHAEF, worked there too and recalls:

We moved from Rotunda to a base situated underneath one of the Underground tube stations. It was in the area of Goodge St station, we could go down to that level, then descend further to our office. Train passengers must have wondered where we were going, but all the Porters and ticket

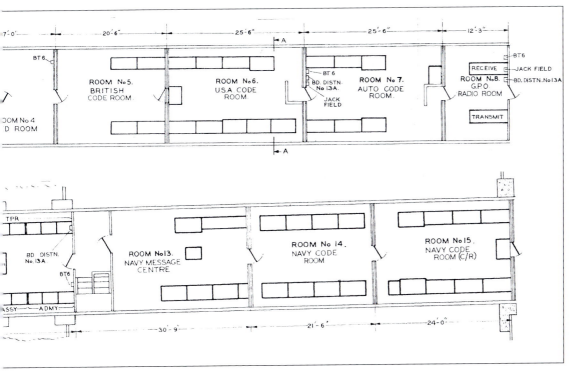

collectors must have known what was going on. There was also a rickety old lift on Tottenham Court Road we could use. It was a terrifying thing not for the public; I think it might have been a lift that maintenance engineers used. It seemed to go down forever into the bowels of the earth. We did shift work – a morning finishing at lunch time, then we went on night duty that night from about 10pm till about 8am. We did an evening duty and an afternoon duty as well but I can't really remember in what sequence. All leave was cancelled now.

A GPO telephonist also has memories of this place and states:

> I think I worked at most of the ministries in Whitehall, and several elsewhere. One or two stand out in my mind for some reason. One was situated below Goodge Street Underground station and was quite a cloak and dagger affair. I was given a telephone number and told to be at a certain spot at such and such a time. I arrived on schedule and a woman appeared apparently from nowhere. She asked me what number I was looking for, my name, and to see my pass (we all had to carry these). When she was quite satisfied she escorted me literally to a hole in the ground, and into a lift, which went down to a level below the underground railway. We could hear the trains going backwards and forwards above us. The switch room was an underground tunnel, and the switchboards were in the centre, which meant that if you happen to stand up suddenly you knocked your head on the roof. I think that these 'boards must have been connected to field telephones, because the lines were very faint, everyone seemed to be shouting at once, and every now and again one or another would close down completely. I can't for the life of me remember what it was called. It may have been that I was never told, because with some of the most secret 'boards they had no names, only telephone numbers.

Other minutiæ

Although the two Goodge Street shelters were occupied by the military, their administration still fell to the New Tube Shelters Committee. Their files reveal a host of fascinating details, such as the fact that entry to Goodge Street North was by the Whitfield Gardens portal (on Tottenham Court Road, opposite Heal's), and to Goodge Street South by way of the Chenies Street entrance. On 29th November 1943 the committee noted that the Bostwick gate entry from the station platform to Goodge Street South could be closed now that the high-speed lift was available from Chenies Street. A substantial radio antenna was erected by the Americans on the two buildings either side of the Chenies Street entrance, which must have altered the cityscape somewhat.

Chancery Lane

With Goodge Street, this shelter was one of the two closest to central London, which is no doubt the reason why it was "adapted and earmarked as citadel accommodation for important operational staff of various Departments if the need should arise, e.g. in the event of a highly concentrated attack by V2 weapons on London becoming a possibility". The decision to allocate 'citadel accommodation' here was taken in January 1944, half to the operational staffs of the London Civil Defence region and Ministry of Works, plus some space for Combined Operations and the Inter Services Research Bureau (alias INREBU or ISRB). The structure was adapted to meet these bodies' operational needs and to provide living accommodation for their staff.

The precise allocation was:
- London Civil Defence Region
  - Report and Control Centre
  - Liaison Officers of Government Departments
  - CD HQ operational staff
- Ministry of Works Engineering Services
- Inter Services Research Bureau (see below)
- Combined Operations
- Flag Officer, London
- Movement Control (War Office)
- Port of London Authority
- Government Communications Bureau (see below)

Inter Services Research Bureau was a cover name for the research and development section of Special Operations Executive (SOE), itself an offshoot of MI6 set up initially to help the Resistance in German-occupied countries and later expanded into a covert organisation of about 10,000 men and women. The Bureau's use of the Chancery Lane location may explain a reference in Leo Marks's book *Between Silk & Cyanide*, which describes his role in agent communication activities. Government Communications Bureau was another cover name, relating to the combined signals intelligence (SIGINT) organisation of the three armed services. It later took the name of Government Communications Headquarters or GCHQ.

Needless to say, these arrangements did not meet with universal approval. ISRB indicated the majority of their communications ran northward and Belsize Park would have been more convenient. The Ministry of Works argued this had no influence on cable routes; lines from both locations would run through the same Northern Line tube tunnels and where these surfaced at Golders Green they would lose protection in any case. Nevertheless, ISRB was content to establish a map room, signals room, operations room and sleeping area at 'Chancery Lane West', as the file calls it.

In March 1944 it was agreed that staff of the Port of London Authority, Flag Officer in Charge and War Department Movement Control could join the merry throng in Chancery Lane. For the London Civil Defence Region Chancery Lane became its 'reserve war room' in May 1944, fitted out to handle ambulance provision, casualty service, rescue co-ordination, heavy rescue, research and experiments. The ponderous instructions issued to selected staff made abundantly clear what lay before them:

The Americans took security down below very seriously. This sentry guards the staircase that led from the platforms of Goodge Street station to the signal centre. The passageway was locked after a more convenient and separate entrance was opened in Chenies Street. [Public Record Office]

When operations start on the Continent, or possibly before, the enemy may include London amongst other targets in an attempt to disorganise our military operations. As it is vital that these operations shall proceed with the minimum of interruption the Regional Commissioners, in common with other departments, have made arrangements to carry on in premises and under conditions likely to be impervious to enemy attack. You, as one of the officers needed to undertake this duty, will realise the vital importance of the work and accept any inconvenience to which you may be subjected during the emergency period. A move of this nature may have to be made at very short notice. You should therefore hold yourself in readiness to move … at once.

The personal instructions also dealt with security and housekeeping matters, noting that although entrances existed in Holborn and on the tube station platform, London Region staff should use the 'special entrance in Furnival Street'. Also that: 'The lift service is not good, there being only one lift which moves very slowly … therefore … it should be used for upward journeys only.'

Construction supplies for creating the new accommodation were to be delivered via the station platforms, which themselves might restrict public shelter provision in the station during the period of adaptation. In the event, the LPTB would not allow this, so the street entrances had to be used. After this work proceeded according to plan at Chancery Lane, the orderliness being broken only on 25th November 1944 when a rocket fell just north of the junction of High Holborn and Warwick Place. Minor damage was caused to the shelter entrance at Fulwood Place, without harming the tunnels or shelter below.

A total of some 1,040 staff positions were reserved in the converted shelter and the army was to guard all entrances. Instructions issued in May and June indicate all staff were to enter by way of the Furnival Street entrance, using the station platform access route in emergency only. In the event it seems that little use was made of the premises and then only by ISRB (which arranged for its telephones, teleprinters and furniture to be removed on 8th May 1945). Four days later the Admiralty advised the Home Office in view of the changed situation the accommodation allocated as an alternative headquarters at Chancery Lane was no longer required.

Clapham Common

A Home Office conference decided in February 1944 to adapt Clapham Common shelter as reserve citadel accommodation in addition to Chancery Lane. Some of the sleeping accommodation was converted into offices, using Kinnear Moodie & Co. as main contractor. The Post Office intercepted the deep level telephone cable that ran through the Northern Line tunnels here and diverted it through the shelter's apparatus room. Some 100 pairs were taken from this cable as well as 100 cable pairs from the surface down shaft 7 and 200 cable pairs down shaft 8. An extensive system of teleprinters, telephones and a 12-position PMBX1A switchboard was also installed (completed on 30th April 1944). The War Office took a shine to the quarters and had half of them earmarked for its use, with its people allowed in from June. The remaining accommodation was for 'pool' purposes, according to the Post Office war diary.

Eastern Expediency

Unfinished tube tunnels provide shelter in east London

IF few people are aware today of London's purpose-built deep shelters, then the subject of refuge created in incomplete tube tunnels is even more obscure. Nonetheless at the height of the blitz in 1940 the unopened stations and running tunnels of the Central Line tube extension provided valuable protection that we shall now describe. Before doing that, however, a little background on this project may help readers put this work into context.

Before the war the Central Line was much shorter than today, with its eastern terminus at Liverpool Street (in the west it went no further than Ealing; the Ruislip line had not been built). Under the 1935–40 New Works plan (mentioned in Chapter 2) new tunnels to the east of Liverpool Street would extend the line to Leyton, at which point tube trains would run over existing suburban lines of the LNER company to Woodford, Epping, Hainault and Newbury Park. The main tunnelling works had been completed by early 1940, but the stations were unfinished and only a small proportion of the tracks had been laid when further tracklaying activity ceased in May 1940. This was the situation when bombing became a serious threat to London's East End and in June it was agreed with the Ministry of Transport that all work should be suspended bar a few minor works that could not be left unfinished. Some track already laid was even lifted for use elsewhere.

Showpiece shelter?

The original 'end of the line' at Liverpool Street was a pair of siding tunnels separated from the station by a crossover tunnel. As part of the eastern extension these tunnels were rebuilt completely and the crossover moved further from the station. In addition twin running tunnels were built beyond Liverpool Street station to Stratford and Leyton, with track laid only in the bore for eastbound trains. No track had been laid in the two siding tunnels, which were intended for trains reversing at Liverpool Street and lay immediately to the east of the station. Reached by a ramp at the east end of the westbound station platform, these siding tunnels were adapted for use as a public shelter in the early summer of 1940. At this time there was a special drive to secure sufficient protection at main line termini to cater for peak passenger loads, and the Liverpool Street shelter came into use during June, in time for the beginning of the Blitz, which started at the end of August 1940. It had accommodation for 2,500 people in tunnels 730ft long. The eastbound tunnel, where tracks had been laid, was used occasionally by trains and the conductor rails were live.

Though forgotten now, for the first twelve months it was one of the most popular and crowded shelters in central London. A Ministry of Health report dated 22nd September of that year gives a convenient description of the arrangements:

The shelter consists of a short length of tube from Liverpool Street Underground station, broadening into a length of larger diameter than the ordinary tunnel, then continuing for about 333 yards as twin tunnels of the ordinary size. It is used by the public through the tolerance of the railway company and without official sanction.

The length of the tunnel appears to be mis-stated and the last sentence is surprising too. It probably represents the original situation, since the shelter was adopted and managed by the City of London Corporation. 'Managed' is perhaps not the best word to use, unless one concedes that its staff here were overwhelmed by their task. In December 1940 Lady Cromer and Mr K. de Courcey of the Imperial Policy Group had cause to write to the Minister of Home Security in words that leave little room for doubt, even allowing for her ladyship's heightened sensitivities. Mr de Courcey wrote:

The situation at Liverpool Street is deplorable. The air defies any description from my pen. It is fetid and overbearingly hot. I saw old people gasp for breath and children white-faced and sickly. Without seeing it, I could not have imagined anything so frightful. I was told by one of the chief marshals that if I visited the shelter at about 3 am I should find a situation about twice as bad. The shelterers are extremely disgruntled and I suspected a low morale tending to sink below danger point. I beg you most earnestly to have fans installed. Then the sanitation beggars description. The stench near the latrines is appalling and the whole condition and system of sanitation are most alarming . . . The lighting is inadequate, then there are some rather nasty old iron fittings attached to the old sleepers, which make it difficult and in some cases impossible to lie down. I heard many complaints about this.

He continues at length in similar vein, mentioning dripping taps making the floor muddy and soaking the bedding that people had brought. Steel bunks were installed subsequently as well as water-borne closets to replace the chemical ones. His general description of the bleak conditions is borne out by photographs taken in November 1940 by the photojournalist Bill Brandt. These show shelterers in the trackless tunnels and people sleeping directly on the tunnel floor and against the metal lining segments of the tube tunnel. In October 1941 wooden bunks were replaced by steel ones and subsequent conversion work made the area far more hospitable. Gratitude was in short supply, however, and the files note that vandalism was a serious problem in the shelter. Timber was constantly being stolen and there were many complaints of damage to work in hand and deliberate breakage of bunks by shelterers.

A section of the westbound running tunnel extending 716ft beyond the end of the existing shelter in the dead-end siding tunnel as far as Commercial Street offered scope for enlarging the shelter. In April 1941 a decision was taken to keep this in reserve, provided that a new entrance shaft with a wide spiral staircase and food hoist could be sunk somewhere from a site over the railway near White Lion Street (since renamed Folgate Street). All publicity was to be avoided, however, noted the file. This shaft was first proposed by the Corporation in February 1941 but by January 1943 the London Civil Defence Region was still unable to come to a decision. By this time the pressing need was over and nothing more happened.

Luxury at Liverpool Street

By 1942 significant improvements had been made to the accommodation in the shelter, which was now described as an economical and well-devised scheme. It was something of a showpiece and was displayed to other local authorities and to official groups visiting from the Colonies, Dominions and foreign countries. The City Corporation felt sufficiently confident to invite the press, a move vindicated by this effusive description given by news photograph agency Popperfoto:

LONDON'S LATEST AND BEST EQUIPPED SHELTER PROVIDES HOME AND SHELTER FOR THOUSAND.

One of London's finest air raid shelters has just been completed at Liverpool Street Underground station. The new shelter, which provides accommodation for a thousand sleepers, is provided with all modern conveniences including waterborne sanitation; it has its own medical aid post and sick bay; a fully equipped canteen; recreation rooms where shelterers can attend sewing or machining classes; take part in community singing or listen to concerts; and an efficient ventilating system, which ensures a plentiful supply of fresh air.

All traces of the shelter, along with the adjacent private shelter and canteen belonging to London Transport, were swept away after the war when the running and siding tunnels were converted to their intended use. Central Line trains ran between Liverpool Street and Stratford for the first time on 4th December 1946.

Ticket entitling the bearer to use the deep shelter at Liverpool Street tube station. Size 5¼ x 3¼in on buff card with red overprint.

[Chris Mees]

Grub up! Not the most appetising of kitchens perhaps but the people waiting at the servery look keen enough to partake. Location is "the newly opened deep air raid shelter under London's Liverpool Street station". This was built in tunnels of the new Central Line extension on which tracklaying had been suspended in May 1940.

[Popperfoto]

Tragedy strikes

It was not only at Liverpool Street that unopened Central Line tunnels were examined for use as shelters and other sections were also considered. The possibility was ruled out between Commercial Street and Bethnal Green owing to the risk of flooding if bombs hit large sewers in the neighbourhood but the unfinished station at Bethnal Green appeared suitable. The decision to use the station for a refuge in its incomplete state led to the worst civilian catastrophe of World War II, albeit little-known at the time thanks to a clamp-down on publicity.

The platforms of Bethnal Green station, 65ft below ground level, opened as a shelter on 11th September 1940 but closed the next day (or three days later, accounts vary) because London Transport believed there was a risk of flooding. This decision was overturned by the Minister for Home Security, Mr (later Sir) Herbert Morrison, after he had balanced the relative dangers of flooding and bombing. During a tour of east London with Admiral Sir Edward Evans, Regional Commissioner for London on 5th October, Mr Morrison reopened the shelter. Its facilities were rudimentary, to say the least, simply because the station was incomplete. The platforms were complete and the walls properly tiled but other circulating areas were still uncovered bare concrete. Crucially, the entrance staircase had no handrail or roof and lighting was initially by hurricane lamps alone, whilst the only emergency exit routes were the long trek through the tube railway tunnels to Liverpool Street or Mile End stations.

Needs must when the devil drives, however, and accommodation was provided for 4,000 people on the westbound platform and trackbed, on part of the eastbound platform and in the crossover tunnel. Barricades were erected to prevent the public reaching the eastbound running line (over which London Transport reserved the right to run engineers' ballast trains).

The shelter area included part of the tunnel to the west of the station but not the shallow 'sub-surface' tunnel leading towards Bow Road. Several major sewers ran close to the station, posing a risk of flooding should a bomb penetrate them. To prevent the possibility of sewage flowing towards Liverpool Street, London Transport had by November 1940 erected bulkheads across the tunnels about a mile west of Bethnal Green station as well as sliding floodgates east of the station. In January 1941 these arrangements were revised to create a new shelter east of the station, using a portion of the platforms. Timber flooring was provided, along with an emergency exit leading up to Carlton Square. An unpleasant incident took place on 30th July 1942, when a large number of Stepney residents forced entry via this staircase, after which a sign was erected telling of grave personal danger to anyone rash enough trying to gain access by this means.

It was an omen of worse to come and the station's infamy rests in the fact that it was the location of the worst single civilian death toll of World War II. The site is marked today by a Blue Plaque memorial, which states that on Wednesday 3rd March 1943 some 173 men, women and children died as they were descending the steps of the official station entrance to seek shelter.

The half-finished station of the new Central Line extension at Bethnal Green was opened as a public shelter in September 1940. At the height of the Blitz upwards of 5,000 people used it nightly but this number subsequently dwindled to a few hundred. The poster on the left states that refreshments can be had at the London Transport canteen. The photo, undated, was probably taken soon after the shelter closed to the public in March 1943.

[After The Battle]

Eye witness

On that night the air raid alert sounded at 8.17 pm and shortly afterwards, an off-duty policeman, PC Thomas Penn, noticed unusual congestion around the entrance to the station (at the corner of Cambridge Heath Road and Roman Road). He saw in the dim light of a single 25-watt bulb that the steps leading to the shelter were jammed with people who had become so tightly packed that they could not move. A genealogy website records that his first instinct was to assess the extent of the trouble and crawling over massed bodies to the foot of the 19 steps, where a woman had tripped, he observed with horror that the pressure of oncoming crowds had jammed over 200 people into the space of a small room. Having sent a message for help, PC Penn again crawled to the foot of the stairs and helped other rescue workers extricate the trapped people, continuing until the stairs were cleared. PC Penn was the sole constable to give evidence at the inquest into the disaster.

An eyewitness account is quoted on the East End Life website. A Bethnal Green woman who was 19 at the time recalled that the station had only one entrance, which was also the exit.

I had gone to the station from our home in Cambridge Heath Road and was just starting down the station steps when the trouble began. The whoosh of a gun or rocket made people behind me surge forward. It happened several times and, as quite a few people were carrying bundles of clothes and bedding, I am not surprised that someone fell over in the gloom in front of us. Soon bodies began piling on top of one another and I was hopelessly trapped. I was upright but it was suffocatingly hot, and people all around were groaning and screaming.

Wardens called out: 'Go back! Go back!' to people at street level but it made no difference. Those on the outside were desperate to get in and didn't seem to realise what was happening. My back was crushed and my hands trapped, and I called out that I couldn't breathe. My tongue was hanging out and I panted like a dog.

The very basic entrance to Bethnal Green station, seen as sightseers and the bereaved gather after the disaster. Today the stairwell is open to the sky but in 1943 it was protected by a corrugated iron roof, with room for two columns of people to enter or leave. [After The Battle]

This shot of the north-east stairwell shows how much work remained unfinished at Bethnal Green station as late as November 1946.

[London's Transport Museum]

It took them three hours to clear the steps and I lost track of time, then I was pulled back up to the street. My clothes were torn and my stockings shredded. I think I was very lucky to be near the surface. Later, my bad back, which I had injured in the accident, meant I could not work for a year and I was awarded £500 compensation. But the authorities made deductions and, in the end, I got only £375.

A survivor of the disaster, Alf Morris, is stated by the BBC website to have been one of the last people to be pulled out of the crush. He retains vivid memories of the scenes of panic. "It's indescribable what went on in them few minutes when most of the people died . . . the screaming, the hollering," he recalled. A local resident, James Hunt, then 16 years old added, "When I arrived here there were all the bodies laid right the way down . . . I helped to get some of the youngsters up, I was only little myself, and I picked up mostly young children." Prompt action ensured that all traces of the disaster were cleaned up within hours. Speaking on a BBC television programme in September 2003, local residents involved in the work said that police stopped buses passing nearby and conscripted able-bodied passengers into a task force for removing bodies.

There had been nearly 2,000 people in the shelter and when casualties were finally counted, it was found that 173 had died (not 178 as originally reported), including 64 children. In addition 92 were taken to hospital. News of the disaster took time to leak out, however. Initially the government withheld information about the tragedy in order to prevent word reaching the enemy but an announcement was made the following evening by the Ministry of Home Security describing a serious accident that had occurred near the entrance to a London tube shelter. The news was not widely reported until the Friday.

Secret inquiry

Eventually, an inquiry was held in secret, the results of which were published in January 1945 near the end of the war. Questions were asked about the behaviour of certain officials and whether the accident could have been prevented. Suggestions were also made that fifth-columnists might have had something to do with the tragedy but these were discounted in the 'report of the Inquiry held by Mr Laurence Dunne into the Bethnal Green Tube Shelter Disaster'. This stated in section 38:

Before going on to deal with the rain and contributory causes of the disaster I should like at this point to deal with two specific allegations which have received some publicity, and which are without any foundation whatsoever. Each may be dismissed with a very few words:–
a. that this was a panic induced by Fascists or criminal persons for nefarious purposes. There were some deaths among men with criminal records. They and their relatives are as much entitled to sympathy as any of the other victims. This story had some local, and I hope limited, circulation. It is an absurdity.
b. that this was a Jewish panic. This canard had a much wider circulation and was, I understand, endorsed by the broadcast utterances of a renegade traitor from Germany. Not only is it without foundation, it is demonstrably false.

The Bethnal Green shelter in calmer times. The two wardens look distinctly uncomfortable at having their photograph taken.

[London's Transport Museum]

The Jewish attendance at this shelter was, and is, so small as to constitute a hardly calculable percentage.

The notion of a Jewish panic later turned out to have been spread by local fascist activists, who had tried to spread dissent before the war. William Joyce (the second Lord Haw Haw) did indeed mention the disaster in his broadcast from Berlin the following Monday but never claimed it was a Jewish panic. Instead he mocked the official statement that there had been no panic, stating this kind of fairy tale could only be told to a child or an Englishman. Along with the reports on Radio Paris and Rome Radio he stated the cause as panic following enemy air raids.

As it happened there was no raid in progress at the time of the catastrophe. People certainly saw a searchlight trained on the sky but the noise came from a salvo of anti-aircraft rockets launched in a test firing from a battery a mile away at the far north corner of Victoria Park. Known as a Z-Battery and designated 19Z, this used a relatively new technique of firing multiple rocket guns simultaneously and certainly created a terrifying sound, one that would certainly scare the living daylights of anyone unfamiliar with the uproar and startled even the few people in a nearby factory who had been forewarned.

Alec Allen, a 'cocoa boy' working as a dogsbody for the unit on the night of the disaster, claimed he was told of a test firing by the commander of the unit. "It was horrendous. The skies were lit up with these rockets. It sounded like the whole battery had been lit up simultaneously," he recalled. Former soldiers from other Z-Battery units in London confirmed the singular noise of the weapon. "It was as if all hell had been let loose, belching out flame and noise as you've never heard it. Everyone else who heard it would be the same as me – petrified," remembered one old soldier.

Unfortunately security restrictions prevented informing the local population and someone shouted, "They've started dropping them!" Word spread rapidly that landmines were erupting and bombs hurtling downwards. Allegations in recent times of military incompetence do not stand up to scrutiny and ignore the need for total security. Suggestions that the battery could have been tested away from populated areas ignore its precise function, to protect the locality of Bethnal Green. Lessons were learnt, however, and local authority shelters were equipped with better handrails and lighting in staircases together with crush barriers and sliding gates at surface entrances. At Bethnal Green the entrance was altered immediately with two shelter marshals on duty over the full 24-hour period at top and bottom of the stairs. At other tube stations barriers were erected around entrances too.

If the catastrophe was a disaster waiting to happen, it is fortunate that it did not occur when the Bethnal Green shelter was more widely used. When opened it had bunk accommodation for 5,000 people with extra space for another 5,000

shelterers. It was popular with its residents, being well equipped to the extent of having its own underground public library. Former shelterer Reg Baker recalled the atmosphere: "You were so close to everyone in those tunnels that you got to know everybody – down in the bunk beds – they were only about four feet apart. We used to sleep in the tunnel on bunk beds either side that went right the way down. It was a full community ... we had a canteen ... we had a church – well, a vicar – and we had a library". In fact the only major shortcomings of this refuge were the overpowering stench of industrial disinfectant used in the toilets and the single main entrance, supplemented by an emergency exit reached by tunnel half a mile away. When the Blitz was at its height, the shelter was often filled to capacity and became a second home to some. Numbers dwindled later on to a few hundred, possibly people with nowhere else to go.

Stratford's shelter

Other authorities had their eyes on the new tube as well. In May 1940 the Regional Technical Adviser of the London Civil Defence Region visited the unfinished works of the Central Line extension and afterwards invited local authority engineers to consider their use as shelters. Leyton Borough Council presented its proposal in June 1940 to use "the entrances to the railway" and a month later a proposition was received from West Ham Corporation. Three public air raid shelters were created as a result in the Stratford and Leytonstone areas.

The first two shelters used the untracked westbound tunnel between Stratford and Leyton stations (the eastbound tunnel contained a working railway track). The ¾-mile tunnel provided two separate shelters operated by different local authorities under separate leasing arrangements with the London Passenger Transport Board. The boundary or division point was a London Transport working site on the east side of Queen Street next to the junction with Henniker Street, where an access and eventual air shaft had been dug to the running tunnels below. West Ham Corporation took over the southern half (425ft) as the 'Stratford tunnel' and created an entrance near Stratford station, reached by a wooden footbridge from the west end of William Street. From there a ramped wooden walkway was constructed between railway tracks down to a 12ft square tunnel 60 yards long that led into the main tunnel.

Leyton Borough Council occupied the northern section (the 'Queen Street tunnel', 'Westdown Shelter' or 'Drapers Field Shelter') and created an entrance at Drapers Fields adjoining Westdown Road and a temporary depot used by London Transport for storing tunnel lining segments and other materials of the new railway (its last traces were erased in early 1947). To reach the tunnel portal the council created fenced asphalt footpaths across the railway depot from High Road Leyton and from Westdown Road; these led to a footbridge over the

About half way between Stratford and Leyton this working shaft was erected to give access to the tunnels being bored for the new Central Line extension. Seen here in October 1937, it later provided ventilation for the public shelter established in the tunnels during the war. Although the route's name was abbreviated to Central Line on 23rd August 1937, the old title remained in use on signs and in all official correspondence for another ten years.

[London's Transport Museum]

railway with steps down to the tunnel mouth from there.

Occupation of the shelters began in September 1940 and although the original intention was to use only part of the tunnel, the public effectively gatecrashed the entire length. Bunks were eventually fitted along the length of the tunnel, with sleeping accommodation for 2,800 people in the Leyton section and for 2,136 persons in West Ham. Canteens were also provided in both sections, with ventilation supplied by the shaft at the mid-point below Queen Street (slightly south of the actual municipal boundary). At this spot a timber and wire mesh barrier with a wicket gate was erected. To be opened only in emergency, its purpose was to create a line of demarcation between each borough's residents but in fact it led to a source of some irritation. To serve a most basic human function, latrines were provided but whereas Leyton's tunnel had these places of convenience set out at convenient intervals, West Ham's 20 cubicles were sited less conveniently all together at the Stratford entrance. For some West Ham shelterers this meant a walk of up to 600yds to answer the call of nature – so they used the nearer facilities 'across the border' in Leyton.

Needless to say, the Leytonians were none too pleased to suffer longer queues for the loos. It became such a bone of contention in fact that the police had to intervene and have West Ham install additional toilets. To add to the displeasure the

latrines had only Hessian 'doors' and partitions, many of which were 'torn and soiled'. Litter bins and candle lights were being stolen constantly, so life in the tunnels must have been quite disagreeable.

Grief at Gainsborough

Displeasure of another kind was felt at another shelter operated by Leyton Borough Council, the next northerly use of the tubes dug for the Central Line to be. Known variously as the Gainsborough, Gainsborough Bridge or Leytonstone Shelter, it was another tunnel entrance shelter. The new tunnels heading off towards Wanstead and Redbridge diverge either side of the original Epping line and enter tunnels north of Leytonstone station close to where Gainsborough Road bridge crosses the line. It was a portion of this new tunnel section that Leyton Borough Council agreed to lease from London Transport in July 1940.

The agreement related to both tube tunnel bores for a distance of 350ft north-east of the Gainsborough Road tunnel portal, at the far end of which a wire mesh barrier was erected. The tunnels beyond here were reserved for the Ministry of Aircraft Production (MAP) for use as an underground factory (described next) and this soon became a source of strife. In September, when air raids on London became intense, shelterers swelled in numbers, broke through the barrier (later replaced by a more substantial screen and picket gate) and occupied the MAP section of the tunnel. Since this was not required immediately for production the shelterers were allowed to stay put until the engineers required the tunnels to install machinery (they were, however, warned this was a temporary concession).

On 25th February 1941 London Transport, on instruction from the MAP, gave one month's notice that the 640ft 'illicitly' occupied section of tube tunnels would have to be cleared and on 14th March signs were posted in the shelter saying it would close on the 28th. Five days later letters of protest reached the Ministry of Home Security (MoHS) and a major argument broke out in the newspapers, not to mention a row between the two ministries. Complaints by the Shelter Committee led to the Member of Parliament for Leytonstone, Mr M. Leigh, berating the government. "The callous decision to close major portions of Gainsborough Bridge tunnel shelter in favour of a company on war work is nothing less that a crime against humanity," he asserted on 23rd March 1941. A few days later two Labour Members, Reginald (later Lord) Sorensen (Leyton West) and Valentine (later Baron) McEntee (Walthamstow West), raised Parliamentary Questions on the subject. Newspapers ran campaigns too. The Minister of Home Security blustered that steps would be taken to provide alternative accommodation for the shelterers but this was clearly impossible and eventually it was

agreed not to move them (in this respect they were more fortunate than their fellows in Redbridge, where a public shelter at the unopened Redbridge station was displaced by the Plessey works, described in Chapter 12).

"Petition Saves Shelter," ran the headline of the *Daily Express* on 4th April, which gave no pleasure to the government. "The plain fact is that we have to choose between shelter and aeroplanes, and there can be no doubt as to the choice," wrote a Civil Service adviser at the MoHS, noting that bunked accommodation in trench shelters was standing idle while people occupied the railway tunnel. It was remarkable too, the file also noted, that 5,000 people signed the petition to retain the shelter, even though nightly attendance was normally just 700, rising in mid-March to 1,000 when air raid activity became more intense. In the event political expediency won the day.

Access to the shelter was by temporary staircases from the south side of the bridge where Gainsborough Road crossed the railway cutting and with no other way out, it was realised that a safety hazard existed. A potential alternative exit would have been through the tunnel bulkhead into the adjoining tunnels used for the Plessey factory but the door here was locked on account of the secrecy of the works. A 5ft diameter escape shaft to the surface was proposed in August 1941 but nothing came of it.

No views have been traced of the entrances to tunnel shelters but this photograph shows how the Gainsborough Road bridge looked in December 1937. Shelterers later walked down temporary wooden staircases both sides of the cutting on this side of the bridge.

[London's Transport Museum]

Photographs of the Westdown and Gainsborough shelters have proved impossible to trace but this linocut drawn in 1941 by N. H. Johnson gives a vivid impression of the Gainsborough Bridge Tunnel. The proportions are not quite right for a 12ft diameter running tunnel, however, and the picture gives a false impression of space.

[Vestry House Museum]

This photograph, shows similar bunks constructed at Liverpool Street or Bethnal Green.

[Railway Gazette]

Rebellion at Redbridge

Redbridge, the next point east on the Central Line tunnel, was another location opened initially as a public shelter and then assigned to aircraft production (see Chapter 12). As a shelter it offered rather little protection, probably less than the Morrison and Anderson shelters that its users had forsaken, simply because it was only just below ground level. In fact the station was built immediately below the surface, so close in fact that stairs and no escalators were required to reach the station platforms.

Nonetheless, the unfinished station provided a refuge of sorts and one that shelterers were unhappy about leaving. Hundreds of people flocked there as soon as the night raids began in September 1940, causing some animosity, as most

of them were not local residents. The condition of trench shelters in council parks was not enticing either; they were extremely damp, forcing people to spend the night on wet concrete floors. The station made a barely more satisfactory shelter; there was no sanitation and people had to sleep on the platform or the rail-less trackbed. When the premises were requisitioned for factory use the shelterers were given notice to quit. Although the station was not closed until an alternative shelter had been constructed and equipped, the shelterers were still not satisfied and a deputation of them was received by the MoHS, supported by a Parliamentary Question on 6th February 1941 by the M.P. for Ilford North, Mr T. E. Groves, regarding "the decision to discontinue the use of the Redbridge tube station air-raid shelter". This time, however, the MAP was not deflected and the shelterers were obliged to vacate their underground quarters to make way for factory workers.

Their departure was not without incident, however, and when they showed signs of refusing to leave, the mayor of Ilford, Alderman C. A. Parman, went accompanied by the Borough Engineer and Chief Warden to reason with them. The shelterers became "extremely threatening" and advanced on the peacemakers with sticks. The Borough Engineer laid out the nearest attacker but others made for the Mayor's car and attempted to overturn it. It is said that only the frosty ground on which the car slid thwarted this effort. A retreat was possible when the Chief Warden arranged a diversion and the Mayor's driver stated that if the crowd would get back a little, the Mayor would like to talk to them. But this was a deceit; when the crowd backed off the chauffeur manoeuvred the car out and away to safety. Afterwards the shelterers transferred to their new quarters without further incident.

Gants Hill and Newbury Park

Further east at Gants Hill a pedestrian subway system and a booking hall for the future station had been built beneath the large (seven-ways) roundabout that had formed a landmark here since the early 1930s. The access tunnels (but not the circulating area that gave access to the Plessey factory) served as a public refuge from air raids and were known as the Gants Hill Subway Shelter. Operated by Ilford Council, it was noted in use in MoHS files dated 1943 and 1944 but not in May 1945. A reminiscence by Sheila West, now in Australia, states, "We were driving home from London one night in 1940/41, before my father went into the army, and it got so bad we had to take cover there. I remember thinking it was great fun!" A police report of August 1944 confirms it was frequently used by casual passers-by and had 250 users nightly then.

At the eastern end of the new tunnel, south of Newbury Park station, an unofficial air raid shelter was also established. This did not last, as long-term local resident Peter Shorer recalls:

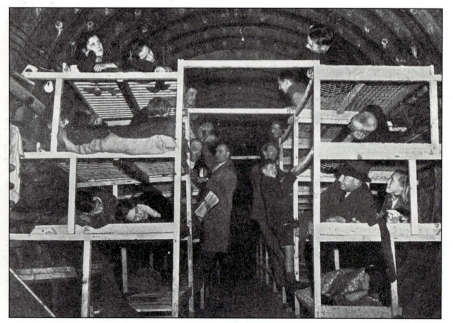

By 1939 the portal entries to Gants Hill station were complete and served as pedestrian subways; later they would become air raid shelters as well. The signs marking the station entrances are still standing today, with inscriptions replacing the plain glass seen here.
[London's Transport Museum]

Below: Smiling faces distinguish this posed shot of shelterers in the Gants Hill shelter circa 1942. The microphone is not a broadcast pattern, indicating this is some kind of entertainment rather than an outside broadcast for radio. Wooden staging for bunk beds can be seen in the background.
[Redbridge Museums]

The tunnels, with no barriers to stop entry, appeared to be attractive to those having access to them and were used as an air raid shelter. After several daylight and night time raids about 1939, this was brought to a halt one Sunday morning when, as usual the locals who had access to the track through the fences of their back gardens assembled some way inside the tunnel. My mum and dad had followed, believing it to be safer under some thickness of ground rather than on the surface in the Anderson shelter or in the house 'under the stairs'. While the neighbours were talking among themselves there was a disturbance at the entrance and in walked a police officer with several constables.

The officer walked straight up to my dad and said in a penetrating voice, "I want you to get your people out of here! It is very dangerous! If a bomb bursts at the entrance it will kill all of you by its blast!" My dad replied they were not his people and he was not responsible for what they did.

But the senior policeman became very imperious and told him, "You will get them out back to their homes and safety at once!" His loud voice convinced many people to move out, so a confrontation was averted and this was the end of the use of the tunnels for that purpose.

This was not the last excitement for people living alongside the railway here, as Peter continues. In about 1941 or 1942 the railway line between Ilford and Hainault was used for firing a large rail-mounted anti-aircraft gun during the night. This was probably to discourage raiders from attacking the fighter airfield at Fairlop. "It would stop at irregular intervals to fire, sometimes outside our house and the sound was dreadful, particularly if you had been asleep! We had got used to the noise of the trains running during sleep times but these guns were something quite different," he declares.

Battle Stations

Disused tube stops awaken

ALTHOUGH unnoticed by the vast majority of passengers, closed stations abound on the London Underground. To some they are an object of curiosity and to the *cognoscenti* a source of considerable interest. Books have been written about them, notably *London's Disused Underground Stations* by J.E. Connor, whilst they have also featured in television programmes. You can even visit them vicariously on a number of websites on the Internet.

Their original construction had been based on over-optimistic estimates of passenger numbers, and in the end the level of patronage frankly didn't warrant the cost of staffing and maintaining them. In a few cases the reason for closure was simply that a more convenient station had been opened nearby.

For all this, they had been solidly built and as the international situation deteriorated in 1938, the opportunity to use these closed stations for other purposes did not go unnoticed by the defence authorities. A list of all disused stations was procured from London Transport in May 1938 and, in the event, six tube stations (three of them closed) took on new strategic roles.

British Museum, on the Central Line, closed in September 1933 when it was replaced by Holborn (Kingsway) a few hundred yards to the east. The latter station had previously been served by Piccadilly Line trains only and the new Central Line platforms enabled it to become a convenient interchange point between these two tube lines, the trams in the Kingsway Subway (later to become a Flood Control Centre for the Greater London Authority) and the buses above.

Brompton Road station stood between Knights-

bridge and South Kensington stations; it attracted so few passengers that, along with other similarly quiet stations, selected trains were scheduled to pass it without stopping. When a new entrance to Knightsbridge station was opened on the Brompton side, the time came to close Brompton Road and the last passengers left in July 1934. Down Street was not a busy station either, lying close to both Hyde Park Corner and Green Park stations. Being off the main thoroughfare and in a district where most people presumably had their own private transport or used taxi cabs, it was little wonder that it was not more widely used. The station closed in May 1932, following refurbishment of Green Park station.

Two other disused Piccadilly Line facilities took on a new role during the war as well, the second Aldwych line platform at Holborn and parts of the old Dover Street station.

The last of the six re-used stations, Post Office, had never closed as such. Instead the station was renamed St Paul's in 1937, while work continued building a new sub-surface entrance and escalators to replace the original street-level entrance and lifts. On account of its differing circumstances and fate, Post Office is given a chapter of its own later in the book; the other stations are described in greater detail now.

British Museum

After closure in 1933 the lifts were removed and the lower station premises sealed off at platform level. Little other alteration was made and the station remained 'remarkably intact'. The street-level accommodation was sold to a major landowner in the district, the Duke of Bedford, and became a Slumberland bed showroom.

The first major air raids of World War II made it clear that better shelter accommodation was required in London and as well as the deep tube shelters already described, consideration was given to using disused tube stations. Four such stations were suggested for possible conversion during a meeting between London Transport and the Ministry of Home Security, one being British Museum. An article by J. E. Connor in *London Railway Record* (January 1999) records that following a visit to this station by a Mr Escilt of the Ministry of Home Security, Air Raid Precautions Department, he reported on 8th November 1940 that this was "a station without platforms, but flat surfaces by rails. It could be used as a shelter by provision of half brick wall between track and platform space, and provision of access and means of sanitation. The access may, however, prove difficult, as the lift shafts have been walled off from the station and the upper portion of the station disposed of".

Authority for conversion having been given, the street-level buildings were requisitioned by the Ministry of Home Security under Regulation 51 of the Defence Regulations 1939 and work put in hand to construct full-height walls for protecting shelterers from passing trains. Construction was

"well in hand" by 27th February 1941, with work in progress on provision of bunks and ventilation equipment too. Connor continues:

The bunks were to be situated on two levels within the station tunnels, and to enable this, a floor was erected above former platform level. The two levels were connected by means of temporary wooden staircases, and these were positioned beside the eight cross-passages. At the east end, close to the original entrance stairs, a canteen was provided on the eastbound side, with benches and stools nearby, where shelterers could sit to eat. Adjoining this, but separated from it by the white-tiled tunnel wall, was an area designated for children to play in, whilst beyond this were the toilet facilities. The Ladies' lavatories were at platform level, with the Gents directly above on the temporary upper floor. There were also washbasins, although the proposed number of these was thought by the Ministry to be rather high, so following correspondence between them and the local council in April 1941, the total was reduced.

The shelter finally opened in September 1941, with accommodation for 625 people. Day-to-day management was by the Metropolitan Borough of Holborn, as a sign at the street entrance testified: 'M.B.H. Public Air Raid Shelter – Admission by Ticket Only'.

Reminders of shelter use remain on the platforms at British Museum station. The style of printing is remarkably dated for the period.
[Pendar Sillwood]

This wartime poster surviving at British Museum station entreats shelterers to act responsibly. Note how crazed the glazed bricks of the walling have become.
[Pendar Sillwood]

Brompton Road

The convenient location of this station with its combination of underground accommodation and a two-storeyed building above ground made this station an attractive proposition. It was no surprise, therefore, that two government departments showed interest in using this as secure accommodation, but since neither body was aware of the other's intentions the negotiations soon descended into tragic-comedy. The Office of Works and Public Buildings was interested in storing art treasures from the Victoria and Albert Museum there, whilst the War Office had other designs on the place.

Ostensibly His Majesty's Office of Works had prior claim, having negotiated with the LPTB to use the tube station to store exhibits from the nearby Victoria and Albert Museum in the event of emergency. Independently the Commander 1st Anti-Aircraft Division, Territorial Army, had held a meeting with London Transport on 24th May 1938 with a view to locating the Inner Artillery Zone gun operations room in the lift shaft of a disused station. Brompton Road was ideal since the building above the station could serve as quarters for the personnel manning the operations room in war conditions. Two months later London Transport agreed to lease or sell the property to the army, at the same time confirming a licence to the Museum assuming that joint occupancy would not cause problems.

This was not to be, however, and when word reached the Museum in September 1938 that the station might be needed for storing explosives or ammunition, it complained that this would make the station totally unsuitable for safe storage of national art treasures. An immediate refutation from the War Office stated its sole intention was to use the premises as Operations (Control) Room for the guns of the Inner London Defences, 1st Anti-Aircraft Division and a subsequent letter to the Office of Works apologised, but the scheme had to proceed in the interests of national security.

In justification the OC (Officer Commanding) 1st AA Divisional Signals stated, "Brompton Road station is ideally situated and a most suitable site for the Gun Operations Room of the Inner Artillery Zone". He had investigated the question of provision of communications to the station with the telecommunications department of the GPO, and ascertained that it would be possible to connect Brompton Road station by cable through the tube to the GPO cables in the underground system. "Safety of lines will thus be assured." Accordingly the War Office intended to purchase the westbound platform and the lift shafts for £24,000. "The lift shafts are suitable for the construction of three or more operations rooms and an apparatus room; these rooms can be connected by a spiral staircase. The LPTB is prepared to build the operations and apparatus rooms and to make the ground level bombproof."

Thus it came to pass that the War Office secured the station for its exclusive use and on 4th

Operations room of the 1st Anti-Aircraft Division located in one of the lift shafts of Brompton Road station during World War Two. Women volunteers of the Auxiliary Territorial Service (A.T.S.) plotted aircraft movements, enabling the army officers in charge (on the dais) to command firing at remote artillery gun sites. Although functionally part of the army, Anti-Aircraft Command came under the operational control of RAF Fighter Command. This photo was used to publicise the booklet Roof Over Britain, one of the many morale-boosting publications on sale to the public at low cost during the war.

[London's Transport Museum]

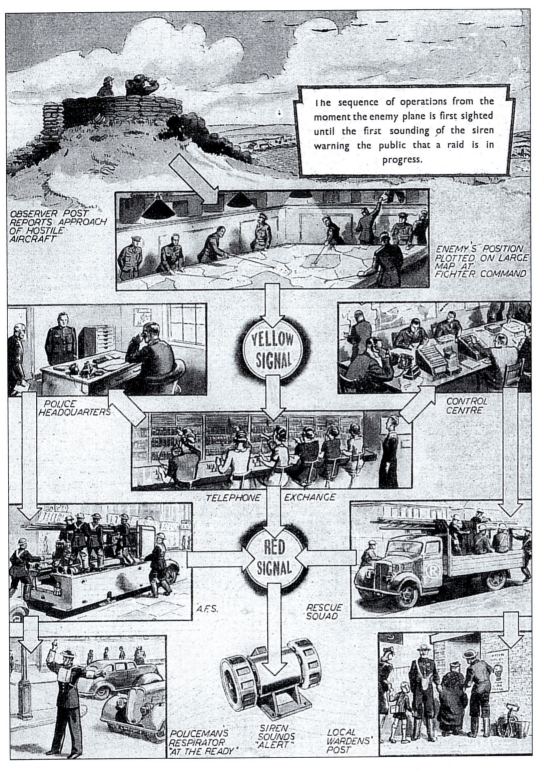

The sequence of operations from the moment the enemy plane is first sighted until the first sounding of the siren warning the public that a raid is in progress.

OBSERVER POST REPORTS APPROACH OF HOSTILE AIRCRAFT

ENEMY'S POSITION PLOTTED ON LARGE MAP AT FIGHTER COMMAND

YELLOW SIGNAL

POLICE HEADQUARTERS

CONTROL CENTRE

TELEPHONE EXCHANGE

RED SIGNAL

A.F.S.

RESCUE SQUAD

POLICEMAN'S RESPIRATOR "AT THE READY"

SIREN SOUNDS "ALERT"

LOCAL WARDENS' POST

This diagram indicates the Brompton Road anti-aircraft operations room's vital role in the defence of London. Reports received here from observation posts would be passed to ARP control centres. Within two minutes sirens would be sounded and all police stations and ARP wardens' posts alerted.

November 1938 the Commissioners of Crown Lands purchased the street-level buildings, lift shafts and certain passages for the agreed price of £24,000 (the museum was awarded the consolation prize of finance to build a bombproof chamber in its own basement, as detailed in Nick McCamley's book, *Saving Britain's Art Treasures*). Conversion of the station for its new use then took place. Brick walls were built on the outer edge of the platforms to create rooms inside, while intermediate floors were built in one of the station's two lift shafts for the operations centre. Of the two walled-off platform tunnels, the eastbound was used as the teleprinter and communications centre, and the westbound one was used for a rest area and staff accommodation. Because the platforms are bricked off anyone alighting today at Brompton Road must use a small stub platform at one end. There is now

This view of the operations room at Brompton Road station gives a better impression of the size of the place. A pneumatic tube carrier system provided internal communications (note the prominent pipework) whilst along the desks are arranged a remarkable collection of telephones, including Post Office 232 and 332 types, a House Exchange System instrument and two examples of the Army 'Tele. F' field telephone. In the background is a wall map showing locations of the gun sites and above it the RAF 'sector clock' with its face marked out in triangles painted sequentially red, yellow and blue dividing the hour into 12 five-minute segments. This arrangement provided an ingenious means of indicating and ensuring the 'freshness' of the plots displayed on the large circular plotting board. For as long as the minute hand was in a red area the plotters would use red markers on the circular board. When five minutes were up and time moved into the yellow section the A.T.S. girls would start using yellow markers. With time in the blue segment came a change to blue markers for current plots along with the removal of any plots using red pieces. When the minute hand finally moved into the next red triangle it was time to remove from the table any plots with yellow markers and so forth while raids continued. Removing plots of the previous colour in this way ensured that visual information could never be more than 10 minutes old.
[London's Transport Museum]

only a small brick wall at around platform height that probably originally supported a wooden platform since removed.

Throughout the war the station was used by the 1st Anti-Aircraft Division in which commanders of the anti-aircraft artillery, searchlights, balloon barrage and fighter squadrons oversaw the map on the plotting table. The plotting staff received details of enemy raids by telephone from Observer Corps centres, which in turn passed on reports from posts dotted about the country. The raids were plotted on the map table so that commanders in the gallery could see at a glance the numbers of the enemy and the routes taken. On this basis orders would be sent out to the fighter aircraft squadrons telling them where to fly to intercept the enemy. The plotting staff, incidentally, were known as 'A.T.S. girls' and the Auxiliary Territorial Service was a corps of female volunteers formed in 1939 to work mainly at anti-aircraft sites.

A vivid impression of day-to-day operations in 1943 is given by retired Lt. Col. B. N. Reckitt in his book *Diary of Anti-Aircraft Defence 1938–1944*. He explains that the original operations room of 1939 was on the ground floor of the station, at street level. Although used only as an office, it retained its original plotting maps and was kept in that state for the edification of distinguished foreign visitors to whom it was impolitic to show the real methods of control. The operations rooms actually used for most of the war were at a lower level, built one above the other in one of the station's former lift

shafts. He continues:

The top room of the lift shaft was called GOR I (Gun Operations Room 1), the room of the General Officer Commanding who had the picture of the progress of a raid plotted on a large map table below the dais, and where he was in touch by telephone with the R.A.F., A.R.P. and Fire Services, with the searchlights, and with every gun site. An elaborate system of coloured lights showed which were actually firing, provided always that the telephonists on the sites remembered to 'key-in' the appropriate code. Their forgetfulness was a continual source of trouble with the G.O.C.

GOR II was mainly a telephone exchange and centre of information for Intelligence officers. GOR III, deeper down in the lift shaft, controlled the northern London area and below it GOR IV the southern area, and each of these two was in the charge of a Regimental Commander drawn from the respective areas on a rota basis, by night. In each room the progress of a raid was plotted on maps as in GOR I. The main job of the controller was calling out the gunners for action, plotting the courses of enemy aircraft to them, directing their radar sets to search on the bearings of approaching raiders and ordering 'barrages' in the event of saturation attacks. This occurred when there were too many enemy aircraft for radar sets to pick out a single plane for engagement.

GOR V was an emergency room at the bottom on the station platform. It never had to be used. In the passage down to it the controllers and their assistants had to sleep with the lights continually on, in a strong draught and with GPO engineers passing up and down to look after the enormous switchboards, which were also on the old platform. The inn in Brompton Road between the station and the Oratory (The Gladstone) was generally known as GOR VI. When on duty it was the furthest one could go for refreshment.

The Brompton Road operations room took part in an interesting experiment carried out with the Army. A specialised kind of radar, known as ground-controlled interception or GCI, situated on the ground scanned the entire dome of the sky overhead to produce a live map of the sky. On this map were plotted all aircraft, hostile or friendly, flying within a radius of many miles. The display tube was known as a plan position indicator (PPI) in which a rotating beam swept the face of the cathode ray tube rather like the second hand of a watch but far more rapidly, producing the display now familiar at air traffic control centres. Back then it was entirely new and one of the first installations was the Army's anti-aircraft gun installation in Hyde Park during July 1941. As a further novelty a remote display and control were provided in the operations room in the tube station, about a mile away. A special linking cable was provided, using BBC equipment, and it was said that the display at Brompton Road was the equal of Hyde Park's. Maurice V. Wilkes recalled the project in his book, *Memoirs of a Computer Pioneer*, which notes on page 67 that:

> The remote display was to be located in the operations room of the 1st A.A. Division, which was underground in a disused tube station in Brompton Road. Someone suggested that it would be worthwhile consulting H. L. Kirke, the chief engineer of the BBC, with regard to the transmission problems involved. 405-line television was operating in London as early as 1936 and was only closed down on the outbreak of war. The BBC had, therefore, much experience of the transmission of video signals. I went to see Kirke in his office and very much enjoyed meeting him.

Edward Pawley fills in some technical details in his book *BBC Engineering 1922–1972*, stating on page 290 that among the miscellaneous projects on which the BBC gave advice was the setting-up of a video circuit over a cable pair, using the equipment that had been developed by the BBC before the war, to operate a plan position indicator for gunnery control.

The operations room controlled a large number of sites around London and because the way they functioned sheds important light on the way the overall system worked, an impression of life at one of these batteries is given as an endnote at the end of this chapter.

Returning to Brompton Road, virtual tours of the station made in recent years and presented on the Web show that many reminders of wartime use remain, including an Ordnance Survey map of south-east London with markings showing the anti-aircraft air defences. This survives on the wall of one of the operations room floors and was featured on the children's television programme *Blue Peter* in summer 2000. In some places, too,

walls still carry original notices signed by the commanding officer of the day. Another survivor is a cinema screen used for screening information films to staff painted on the wall at the end of one of the bricked-up platforms. It remains complete with its 'no smoking' warning painted beneath.

Pencil marks on a London Transport plan reproduced on page 45 of *London's Disused Underground Stations* indicate that a separate exit was constructed to Brompton Square, to the north-east and a user of the building confirms that a pedestrian tunnel runs from the lift overrun pits to a rotting wooden staircase to ground level. The exit appears to be a squat brick structure with a concrete cap and small door next to an electricity kiosk inside the railings of Brompton Square, facing Brompton Road. This feature may have been added after the war since Nick McCamley's book *Cold War Secret Nuclear Bunkers* mentions that Brompton Road was hardened for further use as an anti-aircraft operations room (AAOR) in the early 1950s, and this might well fit with the need for more accommodation and another shaft.

Brompton Road's inadequacy as an AAOR was now acknowledged and a memo from the Director of Military Operations to Vice Chief of the Imperial General Staff (the No 2 position in the army) in November 1951 stressed the urgent need for better protection of military headquarters in war. Six premises, including the headquarters of 1st A.A. Group were noted. In the event, the World War II combination of ground-based observers and radar stations was replaced in the early 1950s by the more sophisticated ROTOR radar stations backed up by new control centres. For this reason post-war use of Brompton Road as an AAOR did not last long, being replaced by two new centres constructed from 1951 onwards and opened in 1953. Lippitts Hill in Essex on the south side of Epping Forest covered the London North G.D.A. (gun-defended area) and Merstham (Bletchingley Road) in Surrey controlled the London South anti-aircraft zone. With the demise of AA Command, both centres were themselves superseded a few years later when higher-performance attack aircraft replaced gun defence. Other strategic uses were found for Brompton Road and at one time it formed offices (not headquarters) for the London District.

An interesting might-have-been occurred in 1987, when the site was earmarked for a new £1 million bunker. On 22nd May the *London Daily News* reported that the London Fire and Civil Defence Authority had decided to house its control room in the station. The bunker, intended to accommodate 60 civil defence staff, would act as an emergency co-ordination centre for west London following nuclear attack. It was one of four bases and was to be ready for occupation within two years. Later, on 19th October, the *Daily Telegraph* expand-ed this story, affirming: "The closed Brompton Road Underground station is being converted into a nuclear fallout shelter for local borough councillors to control north-west London in World War III. The station formerly housed the London anti-aircraft control centre; now, 60 officials will be self-sufficient in a 70 ft deep bunker for 30 days."

Labour councillors were deeply opposed to the scheme, however, and deputy opposition leader Alf King declared: "This takes money away from our already deteriorating fire stations." In the event nothing was built.

Dover Street

Dover Street is not a name to be found on today's Underground map but technically it's not a closed station either. The station was renamed Green Park on 18th September 1933 when its old entrance in Dover Street (a side street) was replaced by a far more convenient entrance on the main thoroughfare of Piccadilly. New escalators linked the original platforms with the new booking hall, leaving the old station building, lift shafts and passages without a use. With the outbreak of war, however, this changed. Originally the abandoned section of the station was earmarked for Winston

Churchill and plans were being put forward for his occupancy. Floor space of about 50ft square was available and plans were drawn up in October 1940 for the Prime Minister's bedroom, bathroom/toilet, a private office, a secretary's office and a conference room. In December this location was abandoned in favour of Down Street, after which London Transport decided to fit out the area to accommodate the Chairman, six Heads of Department and their personal staffs, about 25 people in all. These facilities were to be used if the main headquarters building at 55 Broadway had to be evacuated and similar emergency offices for the three Operating Managers and their staffs were built on the disused Aldwych branch platform at Holborn, whilst the Engineering headquarters had already been removed to South Kensington. All three locations were conveniently accessible from one another by the Piccadilly Line.

By the end of July 1941 the work was almost complete and ready for occupation, with access available from Green Park station as well as via the original entrance. The telephone switchboard provided for this emergency headquarters had connections to the main RL automatic telephone system of London Transport, to Scotland Yard and to the Railway Executive Committee headquarters at Down Street. As mentioned in Chapter 1, a single passageway at the Dover Street entrance to the station was also used for storing valuables of the London Museum.

Down Street

It was inevitable that the railways would become involved in the government's planning for Air Raid Precautions in 1938. Each of the 'Big Four' railway companies made arrangements for functioning under attack conditions (see Chapter 18) and in addition a so-called Railway Executive Committee (REC) was set up by the Ministry of Transport. The panel comprised of senior management from the four main line railways (GWR, LMSR, LNER, SR) and the London Passenger Transport Board. Initially its purpose was to advise the government on how rail transport should be planned and operated in the event of war. On the outbreak of war, however, the railways came under direct government control, with the REC acting as co-ordinating body between the Ministry of Transport and the individual companies.

Protected headquarters for the REC were an absolute necessity and the initial scheme was to strengthen the basement of Fielden House, headquarters of the Railway Companies Association, a body similar to the Association of Train Operating Companies today. Located in Great College Street, Westminster, SW1, the building's vulnerability to bombing and flooding led to a search for an alternative site deeper underground, such as a disused tube station.

The tale of how Down Street was selected and equipped is told in great detail in two articles by Charles E. Lee in the *Railway Gazette* (November

The basement of Fielden House in Great College Street SW1 was the original refuge of the body set up to supervise operational control of the railways in World War II. The pre-war headquarters of the Railway Companies Association, it remained in railway use for a couple of decades after the war.

These were the working conditions for senior officers in the Operating Office of the Railway Executive Committee deep under Mayfair. The charts and small flags below the clock indicated the composition and location of every military ambulance train and casualty evacuation train in Britain. [Science Museum]

Not an inch of space was wasted in the former tube station. The passageway the typist is negotiating is only 2ft wide at floor level. [Science Museum]

17th and 24th 1944). Mr G. Cole-Deacon, secretary of the Railway Executive Committee, was responsible for the design of the offices. The LPTB was put in charge of all structural work, installation of the passenger lift, air raid protection, ventilation and plumbing. Fitting out and electrical, radio and telephone installations were handled by the LMS Railway. Work was started in April 1939, but by the time war broke out it was only half finished. When on 3rd September the staff of 75 walked down the spiral staircase – a lift was not installed until months later – the rooms had no doors or ceilings. Everything was covered with black dust and in the passages of the tube, with its sloping tiled walls, there was not room for two persons to pass. New works on the station, disused since 1932, were on similar lines to those at Brompton Road and British Museum and involved walling off the platforms and providing meeting rooms, kitchens, dormitories and other facilities by partitioning the space remaining on the platforms. Further offices, meeting rooms and a typing pool were provided in the low-level subway leading to the platforms from the lift shaft, with gas-proof doors provided at appropriate points.

A few months later the offices were transformed. Mr Cole-Deacon had been a yachtsman and his experience at sea enabled him to utilise every inch of space. The offices were in a short time electrically controlled for ventilation, heating, cooking, lighting, and sewage. Each room had a telephone. Switches were installed that started up a diesel generating plant automatically to light the offices when the main supply was cut off. Perhaps the best way to describe the offices created in the old station (said a report in *The Times*) was to compare them with the cabins of a modern liner (they were in fact fitted out by the LMS Railway's carriage works). Besides conference

rooms, with pictures on walls constructed of the plywood used for making bus bodies closely resembling oak panelling, there were dining rooms, kitchens, bathrooms, and bedrooms. The principal rooms had wireless sets built into the walls.

Churchill's war cabinet

One section of the offices was called 'No. 10' and was built specially for the use of Mr Churchill and the War Cabinet; it was Churchill who gave it its name. It was early one evening in the autumn of 1940 that a senior Cabinet minister entered Mr Cole-Deacon's room unannounced. He said he would like to see over "this underground hive of industry", as he called it. He seemed unimpressed until he came to the officers' mess and kitchens and the bedroom quarters. Then he said he had been instructed by the Cabinet to find safe quarters for Mr Churchill, who was absolutely fearless in the raids and if he had his way would prefer to stay at Downing Street. After saying he did not think the offices would be suitable, the minister left, but a short while afterwards telephoned to say that Mr Churchill and several members of the Cabinet would arrive in 20 minutes time. They came at 7pm when a raid was at its height, and an hour or two later a meeting of the War Cabinet was held in the railway conference room.

Thereafter, Mr Churchill and his ministers made use of the premises whenever necessary.

Mr Churchill was concerned at the interference with the work of the Railway Executive Committee and asked whether it would be possible to construct another suite of offices for the use of the War Cabinet. Mr Cole-Deacon told the prime minister that if he could use an air-shaft for the purpose a complete suite would be ready for use within six weeks. At the end of that period the work was completed and at the same time the heavy bombing of London ended, so that the suite was never used for its intended purpose although both Churchill and his wife used the place as alternative sleeping quarters from March 1941 onwards. During the bombing Mrs Churchill used the platform exit and would travel by tube train to various stations on a surprise visit to platform shelterers. Churchill referred to Down Street as 'The Barn', a name used also in Crossbow committee files. He appreciated, apparently, the ability that working here gave him to

Visitors arriving at the Railway Executive Committee headquarters by train had to travel in the driver's cab and negotiate a very short platform. The signal seen would stop the next train for anyone leaving.

[Science Museum]

The facade of the station is still clearly visible today on Down Street. [Pendar Sillwood]

continue his work through the air raids – and as a retreat from the distractions of the Cabinet War Room. His access was relinquished in November 1943, however, when it was decided that he should use a different shelter, codenamed 'ANSON' if bombing recommenced. ANSON is part of the Rotunda construction and is discussed separately in Chapter 9.

An amusing story tells how one evening the Prime Minister arrived at his room (which in the daytime was Mr Cole-Deacon's office) and picked up some papers that the secretary and the chairman of the Railway Executive Committee, Sir Ralph Wedgwood, had been discussing. They were the plans for an intricate railway scheme including the provision of additional lines for shifting traffic from east to west. The plans had not reached the stage for placing before the Cabinet. They were to be considered by the Railway Executive Committee next day, but Mr Churchill, eager to get to work, thought they were for his perusal. He read through them, grasped what was intended to be done immediately, and made marginal suggestions that were adopted by the members of the Committee at

their meeting next morning. The Committee were, however, unaware that the P.M. was the author of the suggestions, as the fact that Mr Churchill and his Cabinet colleagues were using their headquarters as an air-raid shelter was at that time one of the most carefully guarded secrets of the war.

Central incident control

All this discussion about Churchill should not distract attention from the main work of Down Street, controlling the railways. One of the most important tasks during the period of the bombing was that of repairing damage to railway tracks. An 'incident' was reported to the control room at Down Street and, whatever the hour of the day or night, the provision of an alternative service was arranged with as little delay as possible to take workers from their homes to the war factories. At this time the maps of the railway systems on the walls of the control room were studded with flags to show where bombs had fallen. The control room was in constant communication with the Admiralty, War Office, Air Ministry, and other Government departments. At the shortest notice arrangements had to be made for moving men, guns and ammunition, including sea mines, from one part of the country to another. During the D-Day invasion period more than 70 ambulance trains were run each week, and as late as 1946 the control room was still having to arrange for more than 2,500 special trains in a period of seven days.

Throughout the war the occupants of these offices 100ft below ground were entirely safe except for the possible danger from flooding that never in fact happened. To prevent any sabotage and ensure that people who did not 'need to know' the actual location of these quarters, an arrangement was made with the Post Office that letters could be addressed simply to R.E.C., London SW (most likely they were delivered to Fielden House, which was in SW and then brought by messenger to Down Street). The GPO telephone line (WHItehall 6146) was also transferred from Fielden House in Westminster to compound the misdirection (it is not known whether similar arrangements were made for other secret installations).

The station's pre-history had begun when it was opened in March 1907. Located only a few blocks away from both Hyde Park Corner and Dover Street (Green Park) stations, Down Street was never a busy station and was closed on 21st May 1932 following the refurbishment of Green Park station. Part of the platform area was demolished to make way for a new double-length siding west of the old station and the lift shaft was converted into a ventilation system but no other alteration was made until the accommodation was selected for the REC headquarters. After conversion access was by train, travelling in the driver's cab and alighting at small platforms in either direction, just as at Brompton Road. Signals were installed to allow personnel leaving the station to halt a train there. Entry was also available via the doorway in the old station entrance at 24 Down Street, although for some visitors this might have created security problems, incurring the risk of recognition. This entrance had a permanent guard of two uniformed police officers.

Holborn

When the Piccadilly Line was built two platforms were provided at Holborn for the Aldwych branch. One is well-known and was in use until the service on this line ceased in 1994; the other was tucked in between the northbound Piccadilly and the other Aldwych platform, located somewhat to the south, such that its extreme northern end abutted the extreme southern end of the eastbound Piccadilly. It was connected to the latter by a cross passage, the door still being there today.

During the second world war it was converted into a labyrinth of offices, with a central corridor running along the old platform edge and feeding platform level offices on the west side. On the east side the trackbed allowed two levels to be constructed, the upper being used as dormitories. There must have been about 50 offices in all as well

as a kitchen and canteen at the far south end. Two separate telephone exchanges (one Post Office, one London Transport) served the offices; both were connected to the London Transport main railway (RL) automatic telephone system, the Control office at Leicester Square, the dispersed London Transport headquarters at Dover Street and the Railway Executive Committee headquarters at Down Street. After the war the place was briefly used as a staff hostel for people who had lost their homes.

Post Office

Post Office (St Paul's) was the third station revived for war purposes. The work carried out here was more radical than at Down Street and Brompton Road and is accordingly given separate treatment (see Chapter 11).

```
┌ ─ ─ ─ ─ ─ ─ ─ ─ ┐
  ENDNOTE
└ ─ ─ ─ ─ ─ ─ ─ ─ ┘
```

Anti-Aircraft Batteries

To defend the airspace over London anti-aircraft firing positions were established all over London where there was room nearby for living accommodation (normally in hutting). From the outset traditional H.A.A. (heavy anti-aircraft) guns were used to fire explosive shells, whilst from 1943 onwards an alternative (but less efficient) means of shooting down aircraft was to send many projectiles (rockets) in sequence to create a frame or 'box' that would ensure that an enemy plane flying through the box would be hit. The latter method was known as a Z-Battery, in which rockets were fired in sequence from typically 64 separate projectors (launchers), the Z indicating the site fired rockets rather than shells. Acting on instructions from the GOR at Brompton Road relayed to individual Z-Battery sites, the commander at each site would have his men rotate the projectors into the required compass direction (the gunner on the left side of the launcher) and elevate them to the correct vertical elevation (the right-hand man). At the appropriate moment the commander in his protected accommodation would press his firing button to detonate the salvo.

Batteries of this kind were established at locations including Victoria Park (19Z, mentioned in Chapter 7) and Dulwich Golf Course (18Z), which Alan Gildersleve recalls:

> When I was in the Home Guard on the anti-aircraft site we had a telephone line to a lift shaft at Brompton Road tube station (GOR) gun operations room. They used to ring us on a lateral line with Tele. Fs when an air raid was starting to appear and I had to answer it in the command post at Dulwich. We had 64 rocket projectors, each with two rockets!
>
> Communication with GOR was very formal, there was no opportunity to chat. We just used to get a ring on a Tele. F to say things such as, "There is a large area of Window over the Dagenham area," or "What is your Bovril?" and sometimes, "All sites

take posts!" followed perhaps by "There are 50-plus bombers over the Dover area." Also "The colours are Red, Red, Mike" or whatever they were that night. ('Window' was the name given to a countermeasures device in which small strips of aluminium foil were scattered at high altitude by our aircraft to confuse enemy bombers.)

'Bovril' was a code word for strength, taken from the old advertising slogan, 'Bovril For Strength', and the question meant in other words, "How many projectors can you man this evening?" "All sites take posts" meant "Take up position – ring your alarm bells, wake up all the gunners and report ready for action!" The 'colours' were the colours that our own aircraft would be flashing to identify them, followed by a Morse code letter flashed on a white light, such as red, red, dash, dash. This was changed every night and we put it up on the Littlewood's board, which was a board full of letters in which we knew where the code was hidden, e.g. aghiltsdghjRRMasdfghklmmb. The code was not printed in capitals though! The first letters were the initials of the colours and the third was the Morse letter. One could of course have many combinations, Green, Blue, Foxtrot for instance. The Littlewood's board was a largish wooden panel covered in letters, similar to a full-up Scrabble board, and probably gained its name from its similarity to a Littlewood's football pools coupon.

Incidentally, unusually for a Home Guard, I was a Lance Bombardier but we wore the KRR (King's Royal Rifle Corps) badge and the red flash with a bow and arrow on it. We were known as a Z site and I did have a bit of conversation with a chap at my then job, who was also a Home Guard at the Southwark Park Z site. Actually he got a commendation for inventing a sort of rotary chart for use on the semi-automatic plotting tables, which was adopted for all sites. These tables were in the command posts like the one where I was working and were for plotting the course of the incoming enemy aircraft, culminating in the order to "Stand by, Fire!" over the sound powered telephone to the gunners out on the site. We never claimed a hit though, as the heavy ack-ack gunners always got in first! They were up at the top of our site.

The huge rockets were fired by a No. 8 battery, a 3-volt torch cell slightly bigger than the modern AA size! I can remember all the commands for setting the angles of elevation and direction and the drill for misfires, etc. The noise was diabolical when they all fired and one was only a yard from the back of the two rockets, with just a screen between one's ears and the rockets. Our 64 rocket projectors were on a large golf course on the side of Sydenham Hill. This was private ground but some sites were in public parks. There was a perimeter fence around the bit we were using with a guard in a hut at the entrance who asked for a password if he did not know you.

There was a joke told us by our officer that someone came in not knowing the password. The guard said the first half and the visitor had to reply with the second half. Anyway one day a visitor arrived and the guard said "Halt! Who goes there? Swiss." The visitor made an inspired guess and said "Roll". The guard replied, "I'll give you bloody 'Roll', it's 'Cottage'!" Obviously the visitor was known to the guard. As you can imagine the security was not exactly very secure.

The site was manned by the regulars 24 hours a day and joined by the Home Guard at night. There were many 'Maycrete' huts for the gunners to sleep in but I was usually in the command post, which was a Nissen hut embedded in concrete. It had a direct hit one night when I wasn't there, which killed a Home Guard man and badly injured a regular officer. A new Nissen hut was put up rapidly but with no concrete and a fireplace that spewed out smoke instead of it going up the chimney – I had to sleep in that! The phone kept ringing and waking me up to answer it so I did not get much sleep.

A 'lateral' telephone line was one that connected one site to another or to GOR. We had one to Clapham. One day it rang and a voice said, "Could you please come and remove your ironmongery that has just landed on our site?" One of our rockets had misfired and landed on the Clapham site! The lateral lines were operated by Tele. Fs and used a Post Office tie line pair permanently connected through.

We used a lot of sound-powered telephones to the gunners out on the site; this sound-powered system was very good and no electrical supply was needed (one just shouted into it). I also operated a small universal call switchboard made by TMC, which also connected to Tele. Fs and Tele. Ls around the site and also to the Post Office telephone exchange, so that the various officers could ask me for a number over their Tele F and I could dial it out and plug it back to them. All very interesting, I can assure you. It was also my job to ring the cooks at 5.30am to wake them to come and cook breakfast for the gunners. One day I had a trainee and he turned the wrong handle and rang all the alarm bells around the site, and called out all the gunners instead. They were not at all pleased when they met us at breakfast!

Incidentally, the GPO was fully aware of the connection to our 10-line universal call board. Their line terminated on it and incoming calls came in just like on a PBX switchboard, then connected by the operator (sometimes me) to the extension required. All extensions were Tele. Fs or Tele. Ls. If it was a Tele. L one could listen in and hear the person coming to answer the 'phone! They had no cradle switch and were live as soon as one plugged into the line. No secrecy here! To make a call from these one pressed a button and a signal was sent to the PBX to operate the doll's eye. (Teles. F and L were magneto field telephones used by the Army; TMC was the Telephone Manufacturing Company, which happened to have its factory in Dulwich.)

A New Tube

The GPO's own deep-level cable subway network and its links to the tube railways

J UST as the existence of the Post Office tube railway would surprise many otherwise well informed people, many folk will be equally surprised to learn that the same organisation built another, equally elaborate network of tunnels under London used for carrying telephone cables. The notion of a tube network for cables is not as radical as might seem, however, given that pneumatic tubes and telegraph cables had been driven underground since Victorian times and in view of the Post

This illustration from the pre-war boys' paper Modern Wonder shows graphically the tangle of public utilities lying beneath most British streets. It was this that led the Post Office to find less hazardous routes for its telephone cables in subways at a deeper level.

Office's experience in tunnelling its one railway. Nevertheless, the extent of this system, now in the hands of British Telecom as a result of the separation of posts and telecommunications in 1981, is quite remarkable, comprising a network of mainly seven-feet diameter tubes covering a route length of around 12 miles.

Its origins go back more than a century, and the virtue of carrying telephone cables (and other public utilities) in subways or tunnels below ground was recognised as long ago as 1860. From this time onwards tunnels for shared services were constructed under all the major street improvements, including Kingsway, Aldwych and Charing Cross Road as well as the Victoria Embankment. Subsequently they were incorporated also in tube station booking hall developments (Piccadilly Circus, Leicester Square and others), with the hope that an integrated system might one day be formed. Most of these subways are semicircular brick tunnels about 16 feet in diameter, running about three feet below the pavement. Rectangular openings are provided at frequent intervals for access to the pipes and cables. Currently, London has nine miles of joint use service tunnels carrying water, electricity, gas, telephone wires and now cable television (previously some also carried telegraph wires, hydraulic power conduits and pneumatic telegraph tubes).

The obvious advantage of subways was saving the need to dig up roads whenever alterations and new connections were needed. Another benefit soon realised was that faults and problems are less likely to occur thanks to the lack of disturbance. Shared use has its disadvantages too, as a disastrous explosion at Holborn proved in 1928, following a gas leak.

Subways provide some protection from aerial attack in conventional warfare, a fact recognised in one of the conclusions of the Air Raid Precautions Subcommittee of the Committee of Imperial Defence formed in 1924. As a result of its recommendations, the Post Office made plans for an emergency communications system making use of tunnels belonging to the tube railways, and these were put to good use during World War II.

The radial scheme

The 'Victory' issue of the *IPOEEJ* explains how the tube railways were used extensively to give deep-level protection for a few miles for important defence and public trunk telephone cables. The scheme adopted entailed the linking up, by circumferential cables, of the radial cable routes of the tube railways at a number of selected interception centres located not far from the emergent points. In this way interruption by bomb damage to any of the radial cable routes could be restored readily by suitable re-routing of the circuits over the circumferential cables at the interception centres.

That was the theory anyway, although a typescript document (undated) in the BT Museum

entitled The Work of the Engineering Department during the Present War concedes:

> In one case this did not protect the cables and a bomb smashed in about 60 feet run of tunnel, cutting two important cables. The tunnel began to fill with water and sewage, and if temporary repairs were to be effected they had to be done very quickly. After great difficulties, the engineers managed to force two lengths of steel tube through the clay filling the tunnel and temporary cables were drawn through. It then became a race between the jointers making the connections between the old and new cables and the rising flood of water. The work had to be perfectly done if it was to be of use and the smallest pinhole would cause failure. The jointers won with seven feet of water in the tunnel and barely room to escape.

This incident occurred in the Northern Line tunnels at Eversholt Street, near Euston, on the night of 21st–22nd October 1940 and it was certainly exceptional. With the bomb passing through 47ft of solid ground, it was the deepest penetration by any enemy bomb in London. The same night both Euston and Mornington Crescent tube stations had to be evacuated between 10.30pm and 3am owing to flooding caused by the explosion.

The radial scheme was started in the late autumn of 1940 and completed during the following year, involving the laying of 250 miles of cable of which 116 miles were in public tube railway tunnels, another 20 miles in the Post Office Railway and a short but vital section in the 12ft diameter pilot tunnel under the Thames at Dartford, constructed before the war in advance of the main road tunnel. In addition a large repeater station for trunk cable routes was built next to the North Circular Road, aimed at linking arterial trunk routes without the need to head to or radiate from the centre of London. Known first as the Hendon Ring Main exchange or Hendon Sub-Trunk Centre, then later

Havoc was caused on the night of 21st–22nd October 1940 when an enemy bomb penetrated 47ft of solid ground to rupture the Northern Line tunnels at Eversholt Street, near Euston. Post Office jointers fought a battle against time to repair two crucial trunk telephone cables in flood waters that reached 7ft before their work was over. Immediately north of the cave-in, the picture shows the fused cables and sewage that had already risen to rail level.

[London's Transport Museum]

For three decades motorists passing the gaunt outline of Brent Building on the North Circular Road had little idea it was built as a desperate move to safeguard the nation's communications integrity. For this reason alone it escaped the wartime ban on new construction projects, but its austere no-frills architecture betrays the bleak era of its birth. [British Telecom]

London's Ring Main ensured the survivability of through communications.

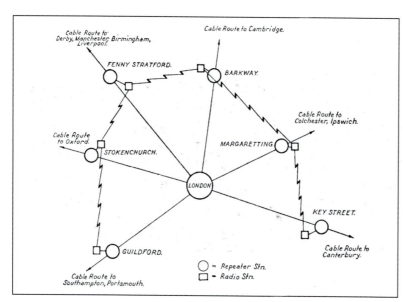

Sites for the radio terminals were selected on high ground within a few miles of the repeater stations to obtain transmission paths of between 25 and 35 miles and the radio equipment used frequencies in the band 45–50MHz that had been allocated to the BBC's Alexandra Palace television station, which had opened in 1936.

Cabling the tubes

The precise purpose of (and routes taken by) Post Office telephone cables laid in London Transport tube tunnels is not well documented. Most information is thus circumstantial and in a few cases, speculative. The plan reproduced in this chapter from Harbottle's IPOEE paper illustrates the trunk cables radiating from central London and reaching the surface at Golders Green tunnel mouth and Belsize Park station (Northern Line north), Manor House station (Piccadilly Line), Mile End station (unopened Central Line), South Wimbledon (Northern Line south), and Shepherds Bush station (Central Line). These locations are clearly captioned, as are a number of locations and buildings in central London, which are also access points to the tubes.

The railway stations are Moorgate (for Wood Street exchange) and Elephant & Castle (purpose unknown) on the Northern Line, St Paul's (electricity control centre) on the Central Line, Waterloo (transfer point to Waterloo & City Line) and Trafalgar Square (transfer to Whitehall tunnels) on the Bakerloo Line, Brompton Road (anti-aircraft HQ) and Green Park (Devonshire House) on the Piccadilly Line and Paddington and Eastern District Office (P.O. Railway). Devonshire House, opposite the Ritz Hotel in Piccadilly, is a massive mansion block situated on the block formed by Piccadilly, Berkeley Street, Mayfair Place and Stratton Street. Before and after the war it was best known as the head-quarters of the Rootes Group of car manu-facturers, but during World War II it housed a number of government departments and served as communications headquarters for MI8 and the Special Operations Executive (SOE). One other connection shown on the plan is Duke Street, the American commun-ications centre in the Selfridges Annexe described in Chapter 6, where the SIGSALY scrambling apparatus was also housed (see Chapter 10). The cable connection is with the Post Office Railway tubes. No BBC cables are shown on the plan, although Broadcasting House itself is marked.

Independent cable tunnels

Access to tube railway tunnels was not gained easily, however, and the Post Office realised it would achieve maximum flexibility only if it built its own tunnels, despite the significant capital cost. The process of building and extending these tunnels has a parallel with the development of London's underground railways and readers familiar with this process will recall that the initial constructions were in fairly shallow ground, followed later by tubes at

as the Brent Building, this was opened for telegraph circuits in October 1944 and for telephony in February 1945. It was strategically important enough to escape the ban on new building construction and stood on the north side of the North Circular Road. Plans of the early 1950s allocated it a key role in the hardened national trunk telephone system but it was later put to other uses and was demolished to make way for the Brent Cross shopping centre.

A more radical solution was adopted towards the end of 1943, when the possibility of heavy attacks on the London area was considered to justify additional measures to safeguard communications between London and other parts of the country. A scheme known colloquially as the 'London Ring Main' was provided to interconnect repeater stations ringed about London at a radius of some 30–40 miles, using the latest design of multi-channel radio-telephone equipment. Using mobile equipment selected repeater stations on different cable routes radiating from London could be linked quickly so as to divert circuits to alternative routes.

significantly deeper level. The Post Office cable tunnels developed along similar lines.

London's first tunnel for the exclusive use of telephone cables was a short one in Wood Street (1925) but this was a one-off. The genesis of today's network lies in a small-bore (7 feet diameter) tunnel linking Holborn telephone exchange in the west with St Martins-le-Grand and the Citadel exchange (Faraday building). Started in 1941 and completed the following year, it is just over a mile in length and runs at a depth from 80 to 100ft below ground to be safe from bombing.

The need for conserving iron during the critical period of the war meant that the greater part of this tunnel was lined with reinforced concrete segments instead of the customary cast iron. The clay spoil excavated in the process was taken away and dumped in disused gravel pits west of London. To speed cabling operations, specially designed roller skates were used for the first time to bring the cables to the appropriate section of the tunnel. In total some 72 miles of cable was laid in this and other Post Office tunnels during the war (other tunnels included the Post Office Railway, which also provided a valuable protected route).

This diagram of the routes taken by telephone cables in London Transport and Post Office Railway tube tunnels is redrawn from fig. 16 of an IPOEE 'read paper' given in 1946 by R. H. Harbottle. To improve clarity, the PO's own cable-only tunnels are not shown here.

Strict secrecy was observed during the construction of the cable tunnels and the soldier's fixed bayonet is not just for show. His insignia indicate he is attached to the Home Guard, the COL on his shoulder standing for City of London and 19 being his battalion number. The rifle he is holding looks like either a .303 Enfield P14 or more likely a U.S. Lend Lease P17 model. The location is under Newgate Street, at its junction with Warwick Lane, looking north towards King Edward Building.
[British Telecom]

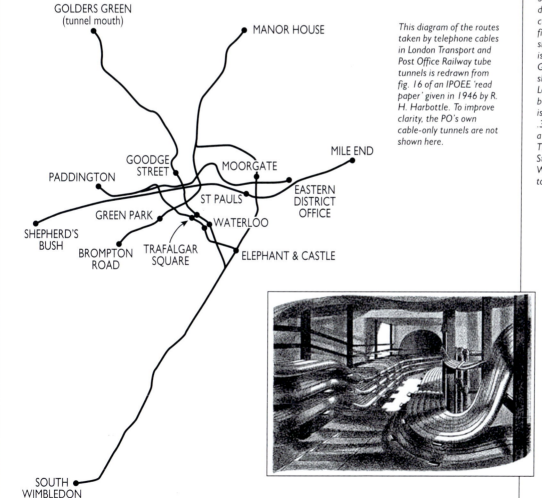

Cable tunnels were not a new idea in 1941. Short tunnels had already been constructed, with their strange artistic character recognised and used in Post Office publicity material. Strategic tunnels of substantial length were nonetheless an entirely new notion, kept strictly secret until the end of the war and little known even today.   [British Telecom]

To confuse any enemy agents, materials needed for constructing cable tunnels in the City of London were brought in by the Post Office underground railway (Mail Rail), and the spoil removed by the same means. These skips were brought from the surface at Mount Pleasant, then unloaded here at King Edward Building station. The motor unit of the train was built at Preston by English Electric Ltd in 1930 and despite being one of the oldest vehicles, was in use until the line's closure in September 2003. On the siding behind is one of the original battery locomotives, also supplied by English Electric Ltd. [British Telecom]

Connecting Whitehall and the national network

An equally vital cable tunnel was constructed beneath Whitehall to serve the ministries and service headquarters in this district. Since this tunnel system was bound up intimately with the Cabinet War Rooms, the Admiralty Citadel and the Rotundas, full details of the tunnels local to these buildings are given in the next chapter.

The Whitehall tunnels provided secure connections to government buildings locally, but the onward link to the national network was still vulnerable. This called for a fully protected cable route connecting government and armed services users in Whitehall with the Citadel main trunk exchange at Faraday Building, a mile and a half away in Queen Victoria Street. Constructing a new cable tunnel over this distance would have taxed the nation's resources sorely under wartime conditions. Instead the linking cable was taken through tube train tunnels, the work being carried out in 1942. Starting at Trafalgar Square station (since renamed Charing Cross) the route followed the Bakerloo Line to Waterloo, where the cables were routed underneath floors to reach the Waterloo & City Line, along which they were taken to a point below Queen Victoria Street and then via Post Office tunnels into Faraday Building. Post Office telephone cables also ran northbound to Oxford Circus station, where a connection from the northbound Bakerloo Line platform led to the Post Office Railway directly underneath, which runs along Margaret Street.

To simplify interconnection between the Post Office telephone system and these railway tunnels, an underground transfer point was built at Trafalgar Square station (now Charing Cross). Work on this was put in early on and an entry in the Telephone Branch War Diary for September 1939 states: "Tube Cables. MDF at Trafalgar Square – building work completed, ironwork being erected." A further entry for the same month from the Chief Regional Engineer's War Diary elaborates:

The necessity for the installation of cables associated with certain vital requirements for defence services at sufficiently deep levels was realised long before the war, and many cables have been provided in London Passenger Transport Board tube tunnels. Subsequently, it was decided to construct a special tunnel at an approximate depth of 100 feet under Whitehall, from Trafalgar Square to King Charles Street, for the housing of cables for intercommunication between Government Departments concerned with national defence and for connecting cables between the various Whitehall offices and the trunk and toll interception cables in the London Passenger Transport Board tubes carrying defence circuits.

Access to the tunnel will be provided at Trafalgar Square (station) and Whitehall Exchange, cable access only will be provided at the Government building where the centralised private branch exchange (Federal) is to be installed, and at other important Government buildings. These cables will be taken through bore holes to laterals branching from the main tunnel. The distribution frames, audio and voice frequency equipment and power plant will eventually be provided in this tunnel. The work has not yet been commenced.

In the meantime, all existing and additional cables in the LPTB tube tunnels will be terminated on a small distribution frame which is now being installed at Trafalgar Square station. This is involving the provision of 12 cables, varying in size from 54/20 to 308/20 and three existing cables are being re-routed. The total cable mileage is about 107 miles.

the trunk and toll telephone services at the height of the blitz. It was not enough that the structure should be capable of withstanding every type of bomb; it had also to be able to withstand a siege. Into the building went 40,000 tons of concrete, 2,200 tons of reinforced steel, and onto it went a concrete roof seven feet six inches thick. It was completely self-contained, with its own continuous water supply, enough food for three months, and sleeping accommodation for off-duty personnel. Work was begun on the building in May 1941, and continued day and night until completion – STC's transmission equipment was being installed on the lower floors while the concrete was still being poured into moulds above. To ensure a constant supply of concrete a

The massive construction of Citadel exchange meant it enjoyed a long life, not closing until the first weekend of August 1989. [British Telecom]

A fully protected route for vital telephone cables between Whitehall and the Faraday trunk exchange near Blackfriars was created using the tunnels of the Bakerloo and Waterloo & City lines of the underground. This bulkhead pipe connection to Waterloo & City Railway is seen from Post Office tunnels near Faraday South and like others does not provide a walking route for people.

[British Telecom]

The construction of a further tunnel in Aldersgate Street, which will be associated with the emergency arrangements at Headquarters and King Edward Buildings, started in the middle of the month. The consent of the authorities for this work was secured with the utmost celerity, and work commenced immediately afterwards.

The Faraday Citadel

Citadel telephone exchange, in Godliman Street just south of St Paul's Cathedral, was constructed on citadel lines and was intimately connected with the deep level cable tunnels. This description, taken from the history of Standard Telephones and Cables Ltd, *The Story of STC 1883–1958*, says almost everything necessary.

The construction by the British Post Office of the fantastic building known as The Citadel, a huge concrete structure at the rear of Faraday Building in London, provided STC with another opportunity to help in safeguarding Britain's communications. The Citadel was a keystone in the plan to safeguard

The reinforced low ceiling is prominent in this October 1945 view of the emergency trunk telephone switchboard at Citadel exchange.
[British Telecom]

large mixing plant was erected on a nearby bombed site and an overhead pipeline fed the mixed concrete direct to the scene of operations. When the ground floor was completed, giving protection to the workmen, work continued even during raid alerts.

The building contained an artesian well 600ft deep, yielding 2,000 gallons of water an hour, and the main entrance was protected against gas and possible frontal assault by heavy steel doors weighing four tons and locked from the inside. Three diesel engines, each of 388hp, supplied the energy to drive the large power plant used for the telephone equipment. This Rock of Gibraltar in the centre of London could still have been put out of action if the cables serving the building had not been made immune from enemy bombs. This was done by sinking a shaft eight feet in diameter and eighty feet deep to connect the Citadel with the elaborate system of deep level cables in the underground railways and the specially constructed Post Office tunnel which had been developed in the early years of the war.

The foundations of the building varied in thickness between five feet and ten feet. Below ground the outer walls were six feet six inches thick; above ground three feet three inches. The thickness of the floors dividing the three-storey building was one foot six inches, and the interior was sub-divided by walls two feet three inches thick to minimise the effect of possible damage by blast. The Citadel was bomb-proof, siege-proof and gas-proof, and during the heaviest bombing raids and flying bomb attacks the whole of the trunk services during the night were operated from there.

Marjory Chapman, a GPO telephonist during the war, has memories of Faraday.

They wanted telephonists up in London and I was picked to go there. When we first went up to Faraday Buildings they just had shells of concrete walls for the girls to stay in and the water was

running down the walls. Well it was either that stay or go home through the air raids. I often went home because I preferred it. They had quite a hard time these girls, because if somebody didn't turn up there was always somebody to jump in immediately. There was no question of leaving anything unturned, you know. We had gas masks and we had fire watching as well. We had to do fire watching at home and fire watching up there, and there weren't enough of the men to go round so we used to do night duties as well. All you were concerned with was getting on with your job and seeing that everybody got what they wanted as best you could. Norman Wisdom was one of the telephonists with us at the time. He was a night telephonist and we used to sit on the switchboard and he used to tell us stories about what he'd done. He was very keen on horse riding. It wasn't all that busy at night, but you had to be there, you see.

Cable conundrums

Interesting routes were found for some cables. A case in point was 'a special cable for defence purposes' that was laid in December 1939 from the old St Paul's station to C.T.O. (R), the reserve Central Telegraph Office that was located nearby in the basement of King Edward Building. According to the City Area war diary this cable ran through the long-abandoned 'old parcels tube' (see endnote) and was brought to the surface via the disused lift shaft.

The Post Office was not the only undertaking to provide fallback communication facilities. Cable & Wireless Ltd, responsible during World War II for the 355,000-mile Imperial radio and landline network that reached seventy countries, was acutely aware of the vulnerability of its central London terminals at its Central Telegraph Station in Moorgate (an establishment entirely separate from the Central Telegraph Office of the Post Office at St Paul's). A reinforced bombproof and gas-proof duplicate station was built at the company's head office at Electra House, on the Victoria Embankment, but even this would not safeguard communication if the cables leading to it were destroyed by enemy action.

Accordingly the directors toyed with the idea of providing fallback facilities further away at a safer location. They first considered a remote country house but eventually they selected 'an unpretentious red brick villa' at 12 Hamilton Road in the west London district of Ealing known to proud locals as 'Queen of the Suburbs'. This was sandbagged but not made air-raid proof. Although its caretaker was armed with a revolver and a police constable kept watch outside, most local residents would have been unaware of the home's new status. In the event, the Ealing station was brought into use only once, on 16th August 1940, when a bomb falling in Hammersmith severed the cable from Moorgate to the Atlantic cable terminal at Porthcurno (Cornwall).

Although this facility had been described in the two official histories of the company, it was not exactly common knowledge and in recent times became the subject of a fascinating rumour. Dismissed by many as an urban myth, the story was put into print by a contributor to an Internet newsgroup, Neil Conlon, who related how in the early 1970s a friend of his had purchased a large detached house in Hamilton Road, Ealing Broadway and set about re-decorating it. Conversion work on the basement proved extremely difficult, however, and it was only after considerable time and effort had been spent that a heavy metal door was revealed, with no visible means of gaining entry. Soon afterwards the owner was informed that his property had become the subject of a compulsory purchase order. The sum offered by officialdom was, apparently, very generous and the owner accepted.

'The Mystery of the Door' puzzled the correspondent for many years but was solved when he read Nigel West's book *GCHQ – The Secret Wireless War 1900–86*, which revealed what lay hidden at 12 Hamilton Road had been a 'standby cablehead and radio station' for Cable & Wireless Ltd. The legend was not accurate in every detail, as it was not the basement (a small affair with only 5ft headroom) that housed the cable station. There are, however, extensive remains of old wiring in the rear room on the ground floor.

ENDNOTE

The Parcels Despatch tube

The first proposal for a tube line to carry the mail was put forward in 1855 by Rowland Hill, who suggested a line from the Post Office at St Martins-le-Grand to Little Queen Street in Holborn. The initial proposal was for an 'atmospheric railway' designed by Thomas Rammell, who came up with a scheme by which a stationary steam engine would drive a large fan that could suck air out of an air-tight tube and draw the vehicle towards it or blow air to push it away. A smaller version of this system was later developed for message handling in large department stores and government offices.

Rammell devised plans for a number of lines in London to carry goods and mails, setting up the Pneumatic Despatch Company on 30th June 1859. In May 1861 an experimental 452yd line was laid in Battersea, which proved to be viable and led to a number of proposals that roused little support from the Post Office, although it agreed to make trials of the new system. The first 2ft gauge line ran a distance of 600 yards at Euston, beginning in 1863 and securing Post Office approval and success. It was followed by a longer, 3ft 8½in line from Euston through Holborn to the General Post Office at St Martins-le-Grand, opening from Euston to Holborn in 1865 and to St Martin's-le-Grand on 1st December 1873.

However, because this new service shaved only four minutes off the time taken to carry the mail by road, the Post Office announced in 1874 it would not be using the new line, which was quickly abandoned and the Pneumatic Despatch Company dissolved. The terminus at the General Post Office became a coal and wood store, whilst other parts of the 5ft cast iron horseshoe-shape tunnel were put to other uses. In 1895 there was a proposal to reopen the tunnel with electric traction and a new company, the London Despatch Company, was formed. Some work was done on upgrading the line and tunnels but the Post Office remained sceptical about its worth and work on the new project ceased in 1902 and the London Despatch Company was wound up in 1905. The Post Office finally bought the tunnel in 1921 to use for telephone cables, after which time it became known as 'the old parcels tube'. Several sections of the tunnel have been lost over the years but about three quarters of it is still in use carrying cables. On 20th June 1928 an explosion in the tunnel under High Holborn was blamed on the ignition of coal gas, with one workman killed. During the subsequent excavations to repair half a mile of damaged road, four of the original mailbag cars were discovered (but not, unfortunately, preserved).

Tunnelling work also requires substantial works above ground. This is the gantry and crane used to drive an 8ft diameter shaft and lateral leading to Faraday and Citadel exchanges. The location is the corner of Dean's Court and Carter Lane, around 1941.
[British Telecom]

10 On Secret Service

The Cabinet War Room, Whitehall tunnels, Admiralty Citadel and Rotundas

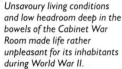

Unsavoury living conditions and low headroom deep in the bowels of the Cabinet War Room made life rather unpleasant for its inhabitants during World War II.
[Imperial War Museum]

BRIEF mention was made in Chapter 3 of the Cabinet War Room and other fortified accommodation for the nucleus of central government. In this chapter we examine this construction and the philosophy that lay behind it.

The subject is easier to understand if we examine how the machinery of government during the Second World War divided itself into three functions. The Cabinet War Room acted as the nucleus of government and housed the war cabinet. The various ministries and armed forces (the 'Services') had their own facilities for maintaining the activities that were called 'due functioning' or the continuing operation of governance. Lastly an

organisation of Regional Commissioners looked after the effects of air raids and other enemy aggression, feeding reports to a central war room at the Ministry of Home Security in order to keep the government informed of the state of the country at large.

Although alternative accommodation had been reserved for the mechanism of government away from central London (including the war rooms provided at Paddock mentioned earlier), prime minister Churchill was determined that the government should 'not be beaten out of London'. Instead plans were laid for hardened accommodation for a substantial proportion of government and services personnel. On 22nd October 1940 Churchill ordered that 'a substantial measure of overhead cover' be provided for the existing Cabinet War Rooms in Whitehall and also instructed Lord Beaverbrook to convert other buildings in and around Whitehall into alternative bombproof citadels.

Cabinet War Room

Of all the subterranean constructions completed during World War II the Cabinet War Room is probably the best known. Following a decision in 1949 to preserve it intact as a memorial of the war, it was made available for inspection by occasional guided tours. In 1984 the main war room was opened to the public as an outpost of the Imperial War Museum and is now one of London's major tourist attractions.

Known variously as 'CWR', 'The Hole in the Ground', 'George Street', 'Storey's Gate' or 'The Annexe', this bunker was constructed under existing government offices bounding on Storey's Gate, Great George Street and King Charles Street. Building work started in June 1938, according to the official guidebook written by Peter Simkins; it was accelerated by the Munich Crisis and many modifications were added throughout the war. Its location was the western basement of the government offices formerly known as the New Public Offices, a steel-framed building constructed between 1898 and 1915. Its steel frame meant it was probably the strongest structure of any in Whitehall and its location was conveniently situated between Parliament and the Prime Minister's office-residence at Number 10 Downing Street.

Originally conceived as a temporary solution, the project soon became more complex and permanent, becoming fully operational on 27th August 1939, exactly a week before the German invasion of Poland and Britain's declaration of war. For the next six years this 'temporary' measure was to serve as the central shelter for government and the military strategists of each fighting service. In late 1940 a bombproof shield was formed at Churchill's instruction by filling the sub-ground floor above the basement with reinforced concrete, then over the winter of 1940–41 a concrete slab 3ft thick and reinforced with steel rails and tram lines was installed above the basement. This was extended to cover the courtyard rooms and the CWR annexe. The apron wall was also built.

The complex lies 50ft below ground and was designed to house, sleep and feed 270 people in 150 offices, rooms and sub-basement dormitories. The structure has a mile of corridors and occupies around six acres of floor space. It was equipped with a mechanical ventilation system, gas filtration system and six lifts; during the war it also contained a BBC outside broadcast studio. A detachment of ten retired Royal Marines, including two corporals, was organised to act on guard and general orderly duties.

The most notable rooms within the complex were the Cabinet Room (in which the War Cabinet met 115 times during bombing raids and where many crucial decisions were made) and the Map Room (equipped with large maps of the Atlantic, the Far East and the British coastline, this was the focal point of the underground site until VJ day, where the direction and progress of the war was charted). Churchill was provided with a bedroom here but it was not to his liking and was used only occasionally for short respite during the afternoon. The Transatlantic Telephone Room makes up the quartet of notable rooms and is described later in this chapter.

It is said that Chamberlain rarely visited the place but when Churchill succeeded him as prime minister on 10th May 1940, he made his presence felt quickly, forming a coalition government and a War Cabinet of five members. The complex remained in permanent use thereafter until the surrender of the Japanese forces in the Far East in August 1945. No longer needed, the rooms were closed and locked on 16th August 1945. The complex came closest to being hit when a bomb fell a quarter of a block away. Churchill's reputed response was: "Pity it wasn't a bit nearer so that we might have tested our defences."

Most inhabitants were probably very satisfied to leave the place, since living was far from easy in the bowels of the earth. An official website states that staff had to carry their gas masks with them wherever they went. If this was a minor inconvenience, the lack of flushing toilets and the need to sleep in tiered bunks with army blankets certainly were more than minor. In fact all but the most senior staff slept in crowded dormitories down in the sub basement (known as the 'Dock'). Other discomforts of living in these underground rooms included insects and rats, whilst the noise of the ventilation system made sleeping very uncomfortable. In the Dock, anyone taller than four feet was forced to stoop to reach his or her sleeping quarters. It was also extremely dark on this level, making the carrying of torches essential. Not

surprisingly, many staff risked the long journey home at night just to sleep in comfort.

In November 2000 it was announced that a museum to celebrate the life of Sir Winston Churchill was to be housed in other parts of wartime leader's bunker network, in an 'historic' area where Churchill's intelligence staff plotted World War II deception operations. Phil Reed, curator of the Cabinet War Room in Whitehall, was quoted as saying he hoped to convert an area "the size of a football pitch" under Whitehall into a museum.

The combined services bunker that never was

Secondary to the Cabinet War Room was the notion of providing a much larger area of protected accommodation for accommodating five war rooms, the complete staff of the combined government services and the Home Security organisation. After preliminary consideration of far more modest schemes, a Cabinet decision in summer 1939 saw the consulting engineer Sir Horace Dalrymple-Hay asked to advise on how best to house up to 3,000 staff underground in a deep bunker running the length of Whitehall. His original proposal was a three-tunnel system running deep below Whitehall, with war rooms provided in two parallel 25ft diameter tunnels, with Post Office cables and other utilities provided from a 12ft diameter service tunnel running between them. The whole affair would take two years to build, at a cost of around £1million, and these considerations, also the resources it would require at a time when three specially devised deep basements were under construction in the north-west suburbs, meant that it was never built. The scheme was turned down by the government in October 1939, although authority had been given already in June for the cable tunnel alone.

Alternative proposals included a single large shelter beneath Horse Guards Parade and a large basement structure that would become the basement of a proposed new building in Whitehall

Cabinet War Room telephonists had slightly more headroom but there was no space to spare. The ring-shaped paper label on the telephone warned users that their conversations were not secure and was fitted to all instruments except the 'scrambler' phones (distinguished by their green handsets).

[Imperial War Museum]

Gardens. In the event no combined scheme came to pass and instead each department opted to construct its own sub-surface citadel, using the cable tunnel mentioned to provide protected communications between them. The nature of this compromise solution is described succinctly by Peter Simkins, who states:

> Top priority was given to the completion of a Whitehall Deep Tunnel, which was intended to offer secure communications and access between these various strongholds, and certain buildings were selected for strengthening, including the Faraday Building in Queen Victoria Street and a steel-framed building in the Horseferry Road.

This decision to adapt existing buildings as citadels followed a year later by consequence of an order given by Churchill on 22nd October 1940, when he instructed Lord Beaverbrook to convert other buildings in and around Whitehall into alternative bombproof citadels. T. H. O'Brien mentions these buildings too in *Civil Defence (History of the Second World War)*:

> In the first half of 1941 the government built some strong steel-framed buildings in central London and four 'fortresses', which came to be popularly known as 'citadels'.

This form of construction was by no means new, but it had the advantage in war that the steel frames would be able to absorb the shock of a direct hit. In this way both the structure and the people within would survive, in theory at least. The actual buildings are identified as Horseferry Road (Air Ministry building, entrance in Monck Street) with the associated Rotundas, the east block Citadel of Faraday Building telephone exchange, Curzon Street House and the War Office citadel in the Montagu House annexe. They are all described in greater detail below.

The War Office citadel

The Montagu House annexe stood on a site now grassed over with Whitehall to the west, Whitehall Gardens to the north, and Richmond Terrace to the south and the former Montagu House (Ministry of Labour) to the east. The annexe had two storeys above ground, used by the Ministry of Labour, and either one or two below ground. The site had, however, been authorised in 1936 as the long-term headquarters for the War Office and was always planned to have a deep bombproof basement shelter. The above-ground accommodation of the annexe was demolished after the war along with Montagu House but the basement – the War Office citadel – remains.

Known as 'The Fortress', the shelter under the Montagu House annexe was completed in December 1941 with a subway connection to the basement of the War Office. It should not be confused with two other underground bunkers known as Montagu House North and Montagu House South, located to the north-east of the annexe bunker beneath where the Main Building of

the Ministry of Defence, opened in 1952, stands today. The southern end of Main Building covers where Montagu House stood, whilst grass grows above the annexe itself. A major function of the Citadel was as a signals centre, handling wireless communications, telephone calls and teleprinter messages. In 1945 it also housed MI10(a), part of the MI10 weapons analysis and technical unit. The bunker played a key role again during the Suez Crisis, when just before August Bank Holiday 1956 Major General J. M. W. Badcock of the Royal Signals began operations planning there.

The Admiralty Citadel

In front of the 'new Admiralty' building, on which work commenced in 1928, stands a 'severe-looking new structure' known as the Admiralty Citadel alias *HMS St Vincent*. Virginia Creeper or Boston Ivy has softened its lines over time, during which its alternative name of Lenin's Tomb has also been largely forgotten.

Standing on the corner of The Mall and Horse Guards Avenue, it was built in 1940–41 to provide bombproof protection for the vital Admiralty operations, wireless and communications rooms and during World War II it functioned as a huge nerve centre through which signals passed from all over the world. From a constructional point of view the Citadel is a two-storeyed bunker, with the main operational level below ground and another providing conference, sleeping and washing facilities at surface level. Above all this is another storey housing air conditioning, gas filtration and standby generator plant, over which is a protective bomb-burster slab covered by 3ft of earth for blast absorption. Grass on top of this earth provides a degree of camouflage. Other features include machine gun slits at each corner of the building (covering enemies attacking from St James's Park or The Mall) and an air intake and exhaust tower that rise above the building. There are separate access routes from the Old Building of the Admiralty both above and below ground.

The overall appearance of the building is not inartistic, made of prefabricated concrete blocks faced with pinkish aggregate. Unlike most British bunkers, a conscious attempt was made to apply aesthetic styling to the building and in this respect it resembles the massive above-ground air raid protection bunkers built by the Germans, which were given very careful architectural treatment. In his book *London Marches On* (1947) Harold Clunn writes with perception, "In structure the Citadel resembles an inverted ship. The whole structure is immensely strong and its foundations are some thirty feet below the ground with heavy reinforced walls above them in several layers. It has not yet been decided whether this building is to remain as a permanency or to be removed as a war-time disfigurement, but it will certainly remain for a long time to come as a feature of the London landscape." Sixty years on it certainly shows no signs of crumbling.

Natural weathering and a mantle of creeper plants have softened the outline of the Admiralty Citadel in Horse Guards Avenue since it was completed in 1941. Few passers-by will be aware that some 20ft of concrete in the roof protect the one-time operations centre inside although the observant eye will spot a number of loopholes or firing positions by which it could be defended in the case of ground attack. The low concrete structure in the foreground is understood to be a ventilation plant room for the Green Park to Charing Cross section of the Jubilee Line.

The external appearance of the Admiralty Citadel gives little clue to what lies inside – or below – it. This is the underground telephone switchroom in October 1945.
[British Telecom]

Occupation began in August 1941 when the first staff took up their desks. The writer Donald McLachlan gives a good description of the use of the building during the Second World War, recalling:

There was an untidy, clattering bustle; hardly one of the small rooms had less than two telephone conversations going on; officers and civilians and 'secret ladies' moving about the narrow corridors with heavily labelled folders and dockets, teleprinter flimsies or illegible sequences of decoded signals. There was a smell of rooms never empty for more than a few minutes, used all round the clock. The Citadel quarters were admirably clean, ventilated and warmed by the standards of those days, but cut off by twenty feet of steel and concrete from the fresh air of St James's Park and the Mall. Indeed, it was probably the best bombproof headquarters in London.

Six hundred yards away to the south in Storey's Gate, the Prime Minister might sometimes wonder during the Blitz whether a direct hit might not bring the Thames flooding into his basement shelter. Not so the hundred men and women of the OIC (Operational Intelligence Centre) working in the Citadel, described by Churchill in his memoirs as that 'vast monstrosity which weighs upon the Horse

Guards Parade'. They had the assurance of safety from even a direct hit – and a bracing assurance it was – but for it they paid the price of complete exclusion from the outside world: no windows, no daylight, no sound of traffic or birds or wind, only the noise of the work being done. It was the engine room of N.I.D. (Naval Intelligence Division).

Kensington and Mayfair citadels

Two less well-known citadel structures of World War II were located in Kensington and Mayfair. The first of these was London's civil defence headquarters, probably the least well known of London's wartime bunkers. Sited in museum grounds at the junction of Exhibition Road and Cromwell Road in South Kensington, it was a surface bunker of reinforced concrete next to the Geological Museum (now part of the Natural History Museum).

For civil defence purposes the United Kingdom was divided into 12 civil defence regions, each under a Civil Regional Commissioner, and London was Region 5. This purpose-built structure, which was ready for occupation by June 1939, had various titles, including London C.D. Region Headquarters, No. 5 (London) Region Control Room and Home Security Region 5 War Room. It controlled the whole of Region 5, comprising all of greater London, including the London County Council boroughs and the surrounding metropolitan districts. It was not a tactical war room as such, but acted as a clearing house for information about air raids, damage, fires and so on received from the local reporting centres in the boroughs and districts. The various agencies working in the bunker could then select the services to be deployed and relay this information back to the boroughs and districts for implementation. The network of civil defence wardens, who acted as incident control officers, helped co-ordinate rescue efforts and directed the deployment of fire, ambulance and heavy rescue units that were supplied by the LCC. The facilities also housed the New Tube Shelters Committee, which handled day-to-day administration of the deep shelters and were conveniently just a short walk from the anti-aircraft operations room at Brompton Road station, where the 1st Anti-Aircraft Division directed London's anti-aircraft activities.

The external walls of the single-storey building were of concrete 6ft thick whilst internally there were two large rooms running the length of the bunker, taking up two thirds of the space, with the remainder divided into four smaller rooms including kitchen and toilets. Originally the citadel was entered from the basement of the Geological Museum, where a tunnel sloped down into the control centre (the covered way is now demolished but the scar is still visible).

Florrie Cowley, a Ministry of Home Security teleprinter operator, provides a contemporary account of work in the blockhouse.

I remember the bunker consisting of one very large room, several large rooms and some smaller ones. In one of the large rooms there were 10 girls

The Control Room at the London Civil Defence Region citadel in South Kensington with maps of damage and current activity. Fire, ambulance and heavy rescue teams were directed from here to attend incidents where local Civil Defence wardens acted as control officers on the spot. [After The Battle]

sitting at telephones, each one a direct link with one of the nine areas of London.

The warden in the roads reported to his senior warden, who in turn reported to his area warden, who phoned in to the girl at the Home Office at Whitehall and to another fixed teleprinter place. Then we numbered it accordingly and sent it to the control room. In the control room the whole wall was taken up by a large map of London and girls were up and down ladders putting in pins of incidents and so on. Now the message went into one of the smaller rooms, occupied by the heads of the fire brigade, light and heavy rescue, ambulance, police, wardens and so on. They then decided what and who needed to be sent to each district.

At 6 a.m. and 6 p.m. we had to teleprint a complete list of incidents in London and everything that was being used. Nothing was ever sent over the bridges (over the Thames), everyone stayed on their own side.

Once a raid started we were the first to know. We had two speakers on the wall, one linked to Stanmore and the other to South London. Suddenly there was a crackle and we were off. The voice would say "London East Purple" or some other area, then the other speaker started "London North Purple". Then we'd get "London West Red" and at the same time "London West Purple", and before we knew what was happening the speakers were both clearly giving out at the same time the area and colour. We had a red phone direct to Scotland Yard; this was a double check as they also had their own system. We repeated as received from the speakers and the warnings were sounded accordingly. Then the incidents were coming through, often before we had sent all the colours to the police or teleprinted the information to the Home Office. The incidents came in fast and furious, what they wanted, how many trapped and so on. Eventually the speaker would sound All Clear in each area, the last incident was dealt with and all was quiet – that raid was over. The next would possibly come in a few hours but for the time peace and a feeling of how dreadfully tired we were.

No girl was allowed to leave the teleprinter room until her relief arrived. Consequently it was great to see one's partner. We worked in threes for three shifts, 7am to 3pm, 3pm to 11pm and 11pm to 7am, fifteen days without a break then four days off. If a member of the next shift was delayed for any reason we had to work her shift as well. The supervisor, who came on at 9am, would work out a rota, sometimes taking a turn himself, if a girl was going to be away for more than a day. Often we left home during a terrible raid with a tin hat on and a special pass so that the wardens would let us through.

One of our other jobs was to send messages in code on a special teleprinter; these were brought down by a man in uniform. What they were and where they came from we never knew but we knew they were sent to the fighting forces. The messages didn't have a single vowel and were sent in blocks of five letters. We had to be very accurate, we dared not make a mistake with what to us was a jumble as it might have made the whole message read incorrectly.

Other buildings to be included as government citadels were the Faraday citadel of the Post Office and 'the bombproof Curzon Street building' in Mayfair. Both were considered by the Crossbow committee and a report dated 17th December 1943 notes the former (built and used primarily as a telephone exchange) 'has a high degree of protection but is not bombproof. It is furnished for Cabinet Ministers but is inconveniently situated'. The Curzon Street premises were, it stated, mainly unallocated as of 8th July 1943, also 'not connected with the Whitehall Tunnel and some way over ground'. Consequently neither was used for strategic protection.

The proper name of the last building is Curzon Street House (1–4 Curzon Street) and exploration of its deep basement while the building was being demolished confirmed it was indeed not connected to any tunnel. The basement was structurally integrated into the office block and was in fact the sole example in London of a bunker and office block constructed as a single unit. Other bunkers were standalone structures and equally protected on all sides, whereas Curzon Street was less well shielded to the rear because the inner wall and roof embedded in the building were much thinner than in equivalent bunkers. Erected in 1939, the building was intended for the use of Home Forces General Headquarters and reportedly it was also made available for the use of the Royal Family should Buckingham Palace be bombed. The building was also occupied at different times by the Ministry of Aircraft Production and Board of Education (government buildings were treated as a pooled resource during the war and differing departments were involved in a constant game of musical chairs).

The Rotundas and the Horseferry Road citadel

As already mentioned, these three protected facilities are normally treated as a single complex, although they were physically separate and each had its own address (17 Monck Street for the office building, 18/19 Monck Street for the South Rotunda and 59–67 Great Peter Street for the North Rotunda). Together they occupied a block bounded north by Great Peter Street and west by Monck Street, with Horseferry Road along the south, onto which the end wall of the citadel building fronted. The entire site was a former gasworks belonging to the Gas Light & Coke Company (nationalised in 1949 as the North Thames Gas Board).

Gas production had ceased here in 1875, having been transferred to the company's vast new gasworks at Beckton, and two large gasholders of the gasometer type 90ft in diameter were built on the Horseferry Road site. These gasholders were demolished in 1937 and a start made on a new steel-framed headquarters building and a protected control room (as ARP preparations) in one side of the south gasholder pit. In 1940 the unclad steel frame and gasholder pits were requisitioned by the government, allowing the gas company to retain the control room. The intention was to create hardened accommodation that would duplicate the Air Ministry's premises in Whitehall, with a

Built between 1940 and 1941 as bombproof accommodation in the wells of two old gasholders, the Rotundas were protected above by 12 feet of solid concrete. Their massive construction is clearly visible in this view of the North Rotunda being demolished in April 2003. The camera is looking north-west from the roof of Romney House in Marsham Street. [Bob Jenner]

rectangular blockhouse and two circular bunkers dubbed 'Rotundas'.

The blockhouse was constructed in the unfinished frame of the new headquarters building, with one storey above and one floor below ground. On account of its steel-framed construction it was and thereafter known variously as the 'Steel-Framed Building', 'The Blockhouse', the 'Air Ministry Citadel' and the 'Horseferry Road Citadel'. The two Rotundas took their name from the circular pits of the gasholders, the resulting circular buildings having half of their three floors underground and one and a half above the surface. Work on creating these heavily reinforced strongholds began in November 1940 and was completed by 21st June 1941 (the North Rotunda was built by Mowlem & Co, and the South by Higgs and Hill Ltd). The architect was Robert Atkinson.

All three structures were intended to survive attack by 1000lb bombs, and one of the corridors in the Rotundas has a clearly visible dent in the ceiling resulting from a hit by a 500lb bomb (girders were used to prop up the ceiling). The steel-framed citadel was built on two levels, whilst the Rotundas were

constructed with three levels internally, 8ft walls and a roof 12ft thick. A vertical bore and underground tunnel constructed in 1942 from tube-type segments connected the complex with the rest of the Whitehall tunnel network (described later). Facilities were impressive; the complex was designed to house 2,000 people in 1,000 rooms and three miles of corridors. It was gasproof and equipped with its own independent water and power supplies intended to function for three weeks in a 'button down' situation. Utility services were concentrated 60ft down in the South Rotunda basement, with four 1,500hp Petter diesel engines driving Brush generators, gasproof ventilation plant and an artesian well. Also here were a 30-position telephone switchboard, 22 teleprinters, eight wireless transceivers and a cipher department.

From 1942 the citadel or blockhouse building housed a substantial section of Air Ministry staff, including the Air Intelligence Section AI2(c) and a radio terminal. With the build-up to D-Day the army's GHQ Home Forces and 21st Army Group occupied all of the North Rotunda and the third floor of the South Rotunda, whilst the Ministry of

Home Security had its war room in the North Rotunda. During 1944 the V1 and V2 threat led the Air Ministry to move into the South Rotunda, whilst the North Rotunda was designated as reserve Cabinet War Rooms (ANSON), although this was never activated (see below). As mentioned above, the bottom floor of the South Rotunda housed the mechanical plant room for all three buildings.

Musical chairs

Correspondence archives show that plans to move staff in and out of the complex were revised constantly and frequently delayed, either for logistical reasons or more simply because telephone facilities were not yet ready. A file note dated 24th April 1941 stated the citadel building would be completed before the Rotundas and needed a temporary switchboard, tie-lines to Federal exchange and Green Line extensions (scrambler telephones) from the main Air Ministry switchboard at Adastral House. By September further tie-lines were being ordered to Adastral PBX and to Station Z [Wealdstone], the latter being proposed as a temporary evacuation place before full communications became available at Monck Street. In November it was stated that the 'South Gas Holder' would be ready for occupation on 1st December but the North Gas Holder not before the end of December.

The Post Office was clearly struggling to keep up with the vast demand for telephone facilities and H. R. Harbottle of the P.O. Engineering Department (War Group), based at Dollis Hill, noted with irritation that originally it was assumed that only the Air Ministry would occupy the Horseferry Road site. Now, however, the Ministry of Home Security had established a reserve headquarters there, although there were no spare telephone lines. In nine months' time an additional cable would be laid in the extension to the Whitehall tunnel now under construction along with the vertical bore to the gasholders. Circuits would then be provided to Whitehall, Federal, Victoria and Trafalgar exchanges. In the event this target suited the continuing game of musical chairs quite well, with GHQ Home Forces set to complete its move from Storey's Gate into Air Ministry accommodation in the North and South Rotundas by October 1942, the Air Ministry relocating into the steel-framed building on completion.

For many working in the Rotundas was a novel experience, as Mary Bateman recalls:

Our place of work was underneath an empty gasometer, a huge round structure used to contain coal gas in the old days (before North Sea gas). When I say huge I mean huge. You could have put quite a few houses inside it. This HQ was named Rotunda, for the obvious reasons it was round, and the rooms all led off circular corridors. Most unusual! They worked us very hard there, and we weren't very pleased to find out some time later that we were flogging ourselves to death, sending out dummy messages, and it wasn't real work at all. We were told we were being brought up to scratch, in readiness for

the future, which would be the invasion of France and Germany; we would be part of it.

Everything was Top Secret and all our mail was censored, which meant all the letters you wrote home or whoever you wrote to were read by an officer and anything that was considered to be risky was crossed out. It was decided that some of us could earn our keep by helping out on night duty at the War Office, on their teleprinters. The War Office girls were allowed to take it in turns to get a little sleep during the night. The powers that be decreed that we should stay awake all night, as they wanted to toughen us up for any hardships we might have to encounter as part of the Invasion Headquarters in the future. A lot of the work at Rotunda was sent out in cipher. Cipher was just groups of five letters that didn't exactly spell anything – for example HZYGD or DNXRM, any combination of letters. Messages that arrived in cipher went to a special office to be decoded into readable matter.

Codename corner

For the Rotundas a moment of greater glory came towards the end of the war, when reconsideration was given to the not yet implemented 'Black Move' plan (also mentioned in Chapter 3) to evacuate key government figures as a final resort, should London become unusable or threatened by invasion. This occurred in 1944 when bombardment from what were termed the vengeance or V-weapons became intense. By this time there was sufficient citadel and steel-framed building accommodation to accommodate around 10,000 key personnel in central London under what were called 'Crossbow conditions', in other words able to withstand attack

The bombproof construction of the Rotundas was put to the test when a 500lb bomb made a direct hit in July 1944 (the bulge in the ceiling seen here has been shored up by girders). This is the tunnel between the South Rotunda and the steel-framed blockhouse, looking towards the short flight of stairs leading up to the latter.

[Richard Lamont]

by Hitler's flying bombs and rockets (see appendix *Notes and definitions*). If the bombardment became severe and prolonged, non-essential workers would be stood down whilst the nucleus would live and work in the citadels and basements.

At this time the Cabinet War Room remained the hub of government. Accommodating around 400, its main function was to collect and process information about all aspects of the national and world situation, to brief the decision-makers and then disseminate those decisions. However, it was realised that the bunker was not bombproof and in July and August 1943 plans were made to prepare the basement of the North Rotunda for possible use by the Prime Minister, his personal staff and a nucleus of the War Cabinet Secretariat.

The codename given to this new facility was ANSON and its lowest floor was set aside for Churchill, his wife, staff and the Cabinet to use, with partitions used to divide the space into rooms. These quarters were ready for occupation on 15th November 1943 and the guards from 'Paddock' were transferred to work here permanently at the end of 1943, but in February 1944 Churchill repeated that he personally had no intention of moving unless London suffered a scale of attack far worse than anything expected to date. Also quartered here from this time was the Home Office Fire Control (not to be confused with the Regional Fire Control at Horseferry House or the Brigade Control at Lambeth).

The Whitehall tunnels revealed

Supporting and connecting the various citadels was a series of communications tunnels dug under Whitehall and Westminster to carry the vital telephone and teleprinter cables linking them to each other and the outside world. This was the most modest of Dalrymple-Hay's alternative proposals, and probably the first published description is found in the following words with which author Douglas Reekie described immediately after the war what had been one of its greatest secrets.

Deep beneath Whitehall in London, centre of Britain's Government, there is a tunnel. It starts near the base of Nelson's Column. It goes nearly to the Houses of Parliament, and then swings away to end beneath and behind famous Victoria Street. It passes under Downing Street, and there is a lift from No. 10, the British Prime Minister's official residence, down to the tunnel. It was that lift Mr Winston Churchill would not use when he persistently refused to go down to his air raid shelter during the worst days of the bombing. The tunnel is nearly three quarters of a mile long and it was not there when the war began.

That tunnel is no bigger than a London tube through which electric trains run. There is a flat floor, along the middle of which a mass of telephone and telegraph switchboard equipment is installed. Teleprinter switchboards and intricate mechanical devices that turn electric impulses into speech and printed words into electric impulses that reach out eventually to the far corners of the world are also there. Engineers are on duty night and day.

Because that tunnel was built in record time there was never any fear that bombs or rockets would interrupt London's communications with the outside world. The tunnel was too deep below ground for a projectile to penetrate to it. From that tunnel, the War Office sent out its million words a day during the war, the million words that organised

Britain's part in the war all over the world. From that tunnel the Admiralty maintained its communications with its commands scattered over the seven seas. Cables took those million and more words outward from the tunnel to radio stations, to the shore ends of submarine cables, to Army, Navy and Air Force headquarters all over Britain.

And several million people who travelled every day on London's underground system, thousands who slept in the bunks on the station platforms during the night of the worst bombing raids, never knew that along the cables, within a few feet of them, were passing coded messages carrying vital war secrets that the Germans would have given their right hands to know.

The cables that fed that tunnel under Whitehall and the rows of instruments and switchboards also had to be protected against bombing, against rockets. They could not be carried overhead through the streets of London, nor even in conduits a few feet below the pavements and roadways of the streets. Those cables also had to be buried deep. There was no time to construct special tunnels for them, so the existing underground railway tunnels were used. The cables followed the tube trains north, south, east and west from Whitehall until the tracks came out in the open in the outer suburbs where concentrated and heavy bombing was unlikely. Night after night, in the early days of the war, after the last train had passed through the stations and the people in the bunks had settled to their rest, engineers worked laying those cables alongside the railway track and beside the existing power cables. They laid them where nobody would suspect they were anything more than part of the normal equipment of the railway – the cables that everybody sees, but to which nobody pays any attention.

The Whitehall tunnel in detail

Although never a matter of secrecy since the end of the war (it was described in fair detail both in Reekie's book cited above and in the Victory Number [January 1946] of the *IPOEEJ*), it has nonetheless been the subject of considerable speculation. It was not included on published plans or mentioned when the remainder of the deep level communications tunnels came off the secret list in 1968 (following a realignment of defence policy at the same time as reliance on civil defence was

abandoned) and was not officially acknowledged until five years later. Even now, one of the Treasury files relating to it (T 219/115, covering the period 1930–1952) is marked at the Public Record Office as 'closed for 75 years' and will not be opened until 1st January 2028. Moreover, the only published plans showing its route are in Harbottle's IPOEE paper (1946) and in Duncan Campbell's book *War Plan UK* (1982).

What can be stated without fear of suppression is that the construction of the Whitehall tunnel was bound inextricably with the need for protected accommodation for essential government departments during the war. Indeed it has been described as a 'complete underground system of accommodation and protected communications'.

Constructed to the order of the Post Office starting in December 1939, the tunnel runs from Trafalgar Square, beneath Whitehall telephone exchange and along Whitehall (12ft diameter), then extended with 8ft diameter to swing west of the Houses of Parliament, terminating eventually in August 1942 at the Horseferry Road citadel. At the same time a protected underground telephone exchange (Federal) was built underground to provide 24-hour service to principal officers in government departments, together with a deep-level teleprinter switching centre.

An interesting insight into how successfully red tape was eliminated in wartime is given in the following extract from the Chief Regional Engineer's War Diary for November 1939.

> The preliminary work in connection with the construction of the Whitehall tunnel . . . commenced this month. Sir Harley Dalrymple Hay, with whom the Engineering Branch had been in consultation for some months concerning the design of the tunnel, will supervise the execution of the work. The circumstances surrounding the granting of the wayleave for a work of such magnitude as this are of interest. Following the disclosure of the scheme to the City Engineer of the Westminster City Council when the extremely secret nature of the work was emphasised, application for a wayleave was made to the Westminster City Council by means of the Department's normal wayleave form for a "telegraph line along Whitehall" and the consent of the Council was granted by return. The execution of the work has therefore been put in hand under this permit.

For a comprehensive description of the tunnels probably the best is this taken from the Victory Number of the *POEEJ*.

> The ultimate scheme represents the accretion of five principal component schemes, which were proceeded with at various times during the war. The initial scheme, commenced in December 1939, was a tunnel 12 feet in diameter, and at a depth of about 100 feet, which, intended at the time solely for cable protection, is connected by short lateral tunnels of 5 feet diameter to the Service Departments and Federal exchange. The latter is a protected exchange in sub-ground accommodation and was provided at the outbreak of the war to give an

Nearly a mile long, the Whitehall subway had 'laterals' (branch tunnels) to the War Office, Air Ministry and Whitehall telephone exchange. Spurs led to the Admiralty and War Office citadels, whilst the southern extension reached as far as Horseferry Road.

[British Telecom]

Tight wartime security meant unauthorised entry into buildings with access to the Whitehall tunnel was impossible, whilst locked bulkheads at deep level meant that infiltrators would not get far. This is the top of the access shaft at the Rotundas.
[British Telecom]

uninterrupted service for the principal officers in Government Departments. Access to the main tunnel for Post Office personnel is provided by an automatic lift and emergency staircase in a shaft at an exchange, which is connected to the main tunnel by an 8ft diameter lateral tunnel. The cables from the buildings of the Service Departments, after being taken through 12-inch steel bore tubes connected to the smaller lateral tunnels, are terminated on the Main Distribution Frame in the main tunnel.

It was obvious that the main tunnel would afford absolute security for telephone and telegraph equipment, the first installation of which was accordingly proceeded with and completed in the summer of 1941 to meet the increasing requirements for defence communications. This equipment, which has been added to from time to time, and now provides for about 4,000 working circuits, includes among the many constituent items, 71 18-channel Voice Frequency systems, 26 carrier systems, 13 coaxial cable terminals and 864 audio amplifiers. During 1941–42 major extensions of the tunnel, which more than doubled its length, were carried out, affording underground access between various Service Departments and accommodating a teleprinter switching centre. In all, a total of 1 mile 740 yards of tunnel has been constructed under the various schemes associated with the tunnel system and six shafts with passenger lifts provided. The tunnel system is connected via the tube railways to the Citadel building [Faraday].

A myth confounded?

Winston Churchill's somewhat poetic description of government citadels linked by underground tunnels (in *The Second World War: The Commonwealth Alone*) has given rise to all manner of wild theories that these (and other Post Office) tunnels played an auxiliary role as secret thoroughfares for government ministers and privileged civil servants. It is certainly true that this was considered before the tunnel was built, back in January 1939, when Sir James Rae of the Treasury told a planning meeting he felt there was much to be said for a tunnel large enough to walk along in order to provide accommodation between the various offices and to provide a certain amount of refuge accommodation. But it was no more than a notion.

Whilst the dimensions of the main Whitehall tunnel (12ft) and some 8ft walkable spur connections into the buildings it served would have enabled them to be used in this way, at least theoretically, the security implications of controlling access to them would have been considerable to say the least, whilst the small lifts and narrow spiral staircases actually built would have been inadequate for any large body of users. An 'official' description in Brigadier Harris's book *Signal Venture* (written in 1951) describes the system as a tunnel for cables and equipment – and no more. Suffice to say that the authors have discovered no historical evidence whatsoever that the tunnels were ever used for any other purpose.

A related speculation is that the Whitehall tunnel and its extension to the Rotundas and the Horseferry Road provided a long-distance underground general purpose walking route between buildings, but this too may be a false assumption. A Post Office document quoted earlier stated that the only personnel entrances were at Trafalgar Square station and Whitehall exchange. This is confirmed by War Office documents at the PRO. Lt Col Meyell, General Staff wrote on 26th June 1942 to Signal Officer-in-Chief, G Ops, stating that a tunnel connected this building (the War Office) to Trafalgar Square station, passing under Craig's Court (Whitehall GPO telephone exchange at rear of Great Scotland Yard), Craig's Court being a VP2 (Vulnerable Point grade 2). Important cables were laid in this tunnel, which was guarded by sentries. Now came the crux of his communication: it appeared there were two other open shafts (giving access to this tunnel), one in Great Peter Street between the Rotundas and one next to the front gate of the Westminster Hospital (then still at Broad Sanctuary). The writer asked should not all three entrances be guarded? The first reply stated no further action was required; exploration found there were locked bulkhead doors at intervals that prevented passage down the full length of the tunnel, which was patrolled by Post Office staff who were satisfied with these arrangements. But then a further order called for a guard to be supplied at the shaft in Broad Sanctuary until the tunnel was completed in about two months' time.

Security in this area was extremely high; from May 1940 barbed wire had surrounded all government buildings in the Whitehall area and surrounding streets were designated 'defended areas' with roadblocks manned by armed sentries. Anyone unable to produce a valid pass would not be allowed entry. Police and military guards were stationed at every street corner along Whitehall from Trafalgar Square to Horseferry Road and whilst the thoroughfare itself remained open, even here barbed wire fences and armed sentries separated the grounds of buildings from the pavement. Buildings themselves were sandbagged and guarded as a precaution against enemy parachutists or fifth-columnist saboteurs.

Sigsaly and the loo that wasn't

When the existence of the wartime Colossus computer was finally acknowledged as 'Britain's best kept secret' in the late 1970s there were many people who just could not believe such advanced technology had been developed so long ago. Another late revelation deserving equal admiration is the secret transatlantic telephone system that enabled Churchill to speak to the president of the United States in total confidence from his Cabinet War Room bunker.

It was in fact the first unbreakable online speech coding system and employed digital cryptography techniques, the one-time digital key being supplied by gramophone discs. Originally named Project X (or X-Ray), it later became known as Sigsaly or Green Hornet, the latter name reflecting the sound of the encrypted transmissions. The soundproofed cubicle in the underground Cabinet War Rooms where Churchill held highly secret conversations with President Roosevelt in Washington had one of the best disguises ever – it was disguised as Churchill's executive loo. Nobody would ever disturb this meeting of minds because the door was provided with a standard toilet lock and indicator. Although beyond top secret during the war, today this inner sanctum can be seen by any visitor to the War Room museum.

Sigsaly was developed by Bell Telephone Laboratories in the USA, incorporating the first implementation of pulse code modulation. This had been invented in 1937 by Englishman Alec Reeves and was not employed widely in telecommunications until the late 1960s. Deployment began in 1943 and because the terminal apparatus for the link was far too bulky to be housed in Churchill's bunker, it was instead housed in the basement of Selfridges' annexe off Oxford Street (used as a headquarters of ETOUSA, the U.S. operations HQ for the European theatre of war). This comprised many racks of apparatus and consumed some 30kW of electric power. Churchill's conversations were enciphered here and transmitted by cable to Scotland, where a short wave radio link bridged the Atlantic to the President in Washington.

The Loo that wasn't. One of the best 'cover stories' of the war was this innocent looking indicator on a door in the Cabinet War Rooms beneath Whitehall. This was no ordinary loo but nobody would disturb the occupant.

The vital need for this totally secure communication facility became clear after the fateful telephone call made on 26th November 1941, by UK Prime Minister Winston Churchill to US President Franklin Roosevelt, informing him of British decryption of Japanese messages reporting that the Japanese were planning to attack Pearl Harbor on 7th December. Unknown to General George Marshall, the U.S. Army Chief of Staff, the Deutsche Reichspost (German Post Office) had broken the A–3 scrambler communication system used on transatlantic circuits. Although the device was considered state of the art, the Germans were successfully intercepting and decoding A–3 calls between Roosevelt and Churchill at their intercept site on the Dutch coast. Remarkably, although all US Defense Department files concerning advance notice of the attack appear to have been destroyed, they had no control over files kept outside the USA and the Gestapo retained their copy (which has been published in the book, *Gestapo Chief, The 1948 Interrogation of Heinrich Müller*, by Gregory Douglas). Thereafter great pressure was put on Bell Telephone Laboratories to create a truly unbreakable encryption system.

Other communications facilities

More prosaic but equally vital to the conduct of government during World War II were the various telephone and teleprinter switchboards already mentioned briefly. Federal, also known as the 'centralised branch exchange', was the name given to a protected underground telephone exchange built in the basement of the Old War Office building (a location also known as Montagu House North). It opened on 15th July 1940 to provide uninterrupted

This may look like Frankenstein's laboratory but it was in fact the apparatus for the electronic coding system that prevented overhearing on top secret calls between Churchill and the U.S. President. Known as Sigsaly or Green Hornet and using digital techniques, it was technically far in advance of its time and remained secret for many years.
[Imperial War Museum]

24-hour service to principal officers in Government departments. From here fully protected cables were taken via London Transport tube tunnels to the Citadel trunk exchange described in the previous chapter. Federal was equipped with 1,137 direct extension circuits to principal officers in 68 departments as well as 179 tie-lines to government PBXs and standard exchange lines to Holborn tandem (for all London exchanges), Toll A and Toll B (serving exchanges in the Home Counties), and Faraday trunks (for more distant locations).

For reasons of control and security Federal was a manual exchange (a PMBX 1A for the cognoscenti) and callers wanting Federal numbers dialled FED (London telephone dials had letters as well as numbers and the code FED was numerically the same as dialling 333). When the low-pitched ringing tone ceased they would hear the word 'Federal', which was the prompt to give both the name and number of the person required. Both name and number had to be given before the operator would make the connection and for security reasons, numbers on Federal exchange were changed regularly, reputedly every fortnight. The Federal exchange did not figure in the public telephone directory or dialling code lists and therefore was unknown to all but those 'in the know'.

Notwithstanding the strict security at Federal some amusing episodes occurred there. A telephonist recalls:

Federal was a War Office 'board in Whitehall. I was sent there on supervisory duties when I was put on the acting list for supervisor. All 'boards had to be covered night and day during the war. There was a large room with beds where operators on night duty could take their official two-hour kip during the night. Federal was a very large office more like an exchange. Now I had been in the habit, since early childhood of having nightmares from which I awoke screaming. I don't have them any more but yes you've guessed it, I had one during a sleep period at Federal. It caused quite a lot of consternation at the time. The military guard was temporarily alerted on the assumption that a member of the Axis had broken in and was systematically cutting our throats, or something to that effect. This episode preceded me wherever I went and I never completely lived it down.

Another exchange reserved for VIP use only was RAPid Falls, described in an amendment dated February 1944 to the Post Office War Instructions D6, section XII 1–3 as a hypothetical exchange in the central 5-mile circle of London to which "a few very important subscribers are connected". Calls to numbers on this exchange were to be given Priority 1 without question whether requested or not. RAPid Falls opened on 20th July 1942 and closed on 23rd June 1945.

The exchange was termed hypothetical because it was not physically a 'real' exchange, merely part of another that was given a separate identity for operational purposes. If you look at a telephone dial (or keypad) you will see that the letters dialled in this case, RAP, were numerically equivalent to 727, the code allocated to PARk exchange, which was located at Notting Hill Gate and covered the Kensington Park neighbourhood. It was, however, normal practice to disguise the location of strategic installations by providing what are called out-of-area lines (and an equally misleading out-of-area postal box number) as already noted for the underground Railway Executive Committee headquarters at Down Street. The identity of these special subscribers has not been discovered yet, however.

Don't tell nobody

Vital as the telephone was in time of war, for rapid dissemination of vital information to multiple destinations nothing beats the printed word, however, which is why essential bulletins, urgent messages and routine correspondence were all handled by teleprinter. DTN was the mechanism; the initials actually meant Defence Teleprinter Network but to far more people they stood for Don't Tell Nobody. DTN was a top secret teleprinter system installed for defence purposes by the Post Office and its scale was colossal. First conceived in 1937, DTN was intended to be equal in capacity to the existing civil network, but by the end of that year it was clear this would be totally inadequate. A far larger system was initiated in a crash programme and by supreme effort the majority was in place in time for the Battle of Britain in 1940. Unlike today's telex system, connection was not automatic and calls had to be connected manually by operators. For this purpose a substantial teleprinter switching centre, the hub of DTN, was constructed in the 12ft diameter tunnel under Whitehall, with the equipment racks all stretched out in one long line.

The Reserve Home Forces headquarters at Wentworth

The beginning of this chapter made mention of the combined services headquarters that was to have been built in tube-type tunnels under Whitehall. Although it was never constructed, it had a counterpart that was indeed built, 29 miles west of London at Wentworth, Surrey.

This was the D-Day control bunker, notable for its location in a private estate between Sunningdale and Virginia Water, close to the world-famous golf course. The estate was commandeered on the outbreak of World War II for use as a military encampment. Equally unusual is its tube-type construction, identical to that proposed for the deep level combined services war rooms in Whitehall (mentioned earlier in this chapter), and its curious orientation that is accurately end-on to central London, requiring long diagonal access tunnels.

Files in the Public Record Office indicate the bunker was constructed in anticipation of a devastating bombardment and resulting evacuation of London. Its location is just south of Wentworth House (now the club house for the golf course) and consists of twin segmental cast iron tubes, evidently taken from London Transport stock, about 100 yards

long, separated by a smaller diameter access tunnel. The latter connects via ramps and stairs at one end directly into the clubhouse, and at the other to an isolated escape exit. The whole is protected on the surface by a massive bombproof slab with a brick ventilation cowl protruding. The slab is now used as a car park.

Wentworth had been earmarked by General Alan Brooke (later Lord Alanbrooke), Commander in Chief Home Forces, as his HQ in the event of an invasion that never in fact came and in due course Wentworth was used as a signals centre by the 21st Army Group in the lead up to D-Day. When last opened for press inspection in 1987 the bunker was found to be in very good condition, albeit with all suspended floors and cabling removed.

Seen in 1943, this complete teleprinter switching station was established in tube-style tunnels under Whitehall to serve official departments.
[British Telecom]

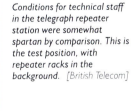

Conditions for technical staff in the telegraph repeater station were somewhat spartan by comparison. This is the test position, with repeater racks in the background. *[British Telecom]*

The Strange Story of St Paul's

Disused lift shafts become nerve centre of the nation's electricity system

O F all London's wartime subterranean structures probably none has aroused more speculation than those at St Paul's. The combination of an uncompleted deep shelter (see Appendix 6) and the underground wartime electrical control centre have attracted an aura of great mystery and secrecy in some publications, whilst the location's mystical connections have not escaped attention either. Nigel Pennick also notes how the rebuilding of St Paul's tube station (described below) destroyed the original Panyer Alley – 'the highest ground in the City of London, subject of one of William Henry Black's geomantic writings'. It is now possible to put all this speculation to rest.

The early history of the tube station

This chapter deals with the remarkable new use found for the lift shafts of the old tube station at St Paul's during the last war. But to understand fully what went on, we need to take our story back several stages to the inauguration of the station at the end of the nineteenth century. The stopping place was opened by the Central London Railway in 1900; named after the country's chief post office nearby, it was in those days called 'Post Office'. The standard low level design of this company's stations provided two lift shafts and a stairwell, with 'in' and 'out' access passages, one either side at right angles to the platform tunnels. These were carried by two overbridges to stairs centrally between the platforms, which were on the same level.

At Post Office station, owing to the narrow and sharply curved street lying above, it was necessary to position one platform tunnel partially over the other. In addition, the small station plot forced the plan axis of the lift shafts (and therefore the access tunnels) to be slanted along its diagonal in order to keep within the boundaries of the properties above. The lower landing was therefore intermediate between the two platform levels, and the short stairs at the ends of the access passages went both up and down from the lift side of the platform tunnels, in an extremely contorted arrangement which apparently constricted the air flow sufficiently to necessitate an extra

ventilation shaft opposite the stair shaft, making four shafts in all.

As part of London Transport's New Works programme under a reconstruction project that started in 1937, Post Office was first renamed St Paul's on 1st February 1937 (alternatives considered were Cathedral, Cheapside and Newgate). Two years later a brand new entrance was created at the station's eastern end, opened on 1st January 1939. The complex engineering works to divert cables and sewers were described in the IPOEE Journal for January 1939. The old booking hall and lifts at a point several hundred yards west on the corner of Newgate Street and King Edward Street were closed, with the new booking hall located underground with staircases from street level at the beginning of Cheapside. Two flights of escalators under Newgate Street led down from there, with an intermediate landing at the upper platform level.

The lower escalator concourse cut through and destroyed one set of platform access passages and stairs, the resulting cross section through an access passage in its roof being used for ventilation. A crude vertical ladder behind a door provides access from the concourse to the original lift landing passage.

With secret subterranea the station had two connections; the first was that one of its escalators was commandeered in 1940 for use at a giant underground ammunition depot at Corsham, Wiltshire, as described in Nick McCamley's book *Secret Underground Cities*. The other was its re-use for controlling London's electricity supply, as described below.

At ground level none of this was apparent from the aspect of the old surface buildings of Post Office station. These were no longer required, and in July 1939 London Transport proposed selling the entire premises, reserving only the small portion required for the new ventilation shaft, although bombing in June 1941 resulted in their partial destruction. The buildings were taken down to first floor level and as described in a *London Railway Record* article of October 1999, they remained as a ruin until demolition in 1973.

A steam shovel clears away some of the debris after bombing laid waste the old Post Office station entrance in Newgate Street. The Grid Control centre 100ft below fortunately was unscathed (unlike this photo).

In 1945 the old Post Office station building on King Edward Street was just an open shell with some emergency patching up. Clues to the protected Grid Control centre below are given by a large ventilation pipe projecting from the top of the stair shaft, and an air intake above it on the roof.

Turbulent times

Being close to the financial heart of London it was inevitable that this area would suffer heavily in the Blitz and in fact the majority of buildings in this area were destroyed entirely. On 29th December 1940 the Central Telegraph Office, lying on the north side of Newgate Street between the old and new entrances of St Paul's station (now the site of British Telecom's headquarters), was set on fire by burning debris blown in from adjacent buildings in one of the most destructive German air attacks of the second world war (this may have been the cause of the flooding mentioned later). The interior of the building was completely destroyed and the damaged upper floors were sufficiently unsafe that they had to be dismantled (the shell of the ground and first floors were subsequently refurbished and re-opened in June 1943). Across King Edward Street, Christ Church was reduced to a shell in a cleared wasteland, along with practically all the buildings on the south side of Newgate Street, whilst the old Post Office station building adjoining was badly damaged.

Fortunately no harm was done to the tube station's old lift shafts below, for which a new use had been found after the vulnerability of London's electrical control centre became apparent in the autumn of 1940. Safer accommodation was required for the control of Britain's electricity generating and transmission services, particularly for the control centre covering south-east England.

Safer haven

In reality the Central Electricity Board (CEB) had left protection of its South East England Control from enemy attack rather late and the Grid Control Centre in Park Street next to Bankside power station (between Blackfriars and Southwark bridges on the south bank of the Thames) suffered several near-misses when the Blitz started. It depended on at least two makeshift standby locations, with no automatic indications or metering other than that available at Bankside, and during raids all the sites were manned. A safer location was sought – and found – in the disused lift shafts of Post Office station and a leasing agreement between the CEB and London Transport made in October 1940 enabled the construction of an eight-storey control complex here.

The design for the St Paul's installation is attributed to Arthur Hawkins, then an assistant engineer in the operations department of the CEB and later to become chairman of the Central Electricity Generating Board and knighted in 1976. To create the new control centre the old station's two lift shafts – which were 23 feet in diameter and 120 feet deep in segmental cast iron – were lined with 18 inches of reinforced concrete as protection against bombs penetrating diagonally and for supporting floors of the same thickness. The contractors, Holloway Brothers, poured concrete for each successive floor only just ahead of an ever-changing design, it is said. The tops of the shafts were capped with bomb-stoppers, that for the stair shaft with a staggered pedestrian access, and for the ventilation shaft with a specially designed labyrinth that would pass 60,000 cubic feet of air per minute. During construction, bomb damage caused the site to be flooded to a depth of 20ft, which did not help matters. In all, 13 rooms were provided, six in one main shaft and seven in the other. Each shaft used 1,563 tons of concrete and ballast as well as 80 tons of steel reinforcing rods.

Fitting out work was carried out by London Transport at the CEB's expense. The original low-level access passages to the platforms were used to house the power distribution and communications equipment, which used the pre-war control's telephone circuits supplemented by a multicore cable three-quarters of a mile long in the tube tunnel linking, via Faraday Building telephone exchange (Queen Victoria Street), into the CEB's own network centred on Park Street, Bankside. An additional telephone circuit connected with the London Transport Chief Engineer's headquarters at South Kensington.

Control was transferred in February 1941 to a temporary room below the equipment gallery using display boards from one of the temporary standby locations. After this, such equipment that could be transferred from Bankside was brought over and lowered down the air shaft.

A fledgling National Grid

The National Control, which was in full operation by the end of August 1941, allowed power resources across the country to be pooled and transferred quickly from one area to another. Staff here co-ordinated such matters as the transfer of power between the area control centres at Glasgow, Newcastle, Manchester, Leeds, Birmingham, London and Bristol; frequency and time control; and the transmission line and generating plant maintenance programme. The centre was equipped with a tie-line diagram with recording meters and error indicators, using equipment from the pre-war emergency control. Communication with the regional controls was by teleprinter. Nationwide control of electricity generation was fully co-ordinated only during winter 1938/39 and it was only with the move to St Paul's that National Control had its own room.

Owing to the fact that each room was only 20ft in diameter, the South East England area control had to be split into two parts. One dealt with the

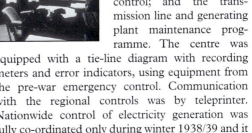

Squeezing two electricity control rooms into the confines of a lift shaft was tricky business, not to mention lowering the substantial equipment racks from the ground. The national control room seen here is a semi-circle. Round the curved perimeter are ranged the Grid diagram which shows the tie lines within and between each region, with Scotland at the top – the influence of Beck's underground map is evident; the instrument panel with recording meters below; and against a window in the partition, so as to be visible from the Teleprinter Room next door, the Main Frequency Meter showing 50Hz. Lighting was diffused and the coved cornice has a bulls-eye air distribution nozzle projecting.
[Roger Morgan Collection]

switching of Grid circuits, into which was transferred the mosaic diagram from the pre-war control at Park Street, Bankside, and the other with the loading of generating stations which had a feeder loading diagram with indicating meters. Communication with the various nodes within South East England was by telephone and by teleprinter with other Electricity Areas around the country. Two separate manual telephone switchboards handled GPO calls on the one hand and internal communication over private wires on the other.

Another section of the facility was the apparatus gallery, constructed in the passage linking the lower lift landing to the station platforms. This had power equipment on one side and communications

The remarkable way this complex arrangement of technical facilities was squeezed into the four shafts of the old Post Office tube station was not helped by flooding caused by bombing all around.

[Roger Morgan Collection]

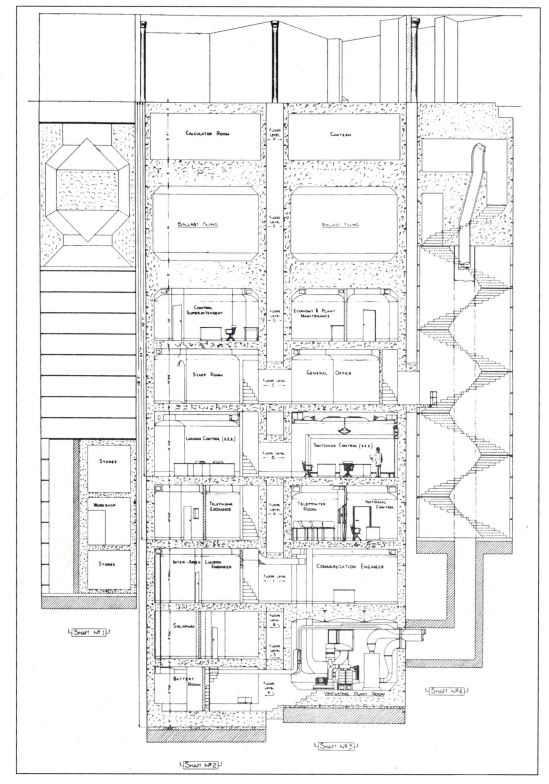

apparatus on the other. Two mains feeds provided primary and standby power sources, whilst there was also an emergency supply from London Transport's 33⅓ cycle system and at ground floor level a 55kW diesel generator. In the last resort the control centre could operate for at least a day from its duplicated standby batteries.

Before long inhabitants of the St Paul's Control had christened their new quarters 'The Hole'. On its lowest levels were a dormitory and the air handling and generating plant, and on the uppermost levels office accommodation and messing facilities. The utilitarian nature of the accommodation was softened by coved fibrous plaster ceilings with concealed uplighting in the best tradition of 1930s cinemas! Watertight doors protected from street or tube flooding.

Progress to Paternoster

"Hundreds of thousands of Londoners must pass the unpretentious entrance to the shaft every day and never guess what lies underneath." reported Wynford Vaughan Thomas in a BBC radio broadcast on 1st February 1949 and this sums up the St Paul's control centre. To class it as one of London's secrets is misleading but its fascination must lie in its obscurity, brought on by fading memories. In its heyday, just after the war, however, it was the subject of press visits and widely publicised as 'the real nerve centre of Britain'. After its replacement by new facilities elsewhere, the centre's prominence faded and with it, public awareness.

Those new facilities resulted from nationalisation of the electricity supply industry, which came in 1948 following the Electricity Act of the previous year. One of the first operational tasks of the new British Electricity Authority (BEA) was to standardise control facilities across the system. This was borne out by a massive cascade failure on 23rd May 1948, which resulted in loss of supply in the now renamed St Paul's control area and its neighbours; restoration was hampered by communication problems. Meanwhile the health of the people down The Hole was of concern, and a temporary resiting on the surface was necessary while the new control system was being designed. The area known as Paternoster Square, south of Newgate Street and north of St Paul's Churchyard, had been flattened by bombing and was selected as a site for the new control room of prefabricated construction.

Opened in 1950, the new control centre was destined to have a fairly short life. Into it were transferred the control and indication equipment from the former quarters in The Hole but the equipment room remained behind, much to the disgust of the telecomms technicians who still had to cross Newgate Street and descend below ground. This part of St Paul's Control remained *in situ* until 1957 when both Paternoster Control and St Paul's closed altogether.

Back to Bankside

In the interim there had been a scheme to replicate Paternoster Control on the eighth floor of Bankside House, but fears of vulnerability from atomic warfare led to Thames North control being established at Redbourne (Herts.) around 1956 and Thames South at East Grinstead (Sussex) in 1957. 'Temporary National Control' remained at Paternoster Square until 1957, when it transferred to the Bankside House (eighth floor) as 'New Temporary National Control'. It was finally rebuilt as 'New National Control' at the same location, opening in 1962. The St Paul's area retained a connection with the electricity industry, however, with the subsequent occupation of new headquarters for the Central Electricity Generating Board (successor in 1957 to the Central Electricity Authority, renamed from BEA in 1955). This new nerve centre was Sudbury House on the south side of the roadway at 15 Newgate Street, virtually opposite the old station entrance. Standing at 205ft tall it was a controversial structure from the outset, as it blocked views of the cathedral.

As already mentioned, wartime bombing had caused extensive destruction in the area around St Paul's and during the 1960s the entire surroundings were redeveloped. Several tall office buildings and a new shopping centre were erected on the old Paternoster Square. In 1973 the road junction of Newgate Street and King Edward Street was improved with a new eastbound filter lane running through the site of the old station building. This was demolished, together with the bomb stoppers of the stair and ventilation shafts, which remain capped below the new road. A new ventilation exhaust tower was constructed in black brick on the triangular road island thus created. Further work was carried out around 1980, when a shaft was sunk in the south-west corner of the shell of the church to construct a new tunnel for draught relief running parallel and communicating with the upper station tunnel via a series of openings at platform level. Subsequent developments are described in chapter 19.

Concerns over the effectiveness of the underground St Paul's control room in 1950 led to the construction of these offices that stood for seven years in Paternoster Square. The two-storey frontage faced Newgate Street, with road access from Warwick Lane on the right, while the apparatus rooms remained in the old tube station lift shafts across the road.

[Roger Morgan Collection]

12 Protecting Production

Unopened tube tunnels boost industrial output

THE main subject of this chapter is the Plessey Company and, although its title today is confined to a brand name recently revived for telephone systems imported from South Africa, for half a century Plessey's production was prolific. Although not one of the best-known manufacturers, this lack of high profile did not hinder its success or turnover. Most of its profits were achieved incognito by making products that never bore its name – telephones for the Post Office and radio chassis (later television assemblies as well) for famous makers that chose to subcontract this work to other firms.

During the 1930s the company was achieving significant growth of its business, which then lay in making components for the aviation, radio and telecommunications industries. In 1936 the company secured three manufacturing licences from American companies, which as Berry Ritchie points out in his history of the Plessey Company, *Into The Sunrise*, tuned out to be a move of crucial national importance. The first agreement was with the Breeze Corporation for the right to use its prefabricated wiring system, the first in the world, using multi-pin plugs and sockets plus flexible conduit to contain the wiring. This wiring was previously done painstakingly over several days by hand but the new system could be assembled by semi-skilled workers and plugged into the finished aircraft within hours. Screening around the wiring looms also shielded radio transmissions from the aircraft against interference by aero engine ignition systems. The second licence, from Federal Laboratories, gave rights to make the Coffman cartridge starter, which literally blasted aero-engines into action in two or three seconds, at least ten times as fast as swinging propellers by hand or using battery-powered electrical starters. The speed of Coffman starters was to be particularly important for RAF fighters scrambling into the air to repel enemy air-raids. The third agreement was with Pump Engineering Service Corporation of Cleveland, a division of Borg Warner, to manufacture aircraft fuel pumps. Plessey was manufacturing all three products in Britain within a year.

Key role

On the outbreak of war Plessey was well placed to play a key wartime role, but space at its works in Vicarage Lane, Ilford was at a premium. Subsidiary factories had been set up in Cardiff and Swindon before the war and some respite came from setting up factories at sites away from London. All the same,

Great secrecy surrounded the operations of Plessey's underground factory and its surface buildings intentionally gave out no clues. Seen here in July 1941 is the eastern end of what was to become Redbridge station. Shops in Eastern Avenue stand behind the tall ventilation shaft, which has since been removed, although the air conditioning plenum plant building itself still stands as a pump house. The camera is facing east and shows the area that is now the station car park, immediately to the east of the station building.

[London's Transport Museum]

more capacity was still needed. Worse, the factory was a potential target for enemy air attack and it later emerged that the Nazis had issued bomber crews with a detailed aerial photograph of the factory taken just before the war. In any case, Ilford's location on the eastern approach to the capital meant it took a severe hammering from bombs, whether intended for Ilford, London or jettisoned at random.

A major strike that badly damaged the machine shops prompted the directors to look for a more radical solution (the raid occurred on 18th September 1940 and badly damaged the production area devoted to making PESCO pumps, used in the fuel line of Merlin aero engines). The works were struck again six days later and again on 9th October. These raids were most likely the result of indiscriminate bombing, since with more effort the raiders could have destroyed the factory totally. Nevertheless the prospect of further destruction posed a major threat.

The idea to use the unoccupied tube tunnelling as alternative factory accommodation reportedly originated with Allen (later Sir Allen but generally known as 'A.G.') Clark, joint managing director of the Plessey Company. He was a dominant character and successfully convinced Lord Beaverbrook, Minister of Aircraft Production, to press London Transport to allow use of this facility. In autumn 1940 arrangements were made for creating a remarkable new factory underground in the tube tunnels nearing completion for the new Central Line between Whipps Cross Road (Leytonstone) and Gants Hill. This was conveniently close to Plessey's existing premises and skilled workforce in

Ilford, and London Transport collaborated with the Plessey engineers in laying out the equipment. The existing factory in Vicarage Lane did not cease production of course and the production facilities in the tunnel were an additional factory, not an alternative one. Plessey also had requisitioned for the company a large timber sawmill at Newbury Park belonging to George E. Gray Ltd when all new building construction ceased in the war. This and a site in Springfield Drive, Newbury Park, became the base for MkI and MkII torpedo manufacture by Plessey's marine department.

Construction for production

The decision to go ahead with the project was taken in November 1940, with work starting immediately and completed in March 1942 at a cost of over £25,000. Considerable effort was involved making the tunnels accessible, installing flat floors and other essential facilities. Access was needed at ground level and the London Transport document known as the 'Plessey tunnel report' states that no surface buildings had been erected at the projected station sites. Instead buildings were constructed of the type most suitable for wartime factory use, being blast and splinter proof, designed without windows to avoid showing light to enemy aircraft. Accommodation had to be provided for the workforce together with electrical switchrooms and refrigeration plant for air conditioning. Electrical substations were built at Whipps Cross Road, Wanstead, Redbridge (opposite Ellesmere Gardens, a quarter mile east of the station) and Gants Hill; these were purely for the factory's needs and had no

Looking rather out of place in the residential area of Wanstead are the windowless brick sheds at a tunnel factory complex known as Cambridge Park. It housed the maintenance engineers and air conditioning plant, for which an overhead gantry was provided to change the filters on this restricted access way. A vertical shaft is in the background, next to the loading bank of a separate building. Behind the fence in the foreground are the sheds for the workers' bicycles. The picture shows the west side of Blake Hall Road close to the junction with Selsdon Road (which was the name of the shaft). The houses in the background are on the south side of Cambridge Park in an area that is now a cutting for the new A12 trunk road.
[London's Transport Museum]

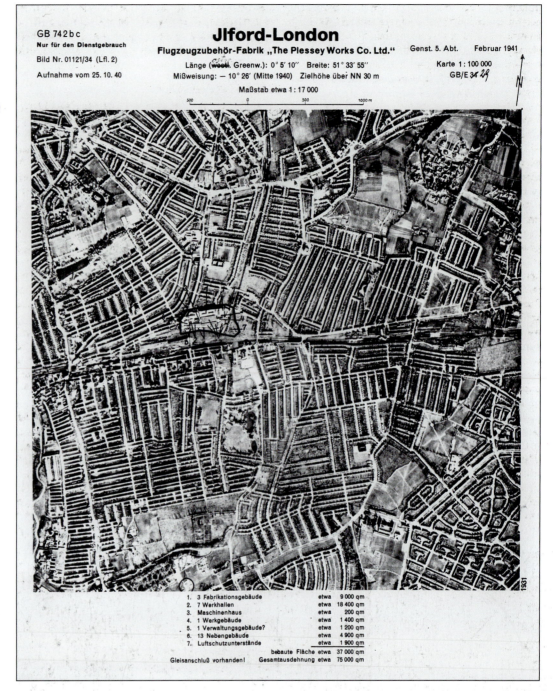

A Luftwaffe (German air force) photograph of 1941 pinpointing the Plessey works as the prime target in 'Jlford' (capital I and J are interchangeable in German)
[Peter Bancroft collection]

The image contains the following printed text:

GB 742 bc
Nur für den Dienstgebrauch
Bild Nr. 01121/34 (Lfl. 2)
Aufnahme vom 25. 10. 40

Jlford-London
Flugzeugzubehör-Fabrik „The Plessey Works Co. Ltd."
Länge (west. Greenw.): 0° 5′ 10″   Breite: 51° 33′ 55″
Mißweisung: — 10° 26′ (Mitte 1940)   Zielhöhe über NN 30 m
Maßstab etwa 1 : 17 000

Genst. 5. Abt.   Februar 1941
Karte 1 : 100 000
GB/E 34 29

1. 3 Fabrikationsgebäude .... etwa 9 000 qm
2. 7 Werkhallen .... etwa 18 400 qm
3. Maschinenhaus .... etwa 200 qm
4. 1 Werkgebäude .... etwa 1 400 qm
5. 1 Verwaltungsgebäude? .... etwa 1 200 qm
6. 13 Nebengebäude .... etwa 4 900 qm
7. Luftschutzunterstände .... etwa 1 900 qm
bebaute Fläche etwa 37 000 qm
Gleisanschluß vorhanden!   Gesamtausdehnung etwa 75 000 qm

potential function for the future tube railway. A new shaft was dug beside the petrol station at the junction of Eastern Avenue and Redbridge Lane; this was for lowering by overhead winch the lathes, milling machines, drills and other plant needed below.

One story that has become confused over the years concerns secret radar work in the tunnels. A letter in *New Civil Engineer* magazine (21st January 1988) stated that during investigations for a proposed M11–A13 link road, 'unmapped' doors were discovered in one of the tunnels near the Gainsborough Road portal, with two short lengths of empty tunnel behind them, located in line between the twin running tunnels. The story was that the chambers were used for secret radar assembly work and were purpose-built during the tube line's construction. Purpose-built they certainly were, at the foot of the shaft from the Whipps Cross substation, but their purpose was to provide a route for the electric cables. In fact these tunnels are shown not only on London Transport's official plans but also in the well-known cutaway drawing of the tunnel factory. The radar plant, known then as the RDF section, was actually a small distance away at Cambridge Park.

This is not to deny co-operation with other authorities nevertheless. A post-war *Railway Gazette* publication on the New Works construction activities states that the concrete overbridges on the Central Line's eastern extension had air raid shelters incorporated in their abutments. This was a cost-effective strategy, as it costs little to build a shelter in an overbridge whereas it costs far more to dig a separate tunnel.

Civil engineering

Close to the River Roding, between Wanstead and Redbridge, the civil engineers encountered much of what they term 'bad ground' and this necessitated a change of plan. Originally the line was intended to run at surface level and cross the river by bridge but in fact the line burrowed under it. Floodgates were installed in the tunnels on each side of the crossing beneath the River Roding at Redbridge, so as to guard against inundation if a bomb managed to hit the tunnel roof. These massive gates were hand-operated (reportedly requiring superhuman strength!) and swung away from the river so that any flood pressure would hold them tightly closed against their frames. Subsequently, when the tunnels were converted for tube trains, additional sumps were constructed to collect surface water draining into the tunnels with new pumps west of Wanstead and east of Redbridge stations. Another combined pump and fan house stands in the centre of the roundabout west of Redbridge station.

From the river crossing as far as Redbridge station the tunnel was built on a cut-and-fill basis, with smooth flat-sided concrete walls cast *in situ*. The remainder of the western part of the tunnel was built using conventional cast-iron tube segments but east of Redbridge station the following 2¾ miles of tunnel predominantly used a new kind of construction with concrete segments (with 12ft 3in internal diameter, three inches larger

than the iron ones). To increase the depth of burial over the shallower parts of the tunnel some of the spoil from making the civilian deep shelters nearer central London was deposited above the tunnels near Redbridge.

A fantastic factory

In twin tunnels just under two and a half miles long, the production facilities occupied 300,000 sq ft of floor space and employed a total of 2,000 workers (mainly female) in shifts covering the 24 hours. Installation of a suspended concrete false floor with air conditioning ducts below gave 9ft 3in headroom to the crown of the tube tunnel. Miniature trains hauled by battery locomotives ran along an 18in gauge railway in each bore to transport materials. Workers entered the underground factory at the unfinished Gants Hill, Redbridge and Wanstead station sites, using the stairs provided at Redbridge and escalators at the other two. (At this time Redbridge was also known as Red Bridge and Gants Hill as Gantshill; these alternative names are found in documents of the time.)

In order to reduce the distance walked underground, additional access points were provided for workers in 15ft diameter shafts at Cambridge Park and opposite Danehurst Gardens, equipped with lifts. According to recollections of surviving employees these were not widely used, although one semi-disabled worker certainly was allowed to use the Danehurst Gardens entrance. Separate shafts at the points mentioned were used exclusively for materials and had electric winches suspended from overhead steel joists built into the shafthead buildings' concrete roofs. Equipment for handling incoming raw materials and finished goods leaving the premises was also installed at the three station sites and at both Gants Hill and

The complex arrangements of the underground Plessey factory captured the imagination of artists – and stretched it too, since Redbridge does not in fact have escalators and those at Gants Hill were not fitted until long after the war was over. Redbridge is in fact London's shallowest tube station and the platforms are just 16ft below ground.

[After The Battle]

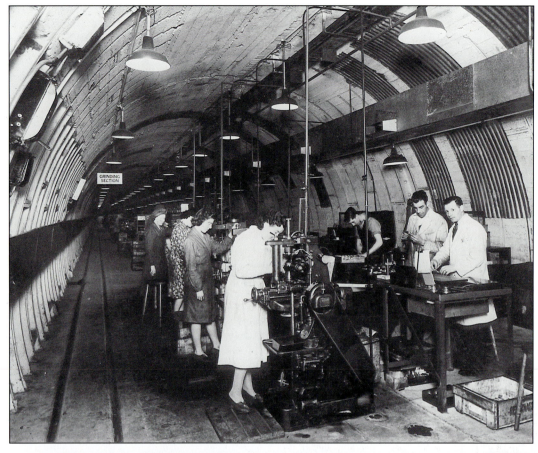

Production line on the Central Line. At peak times 2,000 Plessey workers were employed making essential electrical and mechanical components for the war effort deep below Ilford. Shortage of steel meant that some of the tunnels were made of concrete segments, as seen here.

[After The Battle]

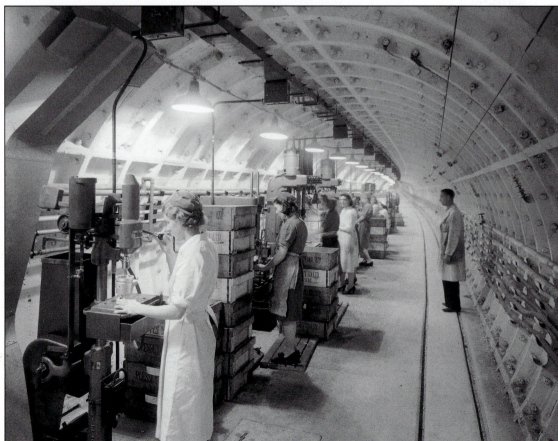

Bright lights, creamy white paint and adequate space made working conditions bearable underground. The concrete false floor and 18in gauge railway track are shown well in this photograph, which shows a section of tunnel made of conventional steel segments.

[London's Transport Museum]

Aircraft industry executives from the USA take the narrow gauge tube train in Plessey's underground factory during October 1942. Allen Clark, joint managing director, is the second passenger from the left, smoking a cigar. For factory workers riding the trains was forbidden but elderly workers were sometime carried unofficially if they could not walk the whole distance.

[Mervyn Hall collection]

Same location, different occasion. Battery loco no. 9 hauls another load of VIP visitors on the manrider cars. The legend on the locomotive reads 'No passengers on locomotives or trucks'.

[Peter Bancroft collection]

This photo of a short train in a 'crossway' tunnel (probably at Danehurst) raises a couple of questions. The lady driver appears to be drawing away from one of the shafts where materials were raised and lowered by hoist. The rearmost truck or trolley of her 'train' is wider than the others and has rubber wheels. 'Mixed' trains of trucks having flanged wheels and others with rubber tyres were commonplace and since the floors were smooth concrete, this did not cause a problem. What is not quite clear is how this train would have reached the 'main line', nor what the rack of cards is for (possibly job cards rather than for employees signing on and off work).
[Redbridge Libraries, courtesy BAe Systems Ltd and Marconi Corporation plc]

Charging of the locomotives' batteries required a purpose-built facility. The batteries themselves were provided with rollers and were slid on and off the locomotives with comparative ease.
[Mervyn Hall collection, courtesy Marconi Corporation plc]

Wanstead one of the escalator channels was equipped as a chute for letting crates and boxes down to the platform.

Products made underground included prefabricated Breeze wiring sets for Halifax and Lancaster bombers, a quarter of a million aircraft pumps, wireless equipment, 22,000 cartridge starters for fighters, gear levers for armoured vehicles, shell fuses and field telephones. The tunnels became the most successful underground factory in the country. The company's war effort, achieved across all its plants between 1941 and 1945, was considerable, totalling 18 million shell and bomb cases, 11 million Breeze connectors for aircraft wiring, 74,000 wiring harnesses, 28,000 PESCO aircraft pumps and 23,000 engine cartridge starters. In addition workers subscribed to buy a Spitfire and this 'Plessey Spitfire', numbered AD381, entered service with 412 Squadron of the Royal Canadian Air Force in Lincolnshire during December 1941.

Conditions described

Eye-witness reports of this strange workplace comment on the unending vista of equally spaced lights in the circular tunnel and down one side, the long single row of machines tended by young ladies in their white overalls. On the other side of the tunnel ran the 18-inch track carrying 'a very serviceable train on its endless journey of fetch and carry'.

Discussion of the factory and its working was forbidden during the war and during this period entry was by production of a pass only. Strict secrecy was observed and even now some of the Plessey pensioners are reluctant to speak about their experience. No public announcement of what went on was made until March 1946 and the only clue that observant bystanders would have seen at the time was the windowless factory buildings and the sheds full of bicycles. The topic saw brief mention in the *Railway Gazette* and the *London Transport Magazine* during 1946 and again in the *Illustrated London News* the following year. Little mention was made thereafter until 1985, when the Plessey Company made major publicity of its wartime secret.

In that year Mr Dennis Barron, then stores manager at Plessey's Ilford site, recalled working below in 1942, when he was aged 16. Quoted in *The Times*, he stated:

> It was strange really, like working in a mine, only you could hear the bombing overhead – a terrific bang and all the lights would shake. Men and women worked side by side. We all liked it because there was such a good group of people working together. Attitudes to work are different now; work doesn't mean much today but then we took our work seriously, arrived at 7.30 in the morning and worked until past dinner time and on Saturdays with no overtime pay.

The tunnel, the newspaper report continued, was equipped to handle raw materials inwards and finished parts outwards on the narrow gauge railway mentioned earlier. There was no passenger service but the battery-driven trains (known popularly as the 'shunters') proved to be ideal for carrying VIP parties on tours of inspection. Mr Barron managed to hitch a ride sometimes to avoid the 20-minute walk through the tunnel to the factory store. Hugh Douglas, a foreman in the factory, remembered the line was so long that he was given a bicycle to get around the machines.

Cloakrooms and water-borne sanitation were installed for the workers, as well as drinking fountains at intervals along the tunnel. For meals a canteen for 600 was established at Redbridge. "I suppose you could call it a canteen," Mr Barron recalled in 1985, "if you only wanted a sandwich. I always preferred to go outside when I had a chance, to walk in the park and to get away from the noise of the smashing chains." In fact the canteen not only fed workers at Redbridge but also distributed hot food in insulated containers to four other mess rooms at Cambridge Park, Wanstead, Gants Hill and Danehurst Gardens seating 400 each. Not all Plessey workers patronised the company canteen, however; at Redbridge an empty shop in the parade was opened by naturalised Italians as a café and prospered well. Workers at Gants Hill fared even better, where a British Restaurant titled 'The Churchill' stood opposite the Plessey canteen, between Barclays Bank and the Valentine public house.

Because access for loading materials at the original station sites of Wanstead, Redbridge and Gants Hill was restricted, additional facilities were created at Danehurst Gardens and Cambridge Park. Electric hoists were built above the 15ft diameter shafts at each of the two places. The structure in this photo remains on the south side of Eastern Avenue opposite the junction with Danehurst Gardens. Used now as an extractor fan house, it stands in the middle of residential housing and must puzzle many passers-by. Those with sharp eyesight may be able to see, apart from the fading 'Tories Out' slogan, the cut-off steel crane joist and the different colour of the brick infill that blocks the opening for the original large ledged and braced wooden access doors. Originally the mechanical horse lorries backed up here for loading and unloading. It is possible, however, that the structure was rebuilt after the war. [Jonathan James]

Welfare matters

An emphasis on welfare meant the workforce was generally satisfied, at least according to official records. Reminiscences of workers and records of the Plessey Trade Union Committee indicate a less cordial atmosphere torn by pay disputes and in 1944, enforced redundancies. Despite this, work continued apace, even during the glidebomb raids of spring 1944 and when a German bomber crashed close by without stopping the night shift. This latter incident took place at Gants Hill on the night of 14th/15th March 1944, when a German Junkers Ju88 aeroplane came down in Woodford Avenue (the A406) outside the Achille Serre dry cleaners shop, straddling the roadway. One of its engines was dislodged in the crash and entered one of the subways of the tube station.

An equally close shave occurred on 24th March 1944 when a Junkers Ju88 A–4 bomber crashed in Redbridge Lane. It was one of 143 German aircraft taking part in a raid over Greater London that night. The aeroplane hit a house at 199 Redbridge Lane, although local opinion has it that the real target was the nearby shaft leading to the Plessey

Plessey's canteen at Redbridge was a substantial building of steel-framed construction with wooden cladding. Food cooked here was distributed to four other mess rooms as well.
[London's Transport Museum]

After the factory closed considerable work was needed to convert production areas into stations for use by passengers. This view of Wanstead station

illustrates how much work was needed to make the place fit for use as a tube station. Here it is still in use for production with its unfinished bare walls and

goods conveyors. Workers can be seen leaving upwards on the escalator; they would use the centre stairs to walk down.
[After The Battle]

Much clutter remained of the wartime Plessey production facilities after the war. This is the Seven Ways roundabout at Gants Hill in 1946, complete with prominent ventilation shaft, checker's hut and other substantial buildings. All of these had to be cleared before the station could be completed. The A12 Eastern Avenue arterial road, opened here in March 1925, runs across this view, leading left to London and right to Southend. The strange appearance of the tower is explained by having shed its outer casing to reveal the internal insulation blocks, then a novel technique but commonplace today.
[London's Transport Museum]

tunnel factory (at the east end of the canteen building and station platform below). Another notable event still remembered vividly by some was at the time of the D-Day Landings in France. As news of the event having started filtered through to the tunnel workers, someone started to sing the hymn 'Abide with Me'. Everyone was crying and the singing spread for the whole length of the tunnel, which must have been very moving.

The standard of health was said to be equal to that of any normal factory, mainly because of the air

conditioning, which supplied six changes of air each hour. "Most of them fought shy of the idea of working in the tunnel when it first opened in the early days of the war," said a factory official to the *Daily Telegraph*. "They found the conditions so pleasant that few of them wished to work elsewhere, even when given the opportunity of doing so." Not everyone shared this view; Andrew Cocker states, "Most of my family worked at Plessey at one time or another and from stories retold during my childhood in the 1960s it was "b – awful working down there."

The scruffy state of the future Wanstead station site in August 1946 shows all Plessey buildings virtually intact (the main block was retained for the station entrance). Features that have disappeared include the unrestricted speed limit on Eastern Avenue, the striped white kerb for better visibility in the Blackout and the pair of concrete K3 type telephone kiosks.
[London's Transport Museum]

Turnouts and other narrow gauge 'jubilee' track sections used on the demolition railway are stacked in front of these buildings at Redbridge station site in August 1946. The car is a 1937 Triumph Dolomite and the buildings in the background housed washrooms, toilets and hanging spaces for coats.

[London's Transport Museum]

Leonard Brown was not very impressed either and did not enjoy working in the tunnel; "It was horrible," he states. In winter it was very cold, with no heating at all (even an official report likens the temperature to that of 'a brisk spring day'). Bombs dropped close enough to blow drawings off tables, so strong was the pressure wave. There was also a certain amount of water seepage, with cold water dripping down his neck sometimes. To cap it all, he was made redundant at the end of the war.

As a night-shift worker Mr Brown did, however, have time to take long walks through the tunnel at lunchtime (1am) and was able to cook his own food on a portable burner that he brought in. He also had a wind-up gramophone for entertainment, which was condoned by the supervisors. Another worker remembers a colleague who ran a

bookmaker's business from his workplace, so there was clearly some time available for leisure pursuits.

Plessey's 'essential workers' with authority to use private cars used the forecourt of a filling station closed for the duration of the war at Redbridge as a car park. With no petrol and no beer for the Red House public house either, buses used the pub's yard. In late 1944 a special bus turn was made next to the war factory buildings opposite the shops where the tower block of flats, Redbridge Court, stands today.

Ways and means

Considerable attention was paid to operational efficiency. Raw materials had to be delivered to the tunnel factory and finished assemblies taken back to Vicarage Lane; for this a fleet of three-wheel Scammell 'mechanical horses' and trailers was used (reportedly painted grey and lettered M.A.P.). Their manoeuvrability and tight turning circles made them ideal for use in confined yards and in truth no other vehicle could have negotiated the tight clearances in the roundabout site at Gants Hill. The same vehicles made similar runs in many residential streets around Ilford; retired engineering staff were issued with lathes on which they produced precision parts in their sheds and garages for assembly at the main Vicarage Lane factory.

A Strowger-type private automatic exchange at Redbridge station control room provided internal telephone communication to 130 extensions. A system of main-operated bells signalled the start and end of shifts throughout the tunnel complex. Oil storage tanks at ground level fed lubricating oil by pipes to every point where it was needed in the tunnel and a compressed air line powered pistols for getting rid of swarf.

Just west of the junction of Redbridge Lane and Eastern Avenue stood a parade of three shops where the company converted a shopfront into its own fire station, complete with 'disappearing' roller doors that opened horizontally and folded sideways; this became a car showroom afterwards until the parade of shops was demolished for the new North Circular Road flyover. Two other fire stations were set up at Wanstead and Gants Hill in addition. The fire appliances themselves were Merryweather trailer pumps drawn by a grey-painted saloon car; their role was to safeguard the surface buildings. Below ground foam fire extinguishers were provided at frequent intervals to extinguish any possible electric motor blaze but there was little else to sustain a fire. No smoking was allowed in the tunnels.

Adjoining the canteen at Redbridge was another temporary building of the army camp type on unused ground behind some advertising hoardings. This served as Plessey's accident centre, supporting the first aid room down in the tunnel. When the air raids were bad and workers could not travel home, it was not unknown to use the beds to rest up. With the end wall knocked out, it later became a workshop for the dealer who turned the fire station into a car showroom.

After the war acute shortages meant that the old Plessey canteen was pressed into service for a year as a booking hall until proper station buildings were built at Redbridge. Around December 1946/January 1947 a covered way and temporary staircase of scaffold poles and planks were built down to the platform. Although indistinct, this unique photograph shows the wooden building, its signage and some temporary lighting made from scaffold poles. This view is taken from the bus lay-by in Redbridge Lane, almost opposite the Red House pub. The station had another entrance on Eastern Avenue and its lights are seen in the background.

[Bob Burrell]

TUNNEL FACTS AND FIGURES

Size	Electric supply	Heating & Ventilation	Miscellaneous
Length: 5 linear miles	Horsepower of production machines: 2,000 hp	Heat generated by machines, operators and lighting: 6,800,000 BthU	Six miles of pipe were laid to distribute air to the machines.
Floor area: 300,00 sq ft	Lighting load: 350,000 watts	Six changes of air per hour provided, which included 2,000 cu ft of fresh air per person for 2,000 people, equal to 500 tons of air circulating hourly in the factory.	Lubricating and cutting oil were also distributed to each machine through a pipeline by gravity.
Cubic contents: 3,000,000 cu ft	100 miles of electric conductor were laid to production machines	In summer 10 to 12 tons of water had to be removed from the air daily. Conversely in winter 5 to 6 tons were added to maintain proper humidity. The full operation of the refrigeration equipment was equivalent to making 400 tons of ice per hour.	
Number of operators: 2,000 per shift	6,000 lamps were installed	150 tons of sheet metal were used to form the air ducts, which included 2,500 branch ducts.	

MAIN PRODUCTION AREAS

Cambridge Park	–	RDF Department (radio direction finding, i.e. radar apparatus).
Wanstead	–	tool room, Breeze connectors.
Redbridge	–	Coffman starters and PESCO pumps.
Gants Hill	–	tool room, coil winding and automatic machine shop.

Rehabilitation

The lease agreement between London Transport and the Ministry of Aircraft production specified a period of 21 years from 1st January 1941, with an option for earlier termination after the cessation of hostilities upon six months' notice by either side. In fact the factory closed in 1945 and it took five months the following year to remove the factory plant plus another seven to break up and remove the concrete false floor, air conditioning and other paraphernalia. London Transport undertook this work, as agent to the Ministry of Supply, and also handled the removal of all factory plant and equipment that was not purchased by the tenant. Jubilee (lightweight sectional) track was laid in the tunnels and diesel locomotives hauled trucks of debris to the shafts, where cranes hoisted load-skips and trays of precast slabs and blocks. Lastly the concrete around the factory railway track was demolished by compressed-air breakers fed from the factory's existing compressed-air main. In all some 12,000 tons of equipment and concrete had to be removed before track laying could commence for the opening that eventually came in December 1947.

Of the four temporary electrical substations built, only the one at Redbridge was retained by London Transport; the rest were demolished in 1946. Further conversion was required at Redbridge and Wanstead, where wartime buildings had to be demolished to make way for the booking halls of the new stations. A prefabricated concrete Horsa Hut building erected at Wanstead as a temporary canteen for Plessey had a remarkable afterlife, first as the local employment exchange and then as a public library (now demolished).

Afterlife

The three new stations of Wanstead, Redbridge and Gants Hill hold the distinction of being the last complete stations designed by the architect Charles Holden, although in Wanstead's case his task was confined to adapting the existing Plessey factory building with new entrance porches. Designs that had been commissioned before the war had to be modified in the light of post-war shortages of money and materials. Thus it was that cement rendering replaced brickwork at Wanstead and timber had to substitute for bronze. Redbridge received a circular building of brick with a 36ft tower, although not immediately; until the new building was finished, the old Plessey canteen soldiered on. As already mentioned, at Gants Hill the embryonic booking hall beneath the roundabout that had served as part of the Plessey factory was now put to its intended purpose, although the most memorable feature of the station is the Moscow Metro-style concourse between two platforms at the foot of the escalators.

Passengers using Wanstead, Redbridge and Gants Hill stations today are reminded of their wartime importance by special wall panels that tell

Until local history expert Norman Gunby instigated a project to erect historical plaques in July 1998, few of today's passengers were aware of the vital role that Wanstead, Redbridge and Gants Hill stations once played. Now wall displays tell the story of London's secret wartime factory.

[Norman Gunby]

Top: Swords into ploughshares? One of the surface buildings of the former Plessey factory was converted in mid 1947 to become Wanstead tube station, ready for opening in December of that year. Meanwhile the enamel sign on the splendid gas lamp post (with its light reflector and winding gear for lowering and raising the Sugg Rochester lantern) still points to Snaresbrook station on the LNER steam line to Epping (closer and more convenient for certain journeys).

[London's Transport Museum]

Above: For other wartime constructions there was no further use, such as this electrical substation at Whipps Cross Road being demolished in July 1946. The power cables reached the tunnels from here by an 11ft 8¼in shaft, probably in the angle of Whipps Cross and Woodford Roads.

[London's Transport Museum]

the story of the Plessey tunnel factory. These displays are now a permanent feature of the three stations and were erected at the instigation of local historian Norman Gunby, who has also written about the factory in his book *A Potted History of Ilford*. Another, less obvious, reminder is on the platform at Redbridge, where oil from the wartime lathes and capstans still shows up and brings back memories to people who worked down below.

Other places for production

The Plessey factory was London's largest underground factory by far but it was not unique. On a smaller scale London Transport created machine and assembly shops in the exhibition subway at Earl's Court, where 150 part-time workers, men and women members of the staff, made munitions nightly while District Line trains rumbled overhead. At 4.30pm they clocked off their regular jobs and performed war work from 5pm to 11pm, at a rate of two shillings an hour. Most of the work was on aircraft parts, which supplemented the work of the organisation's much larger 'London Transport Aircraft Factory' operation above ground in the Chiswick bus works.

News of this enterprise at Earl's Court must have spread, for in March 1942 the London Civil Defence commissioner wrote to the Minister of Home Security with an ingenious scheme to make use of idle hands and empty spaces. His suggestion, that part of the deep tube shelters could be used for production of war materials, found immediate favour and was passed to the Ministry of Aircraft Production (MAP). After due consideration the latter body replied in May that it would like to use Clapham South for production of MAP materials and would discuss further action with the Ministry of Supply, noting nevertheless that the chief problem was shortage of labour, not factory space.

In July the MoHS wrote back to London Civil Defence Region supporting a proposal that voluntary wardens and members of the public could carry out part-time productive work in the shelters. It would have made little impact on overall production needs and the use of unskilled labour would mean that no work of great precision could be undertaken. The scheme came to nothing.

ENDNOTES

The Plessey Spitfire

Early in World War II Lord Beaverbrook originated the idea of 'presentation' aircraft. An individual, organisation or town could present the cost of an airframe (for a Spitfire this was set at £5,000 although the real cost was nearer £12,000) and an aircraft would be allocated to bear the name of the donor (or any caption they chose instead) in (officially) 4in high yellow characters on the fuselage. Many towns and organisations had Spitfire Funds and went to great lengths to raise the money required. Although the total number of Presentation Spitfires is not entirely clear, the number was around 975 aircraft, about 11 per cent of the total production. AD381, the Plessey Spitfire, was stationed at RAF Wellingore, a satellite airfield of RAF Digby in Lincolnshire, joining 412 Squadron on 16th December 1941, after a few days with No. 12 Maintenance Unit.

Further movements are:
- 15th September 1942 to Vickers Supermarine for modifications.
- 28th January 1943 with 64 Squadron.
- 2nd April 1943 transferred to 453 Squadron.
- 17th July 1943 with 129 Squadron.
- 15th August 1943 with 313 Squadron.
- 10th February 1944 to Flight Leaders School, Millfield.
- 7th June 1944 involved in flying accident, category AC.
- 20th September 1944 with Allied Expeditionary Air Force Com. Squadron.
- 23rd June 1945 involved in flying accident, category B.
- Afterwards presumably written off as for many (by then) obsolete airframes.

(This information courtesy of The Spitfire Society and the Airops website)

The Ilford Tube

The huge growth of dormitory suburbs east of London gave the LNER company great difficulty providing sufficient capacity on its inner suburban services and this led to consideration of a tube railway between Liverpool Street and Ilford, following the same route as the surface railway. A proposal along these lines in 1930 was not, however, followed up for reasons of cost. Two years after the formation of London Transport in 1933 the two operators agreed on a more comprehensive plan involving what was to become the eastern extension of the Central Line (following a new route between Liverpool Street and Ilford) and the electrification of the LNER's main line as far as Shenfield. The project's official title was the North East London Electrification Scheme, with a shorthand name of 'Ilford Tube' applied, internally at least, to the Central Line improvements.

Construction began before the outbreak of war, with the first section expected to open in October 1939 (the war meant it was not finished until after the war, in stages between December 1946 and autumn 1949). Much of the work was carried out during non-traffic hours using trains of material hauled by battery locomotive from the Central Line depot at Wood Lane. The return trips brought back the spoil that had been excavated. A large engineering supplies yard and welding plant was built at Drapers Field, on the east side of the LNER line between Stratford and Leyton stations; five battery locomotives were stabled at this depot, which was eliminated once construction of the new lines was complete.

The Plessey Tunnel Railway

Remarkably little information has been published on this railway but this is a summary of the known facts. The battery-driven locomotives, twelve in total, were supplied by the Liverpool company of Wingrove & Rogers Ltd, generally known as BEV (British Electric Vehicles). Produced in two batches, works nos. 2063 to 2068 were delivered between July and September 1941 and nos. 2352 to 2357 in August and September 1942. They were of the company's standard W217 design, used widely in mines and quarries, with four coupled wheels covered for safety reasons by a fairing. One axle alone was driven. The driver's seat was a 'bolt-on' addition and was hinged to allow it to be moved aside to give a shorter turning circle. The company's records give no clue to the fate of the locomotives at the end of the contract, with no indication that they were resold to another customer.

The track was built to the widely used gauge of 18 inches, using rails of 20lb or 25lb weight (per yard of rail). It is understood that stub points of very basic design were used, with a single movable rail. The single tracks ran along the outer side of each tunnel, with 'occasional turnouts at cross passages', but no plan of the track layout has been discovered.

Apart from tours laid on for VIP visits, it was strictly forbidden for passengers to ride on the trucks or locomotives and a warning to this effect was painted on the side of the locomotives. In practice some workers did hitch a ride but stepped off quickly if spotted by a foreman.

London Transport staff making aircraft parts on 10th September 1942 in a subway closed for the duration of the war at Earl's Court.
[London's Transport Museum]

By way of retaliation Plessey workers at Ilford saved enough from their earnings to pay for this Supermarine Spitfire fighter, AD381, for the Royal Air Force. The 'Plessey Spitfire' entered service with No. 412 Squadron in December 1941.
[Peter Bancroft collection]

New Uses for a New War

Deep shelters are recycled for the Cold War; rail plans are renounced

THE transition to peace at the end of hostilities was a gradual process, although for the deep shelters new, more peaceful, uses were found quite rapidly.

As early as 15th May 1945 a meeting of the Civil Defence committee decided to consult the Treasury over the disposal of the deep shelters at Goodge Street North and South, Chancery Lane and Clapham Common, which the War Office had equipped as offices. No staff remained at the last two locations and the Goodge Street premises would be vacated soon. More significantly it was noted that: "However intense the difficulties we face in London to provide office accommodation, it is certain that the accommodation that these long tunnel shelters affords cannot be regarded as suitable space for official staffs in normal conditions. Our storage requirements are great but the limited means of access rules them out except perhaps for 'dead' storage." In other words the deep shelter accommodation was a white elephant and accordingly it was proposed to hand over Chancery Lane and Clapham Common to the Ministry of Home Security, followed by Goodge Street once vacated.

A move came in October 1945, when responsibility for the shelters was transferred to the Ministry of Works, with London Transport deferring its options on their use for any railway purposes. False hopes had been raised, however, on 9th January 1945 when both the *Daily Mail* and the *Daily Express* ran highly optimistic stories about London Transport's reconstruction plans. The *Mail's* reporter enthused for instance:

> Express underground trains which will carry passengers from the heart of London to the suburbs in a matter of minutes; new types of deluxe carriages and the rebuilding of some changeover stations are among the major improvements planned by the LPTB. The expresses will make non-stop runs at high speed beneath the existing tubes, which will carry the normal stop-at-every-station service. Details of London Transport's plan for the post-war era were given to me yesterday by the general manager, Mr T. E. Thomas.

Exactly how two reporters ended up independently with the wrong end of the stick – or whether they did at all – is unclear, but Lord Ashfield issued an immediate retraction and even wrote to Sir Cyril Hurcomb at the Ministry of War Transport to cover his back. The next day an 'Announcement to Press' was issued by London Transport, stating:

> To avoid any misunderstanding arising out of an interview with the General Manager which appeared in certain newspapers today, the London Passenger Transport Board announce that the question of the provision of deep level express railways has not been considered by the Board.

From then on there were no more positive pronouncements on the deep level express tubes and further news on the subject concerned only alternative, non-rail uses.

Troop movements

Following the closure of deep shelters used by the public on 7th May, Goodge Street was the first of the government-occupied shelters to be cleared. It was vacated by the Americans on 29th May 1945 and to British annoyance they made rather too good a job of this, taking back to their Duke Street premises seven electric clocks that were Crown property!

Shortly afterwards, in June 1945, the War Office elected to take over completely three of the shelters it had been sharing, at Camden Town, Clapham South and Stockwell, as accommodation for soldiers in transit or on leave and for army cadets. Their transfer to the London District Leave Hostels Unit organisation was confirmed the following month; subsequently Goodge Street was adopted as well. Bedding and beds were taken over at no cost and most of the existing staff were retained in their old functions. London Transport would continue to provide maintenance services and the responsibility for telephone equipment and calls, previously provided without charge by the GPO, would also pass to the War Department.

The Victory Parade of June 1946 involved some 25,000 serviceman and women, making tremendous demands on accommodation in and around London. Around 3,500 gunners, airmen and guards were billeted on Clapham Common, both above ground and in the deep shelter at Clapham South.

One person who remembers the Goodge Street shelter well is John Stocks, who spent time there in November 1947 while waiting for a ship to Singapore. He recalls:

> Although underground, it was a full army camp, with canteens, multi-level bunks, toilets and showers. It acted as overflow for the main transit camp at Feltham and it was really quite comfortable and warm, by no means insalubrious, and the food was quite good too. My only complaint was that the bunks were a bit claustrophobic, with only 18 inches between them. We used the main Tottenham Court Road entrance, using the bombsite where the American Church is now as a parade ground. Only officers were allowed to use the lifts; everyone else had to use the stairs. In point of fact even the officers had to walk sometimes because some of those leaving the shelter failed to push the gates fully closed. The lift therefore remained at the upper level and any officer wanting to come up had to walk!

We were forbidden to wander anywhere in the shelter other than our officially allowed areas, but since we had been told to lose ourselves during the daytime, the attractions above ground were far greater than any illicit exploration.

Although these shelters were now in War Office hands, one of them also saw civilian visitors. In 1946 Clapham South became London's biggest 'shilling a night' hotel for thousands of boys and girls. In February 2,000 army cadets came to London for parades, spending three nights in the shelter or a tented camp erected on the common by the Guards. Four months later in June a similar number of members of Girls' Friendly Societies from all over Britain were billeted in the shelter when they came to put on a display at the Royal Albert Hall.

Repository for the PRO

Chancery Lane was another tube shelter that attracted new occupiers. In 1945 it came to attract the attention of the Public Record Office, then located nearby in the street of Chancery Lane itself. The PRO stated itself to be interested in storing 400 tons of documents in the tube if it could be assured of four years' occupation and this was agreed on 27th June 1945, with London Transport agreeing not to exercise its purchase option.

Under the new occupancy access to the repository would be solely by the lift shafts and staircases at either end of the shelter, with the doorway from the lower escalator hall of Chancery Lane tube station to be kept permanently shut at the request of both the PRO and the LPTB. In this way "the shelter would be completely isolated from the tube railway systems and should a fire occur in it the question of penetration of smoke into the tube will not arise".

An *Evening Standard* article paints a vivid picture of the shelter and its new occupants:

For two hours, on January 10, 1946 an Evening Standard reporter trudged around the empty, echoing spaces – now being filled with the Public Records of England. There were 12 of us in the tunnelled labyrinth 200 feet beneath the traffic-jammed thoroughfare of High Holborn; a representative of the Public Record Office, a foreman, five workmen, two watchmen, a liftman, an electrician and myself. Between us we made up the total population of an underground citadel that was built to accommodate 10,000. It was here, during the War, in this top-secret, deep shelter, that thousands of Government executives would have retired to carry on the battle in the event of invasion or super air raids. It was here today that I watched workmen wheeling into the bunk-lined, electric-lit tunnels, loads of Government books and documents which had been 'evacuated' to the country during the War. The public records of England are coming back to Town. And 500 tons of them will in future be housed in this underground city built to defy bombs. The deep shelter, built at a very high cost, but never required, has been found to be an ideal depository for some of Britain's most important archives.

When war broke out the Public Record Office had to evacuate from Chancery Lane more than 2,000 tons of official books and documents which had accumulated since the days of the Domesday Book nearly 900 years ago. "It was a colossal task," I was told today. "Contents of about 20 miles of shelving had to be transported by lorry to the country. But the job was done – not one book, document or paper was lost or damaged throughout the War." Among the 2,000 tons of documents were 500 tons of modern departmental records, which were first stored in Canterbury Prison. After the fall of France they were transferred to three depositories in safer parts of the country.

Every day two five-ton lorries, with Public Record Office officials aboard, draw up to the shelter entrance with their loads of records brought from three country depositories – an ecclesiastical

This 1956 photo of Buck Street, Camden Town shows the shelter that had last seen use as the Public Record Office's Camden Town repository four years previously.

[Public Record Office]

Waste not, want not! With nearly all steel supplies diverted to the export drive after the war and soon afterwards to Cold War defence projects, there was an acute shortage for other purposes. Good stewardship of resources saw surplus casualty stretchers of the kind used in the deep shelters (see illustration, page 52) re-used as railings around council flats in many parts of London. Half a century later they still serve their purpose well (note the characteristic kinks in the tubing that formed the supports of the stretcher).
[Roy Smith]

training college near Oxford, a ducal castle in the North, and a casualty ward in the Midlands. For two hours today I trudged around the empty, echoing tunnels, 200 feet beneath the road. They seemed to stretch away for miles, and possibly they did. I saw the bunk-lined corridors, the control room from which shelterers would have been marshalled, modern kitchens which would have provided hot meals on the cafeteria system, endless rows of stools at the food 'bar', and food-storage cupboards which could have stocked sufficient food to withstand a one-year siege.

When fitted with shelving the bunks' steel uprights will make perfect storage receptacles for the official records. Said the Public Record Office official: "We did not choose an underground shelter for safety-first reasons. It is merely that it is available and is ideal for our purpose." Work on the shelving of the bunks will start soon. It may take months to complete. About 80,000 ft will have to be fitted.

Although the racking mentioned was installed, the PRO soon exhausted the capacity of the accommodation and, beginning in November 1947, had to find additional space shared with other government departments at a number of shelters and certain other shelters were also used for storage of government documents (see Appendix 5). Typical arrangements put upwards of 400 tons of papers into each shelter, delivered by covered vans at a rate of 5 tons daily. A change of policy by the Ministry in 1951 caused the shelter stores to be cleared again, with all records moved to above-ground archiving in Hayes, Middlesex.

The Cold War begins

The economic and social problems mentioned previously were soon compounded by political uncertainty as the realities of Cold War dawned. Three years after the end of hostilities planning began in earnest for World War Three, and by 1950 a plan had evolved for the maintenance of government under war conditions. For practical and morale reasons the nucleus of government would remain in London using the same citadels and steel framed buildings as during the previous conflict, with evacuation for the bulk of civil servants. Considered opinion held that although the atomic or A-bomb would devastate city centres, London included, the citadels and their functions would survive, assisted by hardened communications

links yet to be constructed and a new civil defence organisation to be developed. In overall control was to be a Central Government War Room, the plans for which appear to have been somewhat tentative, but it would probably have been established in the Rotundas to perform the same role as the old Cabinet War Room.

Given the difficulty of preparing for the totally unforeseeable, planning for war revolved inevitably around the re-use of existing facilities and techniques. With the threat of aerial attack considered entirely real, particularly during the Korean War (1951–53), the deep level shelters clearly had a role to play, even if the Home Office felt unsure of their precise value. This letter from the Home Office to the Ministry of Transport of August 1947 clarifies the thinking at that time: "The Home Office responsibilities with respect to these shelters have been entirely transferred to the Ministry of Works and our only interest in them is as potential shelters in a future war. By the time that occurs they may have become part of the London Passenger Transport Board system."

Express plans slow down

Although public pronouncement on further rail use of the deep shelters now ceased, their existence was not forgotten altogether and they still received consideration when new railway routes for the capital were put forward by the Railway (London Plan) Committee. A proposed Route 3 envisaged in 1946 a line paralleling the Central Line between Bond Street and Bank, which could have used the Chancery Lane shelter (in theory) but this scheme was rejected by London Transport the following year in favour of a brand-new line running further south. Despite this prospects of rail use were still seen as imminent at a discussion meeting between London Transport, the Ministry of Works and the Ministry of Transport on 5th September 1947. The report stated the quadrupling of the Morden and Northern sections of the Northern Line were 'first priority works' and that quadrupling of the Central Line at Chancery Lane 'may well be necessary at an early date'.

Amongst the proposals contained in the Committee's second report (March 1948) was Route 12 that would duplicate the Northern Line. Its construction was to make use of the shelters at Belsize Park, Camden Town and Goodge Street but the project was rejected by the London Plan Working Party, which, on 29 October 1948, submitted a separate report to the BTC with whose approval it was passed to the Ministry of Transport on 1st February 1949. Submissions made by the Working Party for new tubes were divided into higher and lower priorities, the latter containing Route E, which took the form of a new railway paralleling the Northern Line between Kennington and South Wimbledon and would utilise the deep shelters situated south of the River.

For all this, neither London Transport nor the various government ministries were entirely certain what should be done with the shelters. Under certain agreements made between London Transport and the Ministry of Health, the former had an option to purchase the shelters but agreed not to exercise its option before 9th May 1949. The British Transport Commission also indicated that, provided it retained the option to purchase the shelters at any date they were required, it would be prepared not to agree to exercise that option within five years from 1st January 1948.

This was convenient for the government, which had higher priority uses for the shelters. A meeting held jointly between the Ministries of Works and of Town & Country Planning in January 1950 confirmed that current Civil Defence policy was to retain existing shelters. Surface works lay on requisitioned land under the responsibility of the Ministry of Works and it was not until 1952 that the British Transport Commission was given the right to acquire any of these shelters (except Chancery Lane, under 'strong pressure' from the Post Office) for incorporation in the tube railway system.

Safe haven?

Paradoxically, at the same time that shelters were being held in reserve for use should hostilities require them and financial austerity ruled out any express tube projects, the authorities were reluctant to abandon altogether this possibility. Differing departments had different ideas and the overall position was summed up well in a letter dated 21st August 1947 from a Mr R. Chatterton (Home Office, Civil Defence department) to the Ministry of Works, stating, "Progress in the formulation of a future shelter policy is painfully slow".

In fact progress was being made but 'need to know' policies meant he was unaware of the decisions of a secret Home Defence Committee Working Party. A letter from the Home Office Chief Engineer's branch to the Ministry of Transport of December 1947 affirmed:

> In the first phase of an attack, which may come with little or no warning, it is probable that the function of the underground railways will be mainly . . . evacuation. When this phase has passed there will be a very large demand for shelter of the remaining population. The new main-line tunnels (referring to the large diameter tubes proposed in Railway (London Plan) Committee) could be adapted to meet the requirements of both phases. One at least of the tunnels could have hinged floors constructed in the tunnels, which could be let down to form a continuous floor and thus enable the tunnel to be used for shelter as soon as the emergency arises. Such work should be done at construction stage.

This drawing, taken from a sketch in the files, indicates how a succession of hinged slabs could be lowered from their upright position to form a continuous floorway. Ingenious as it is, there is no indication how the slabs would be supported in their horizontal position nor how they would be manoeuvred from one state to the other. In truth

the mechanism had no more foundation in reality than the rest of this grand notion, although as might-have-beens go, this must rank as one of the most inspired.

Other departments continued to make plans for the future of the deep shelters, oblivious almost certainly of the Home Defence Committee's Working Party. A minute dated 30th December 1950 by the Chief Estate Surveyor of the Ministry of Works refers to the ministry's policy of purchasing all land occupied by surface works of the deep shelters (with a few particular exceptions). Underlying the ministry's reasoning to purchase surface lands connected with the shelters was the realisation that any future rail projects would have no use for the surface buildings, given that the express trains would not be stopping at these stations. At the same time, the British Transport Commission, it was considered, would most likely not exercise its purchase option for the shelters north of the Thames 'as the traffic problem is less acute on this section of the Northern Line compared with the southern section of the Line'.

London Transport clarified its view in August 1952 when its Mr R.M. Robbins wrote to the Directorate of Lands and Accommodation at the Ministry of Works regarding the future of all existing installations. Robbins held a view that in the current economic situation Route E (incorporating the shelters at Stockwell, Clapham North, Clapham Common and Clapham South) would not see any work for at least 20 to 25 years, if ever. Nevertheless if construction became a reality, statutory powers would be required and powers would then be sought to acquire old works in addition to sinking new shafts to meet the requirements of the railway.

Due functioning

At this time Robbins also mentioned a request made to the Ministry for London Transport to be granted use of the shelter at Belsize Park as protected accommodation for 'due functioning' in the event of any future national emergency. We shall encounter

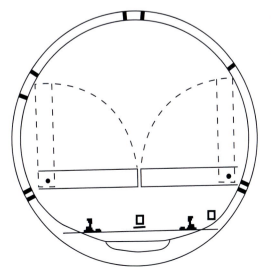

Sketch diagram of the hinged slabs that could convert a tube tunnel for trains into an atom-bomb shelter for people.
Based on drawing in National Archives file HO 205/365]

this term again later, but it simply means the continued operation of 'service as normal' or something as close as possible to normal. This permission was refused on the ground that the government had earmarked sites north of the River for its own essential services, the shelter at Belsize Park together with those at Goodge Street and Camden Town having been claimed by the Home Office.

As the GPO was using Chancery Lane, London Transport was faced with the prospect of having to take possession of the south London shelters although these were considered of little use even if they could be made available for civil defence purposes. However, some importance was attached to the prevention of access from the Executive's stations to the shelters where ample ventilation was also considered essential to prevent smoke penetrating tunnels, platforms or other parts of the stations.

A letter dated 19th August 1952 states that London Transport had abandoned any interest in Goodge Street and Camden Town, although Belsize Park was still of interest. On 26th February 1953 the LTE stated that it reserved its right to purchase the tunnels at Stockwell and the three Clapham stations. The only location where London Transport had made use of these wartime works was in fact at the uncompleted site at the Oval. To improve the ventilation of the running tunnels it was proposed to use the northern shelter access shaft, powers for which were acquired under the British Transport Commission Act of 1950. Subsequently on 21st November 1951 the BTC purchased the shaft standing in the triangular road junction along with obligations to fill in and make good the remaining deep shelter works.

Wasting assets

With the use of any of the shelters by the Board now compromised, the Ministry of Works was pressing for an urgent decision regarding their future. Robbins therefore stated that subject to ratification of the British Transport Commission, the London Transport Executive made the following proposals to the Ministry of Works:

That the Commission's option to purchase the shelters at Belsize Park, Camden Town and Goodge Street be waived;

That the option to purchase shelters in South London at Stockwell, Clapham North, Clapham Common and Clapham South be retained, but that the Commission waive their option with regard to shelter entrances at surface level.

That in respect of the shelters mentioned in (1) and (2) the Ministry be asked to obtain sufficient lands to ensure that access to the shelters is independent of the Executive's stations and that ventilation is ample to prevent smoke from penetrating the Executive's tunnels, platforms and stations.

The Festival Hotel

A far more cheerful event and a clear sign to the people of Britain's resurgence after the war was the Festival of Britain, held in 1951. Coming a century after the first Great Exhibition of 1851, it was intended as 'a Tonic to the Nation', to display the country's expertise in science, the arts and much more. The chief exhibition centre was in London on the rejuvenated South Bank, and early on in the planning process it was realised that London's hotels might not be adequate to cope with the millions of visitors arriving from all over the country and world. In this they were not wrong; the Festival site attracted over 10 million paid admissions. It was also recognised that at a time of austerity not all visitors would be able to afford hotel accommodation and someone had the bright idea of reopening one of the wartime deep shelters to provide low-cost bed and breakfast facilities.

The shelter selected was Clapham South, 'borrowed' from the War Office and titled (with great faith) for the occasion the 'Festival Hotel'. Up to 1,500 visitors paid three shillings a night for bed and breakfast. Reporter Caren Meyer of the *South London Press* described the arrangements for visitors' welfare made by the London County Council on behalf of the Board of Trade.

Deputy manageress Mrs Florence Davison deals with incredible brusqueness and efficiency with all comers and with ubiquitous eyes sees to it that those down from the tube do not miss the cash desk and their 3s. contribution for the night. In navy blue with white spots, large hat and rimless glasses, her short but stocky figure stands at the crossroads of four corridors and with arms outstretched like a policeman, directing the traffic.

"Shove them down there," she commands. "Anyone else for Jellicoe section?" Her daughter-in-law, Ivy, sits at the cash desk collecting the night's money, her son attending the male shelter section.

Even the wartime morale-boosting posters looked fresh when the shelter at Clapham South was inspected in December 1950 before refurbishment to accommodate visitors to the following year's Festival of Britain exhibition. The shelter could house 4,000 people served by limited lift facilities, electric light and ventilation. The original signing and section names were still in use, as the photo shows.
[Peter Bancroft collection]

Normally only parties are catered for but people stranded are given the look-over by manager Albert Cairns and if he likes the look of what he sees they can stay. If he doesn't, he sends them over to Cavendish-rd police station who vet them again. "It's a paradise for pickpockets and pilfering, that's why I have to be careful," Mr Cairns says.

The shelter provides two-tiered bunks in 16 sections on two floors, with three blankets to each bunk and a sheet for women. There are wash rooms with cold water, two canteens serving sandwiches, cakes, tea and lemonade until 12pm and a first-aid room, which is in much demand.

Those staying the night are not encouraged to put in an appearance before 8.30pm at night and by midnight the air is filled with the whistle of mass snoring, the creaking of beds and an occasional cough. But after 6am there is no peace. Tube trains rumble across the ceiling, armies of people walk the corridor overhead. Little girls giggle and teachers admonish them to fold their blankets as they found them and hand in their sheets.

In the middle of all this fatherly Mr Cairns broadcasts the various missing and found items and Mrs Gladys March, one of the attendants, on duty four times a week from 10pm, picks up her alarm clock with which she has awakened those catching the 4.30am boat train and wearily makes her way home. The 1,500 Festival visitors climb up the 192 steps to air and sunshine, or wait for the lift, six at a time.

The shelter site was in fact very convenient for the large coach parking area set up on Clapham Common near Clapham South tube station. A special bus route 'F' operated by London Transport ran direct to the Festival Gardens (Prince of Wales Drive terminus) at a fare of 6d, using six buses allocated from Elmers End garage. The shelter itself was freshly painted for the occasion and no doubt its occupants were grateful for its economical comforts. Stephen Murray of Hunmanby, Yorks, recalls:

I saved hard when an opportunity to go, on a school trip, to the 'Festival of Britain' cropped up. That was a good experience and one I have long remembered, particularly sleeping in part of the Clapham Underground that had been used as an air-raid shelter during the war and was then some sort of hostel.

A year later in 1952 the shelter was used again to house troops attending the funeral of King George VI on 15th February and after that as a public shelter of last resort. A newspaper article on 26th September explained that the War Office had sustained such heavy losses running the shelter for civilians that the 2,500 made-up beds and room for 6,000 more would no longer be available. "We are not a benevolent institution, running hotel accommodation for civilians at a loss. We opened the shelter only as an intermediate measure," said a spokesman. The night staff of 10 were to be dismissed, leaving only two cleaners and the caretaker Albert Cairns, who had spent 13 out of 24 hours there daily since 1942.

The shelter saw action afresh in Coronation year to provide accommodation for visitors from the

provinces. A visit by the South Wales Voice singers to the London Eisteddfod in April 1953 sets the scene.

Having failed to secure hotel accommodation for the party as a whole, arrangements were made for them to stay at the Clapham deep shelters. Here was a new experience for most of the members and there was much amusement at the way in which

The dining rooms looked a bit spartan, however, not to mention the low headroom . . .
[Peter Bancroft collection]

. . . whilst the washing facilities offered little in the way of privacy or creature comforts.
[Peter Bancroft collection]

some sought to adapt themselves to the prevailing conditions. Tasteful light refreshments were served at a canteen in the shelter, the only drawback being that husbands and wives had to part as the ladies were accommodated in a separate dormitory. There were touching scenes at the parting. A wholesome breakfast was served in the shelter and enjoyed by all as husbands and wives had now been reunited, and if the first night was a trifle hectic to the dwellers in the deep, the company slept like innocent babes on Saturday night after having, at the request of the shelter and canteen attendants and others staying there, sung a few songs and hymns.

As the actual Coronation ceremony approached, these visitors made way for troops too numerous to be housed in London area barracks, which was a disappointment to Brixton MP Marcus Lipton. He said, "I had been hoping that children from the provinces would be allowed to see the Coronation Procession from the Embankment and be housed at Clapham one or two nights. As it is, only London children over 10 years of age will be allocated seats on the extended route of the procession along the Embankment."

With Clapham South housing troops, another of the Clapham shelters (probably Clapham North) was used to accommodate the official naval contingent. The *Manchester Guardian* for Coronation Day, Tuesday 2nd June 1953, revealed: "The sailors who are to line the Coronation route in Whitehall, the Victoria Embankment and Northumberland Avenue were out practising this morning on a route they had marked for themselves in Clapham. They are camped in the Clapham deep shelter and their training ground is Clapham Common ..." An article entitled 'Superb Coronation Troops' in *The United Services & Empire Review – The Organ of Imperial Defence* (June 1953) added the information that "the Royal Navy used the famous deep shelter at Clapham. The shelter can take between two and three thousand, and with the exception of 400 sailors at Earls Court all the Naval contingent were at Clapham."

New image

No such limelight fell on the other shelter sites but an unwelcome obligation remained with the Ministry of Works to tidy up the surface buildings. The work of this beautification, described as minor modifications, aimed to remove gas filter trunking, reduce the height of ventilation shafts, remove blast walls where pavements were obstructed, tidy up sites and remove boundary fencing. Finally the buildings should be painted to harmonise with the neighbourhood.

Files reveal that this work was not without its problems. For instance, the paraphernalia of the shafthead buildings was considered highly unsightly, and there was pressure on the ministry to remove the towering ventilation shafts that are so conspicuous in early photographs, and also the water tanks. But as a letter of April 1952 pointed out, vent shafts were needed even where shelters were out of use to maintain the air below fresh and to prevent dampness. Cutting down water tanks to ground level could not be done without destroying the washing facilities in the shelter.

Route to refuge

Although the notion of using the deep tube shelters for an express tube line had been abandoned, plans were proceeding for a new tube linking Victoria with Tottenham Hale that would later become known as the Victoria Line. Back in July 1951 it carried the name Route C and among the upshots of a joint discussion between the London Railway Working Party and the Ministry of Transport was the statement, "There is no doubt the building of the tube would mean a useful addition to the shelter facilities in central London".

For much of the Cold War period the shelter capabilities of a future Victoria Line were not forgotten. MoT reports of autumn 1956 clarify that although no civil defence funds were available for constructing the Victoria Line, money might be provided for creating additional shelter facilities if work started. Moreover, although the line's

Hideous vent stacks, such as this one at the rear of the Chenies Street entrance to the Goodge Street shelter, could be tolerated in war but not forever. In 1956 the decision was taken to remove these eyesores, even though this affected efficient ventilation of the tunnels [English Heritage]

primary purpose was to relieve traffic congestion, "any possibility of it receiving additional support on defence grounds is well worth serious consideration". The line eventually opened in sections from 1968 but there is no evidence that the construction incorporated any civil defence features.

Enter the H-Bomb

Memories of the Cold War are fading fast and many of those who lived through it will be unaware of Britain's state of preparedness, actual or intended. In 1952, for instance, the BBC actively maintained a training centre for Air Raid Precautions at Aldenham, whilst the Post Office was still producing and updating its emergency war instructions. That these were not isolated examples of paranoia is confirmed by many official records now emerging. Early post-war civil defence training films also portray warfare in terms very much similar to those of World War II and indeed many of the preventive and cleaning up measures of limited atomic or conventional warfare would have been along lines that were already familiar.

However, the entire validity of this basis for planning was destroyed by 1955, when the hydrogen bomb with its much deeper penetration depth began to enter the equation. The deep shelters would no longer be a safe haven against the H-bomb, as demonstrated by research commissioned six years later. Document ES 3/57 of the Atomic Weapons Research Establishment (now in the PRO) is a report on a trial conducted in August 1961 at Suffield, Alberta involving a 1/40th scale model and 100 tons of TNT. The trial was made at the behest of the Home Office, who were looking at the possibility of using tube tunnels for public sheltering in World War Three, as had been the practice in the previous war. The aim of the experiment was to assess the effect of nuclear blast on the London Underground system. A scale model was constructed of the Northern Line between Kennington and Golders Green, which was subsequently blown up using TNT to simulate the effect of a 10-megaton ground burst dropped on the middle of it. The main interest was in the damage done beyond the crater by the blast pressure front entering the tunnel via station entrances and via the points where the tunnel had been breached by the crater. There are no prizes for guessing that the damage looked very nasty.

Further complications

A tedious issue arose in 1955 with the imminent expiry of the Emergency Powers Act under which the deep shelters had been constructed. To regularise the situation the Underground Works (London) bill was laid before parliament. Its purpose was to vest in the Minister of Works ownership of land acquired at surface level for the underground structures involved, paying compensation to landowners on the same basis as if they had been bought under the compulsory purchase terms obtaining in 1946. Its other financial

implications were minor, involving a cost of around £50,000 in the first year and £20,000 annually thereafter for maintenance, but it all related to a subject that the government now preferred to keep under its hat. Accordingly the bill was issued in the name of the Minister of Transport; the Home Secretary indicated he was willing to support it but would "rather be left out to try to avoid drawing attention to the civil defence aspect of the bill".

Not only were the deep shelters an embarrassment, they were largely also unwanted assets. An official memorandum concedes with delightful understatement, "with the development of the hydrogen bomb the Home Office became a little uncertain as to the use of these shelters but they eventually decided that on balance there was a case for acquiring them. In any case, they just cannot be left to collapse".

The latter of course was not a fate likely to befall two of the shelters that remained in active use. Chancery Lane was still home to the Kingsway trunk telephone exchange (described in Chapter 14), whilst the Army maintained its use of the Goodge Street shelter as a leave hostel – albeit with considerable reluctance.

A letter dated 27th October 1954 from Major General Johnson of London District Headquarters to the Ministry of Works deplored conditions in the London Assembly centre at Goodge Street. Acute lack of space and toilet facilities in the surface buildings associated with the shelter was drawing adverse criticism against the Army, also affecting recruiting and prompting wives to encourage their soldier husbands to leave the army. A second storey was proposed for the building but the sub-surface works meant the foundations could not bear the additional load. For its part, the ministry's view was that buildings not strictly connected with the wartime use of deep shelters were to be deplored and prejudiced their chances of acquiring these requisitioned sites. Although their sympathies were with the Army, additional accommodation could be offered only underground.

Worst fire since the Blitz

For all the inconvenience of this situation, far worse problems were to come in 1956. Parliamentary questions in February and March drew attention to the "hot, dirty and unsuitable" conditions for troops billeted in the Goodge Street deep shelter, who were "obliged to carry their kit down and up about 200 steps and through long tunnels". The place, worse than "a hovel or the Black Hole of Khosti" in which the young troops were incarcerated was "dangerous to their health" and could "endanger their effective service overseas". The Secretary of State for War conceded all these points but stated no alternative arrangement would be ready before 1957 for the 1,000 troops a week who used the Goodge Street centre.

In the event the soldiers' misery was cut short by a disastrous fire – London's worst since the Blitz – that broke out in the shelter on Monday 21st May

1956. Remarkably no life was lost but the fire took nearly 24 hours to extinguish, with flames so intense that water played on them turned to steam. A total of 500 firemen, working in teams of 20, battled against the flames standing up to waist depth in water and of them, 36 had to be treated in hospital after being overcome by heat and smoke. The fire started in the officers' mess, caused either by a fault in an electrical hotplate or by a cigarette end dropped by a fibreboard partition. Damage to the structure overall was remarkably small, although there was a "good deal of mess" to clear up and a decision was taken not to use the shelter again as a transit camp. Concern was, however, raised that the heat might have dried out the clay surrounding the tunnels to the extent that it might have shrunk enough to affect the tube railway or surface buildings, unlikely as this might be.

The Goodge Street fire delivered many lessons, not least the potential risk in using deep shelters for future air-raid protection purposes. It exposed the inadequacy of the fire fighting methods used and demonstrated also the potential vulnerability of the tube railways from fire and flood occurring in the tube shelters. Although little smoke penetrated to the Northern Line tunnels in fact, London Transport was now acutely aware of the risk. Immediately the Executive demanded either 4½-inch brick walls or air lock doors containing ducts for fire hoses between all deep shelters and tube stations and no time was wasted in making these provisions. At Chancery Lane two of the three links between the station platforms and Kingsway telephone exchange were sealed permanently in July 1956 with concrete bulkheads containing fireproof doors to reduce the risk of fire spreading. Only one single access point was retained, a waterproof door at the centre of the eastbound platform.

Quick wash and brush-up

Although the future utility of the remaining shelters was now in considerable doubt, they could not be abandoned of course, and pressure from civic authorities and other bodies led to the Ministry of Works undertaking a programme of minor 'beautification' measures to alleviate the look of dereliction at most sites. A photographic survey was made in June 1956, giving an excellent impression of the appearance of the tube shelter entrances (and also of the remaining structures in the borough of Southwark). Some of the buildings looked decidedly worse for wear and one still carried the signs directing the public to its two entrances. By December of the following year the ministry's chief architect had prepared a detailed schedule relating to minor repairs and colour washing of concrete surfaces. However, by far the most important work done was reducing the height of wooden vent stacks and removing metal trunking. Both of these operations changed the entrance buildings' appearance profoundly and rendered them visually far less intrusive.

As a result and with memories of the war now fading rapidly, far fewer people now paid attention to the shelter entrances, although vandalism became an increasing problem in the 1960s, with substantial damage being caused to the Clapham South building. Files make repeated reference to emergency telephones being stolen and the need for stouter locks and gates. The risk of maintenance staff being trapped in the lifts was another danger recognised and to alleviate this it was arranged in 1969 for telephones to be installed in these.

Spy saga

The mystery surrounding the shelters was reinforced by a brief incident involving the renegade 'spy catcher', Peter Wright, at one time assistant director of the government security department MI5, who made use of shelter facilities on an unspecified occasion some time after 1958.

Below: The Clapham South shelter was also the administrative centre for the New Tube Shelters and had an adjoining compound where Peter Wright and Tony Sale waited in vain to trap Russian agents. This view dates from June 1956, when wooden signs still advertised the building as the London County Council Clapham South shelter.
[English Heritage]

Bottom: Nearly 50 years on the view is little altered, although the signs of ventilation equipment have vanished. [Jonathan James]

He was using a technique codenamed RAFTER to try to track down Soviet 'illegals' (covert intelligence agents) operating in London. These spies received their instructions by radio from the USSR and by tracing emissions from the local oscillator in their radio receivers, MI5 was able to home in on the spies' whereabouts. Wright related the tale in his autobiography *Spycatcher*.

> We drove our radio-transparent RAFTER van over to Clapham, and made a base in the walled forecourt of the old air raid shelter that ran under the south side of Clapham Common. We took power from inside the shelter and rigged up an aerial, which I estimated would give us a range of about half a mile. I sat with Tony Sale in the cold, poorly ventilated van, watching, waiting, listening. We tuned our first receiver to GRUFF (the Russian transmission) and searched the nearby frequencies with our other receiver to see if we could detect any oscillator. In the second week we got a 'hit', a strange owl-like hoot, modulated with the Morse from Moscow. Someone was listening to the GRUFF broadcast within half a mile of us. Tony Sale looked across at me, momentarily, the scent of prey in his nostrils. We drove … and travelled in every direction. Slowly the awful truth dawned on me. GRUFF must have been right on top of us, listening within yards of the air raid shelter. We drove back to our base and searched the area. Behind a high brick wall at the back of us was a large wasteland car park. GRUFF must have been parked there in a car, or perhaps a van like ours.

The 'wasteland car park', entered from Malwood Road, belonged in fact to the Odeon cinema in Balham Hill and the 'forecourt' was in fact the works compound next door to Clapham South shelter (not Clapham Common as thought by some commentators). Clapham South was the only shelter with an enclosed yard and served as the administrative headquarters for the entire eight shelter system. The gate into the compound from Balham Hill was immediately north of the shafthead structure of the south entrance, with an 8ft high wall surrounding the site on all sides. This is where Wright parked his car while searching for his suspect, who was parked and transmitting in the Odeon cinema car park. The building in between is a temporary structure from World War II then used by a machine tool company. During the blitz of 1940–41, bombs damaged the cinema badly and destroyed the houses that had previously occupied the site. This is why a vacant site was available for the entrance and administrative compound.

Express tubes – the final renunciation

The unfortunate Goodge Street fire of 1956 focused fresh attention on the deep shelters just when, as noted earlier, the Home Office was trying to play down the strategic reasons for retaining them as a last bastion for citizens caught up in a Cold War nuclear holocaust. Reporters with long memories also made the connection with the wartime plans for using deep shelters for post-war railways. The *Daily Telegraph* did exactly this on 24th May 1956, stating that Goodge Street was

> … one of eight built by London Transport under emergency powers in the early part of the war. They were designed as air raid shelters but were all situated near to Underground stations, from which access was provided. Another reason for building them was that they could be incorporated in any new fast track it might be decided to build in future. London Transport was given an option to buy the tunnels but did not make specific plans to use them for either express service or for normal Underground trains. A London Transport official said: "They were not built with the clear idea of using them for an Underground track and we have not prepared any definite plans for using them".

The final renunciation came in 1960, some eight years after the Executive's decision of 1952 not to exercise a purchase option of the north London shelters, when a Mrs Norman Bentwich wrote to *The Times* on 29th July. Obviously remembering the publicity that had surrounded their construction, Mrs Bentwich asked what had happened to the wartime 'stations'. It fell to Anthony Bull, CBE, then vice-chairman of London Transport to respond and in his reply he stated that the 'stations' had been built on the instructions of the Government at public expense as deep air raid shelters and had never been the property of London Transport. Although they had been constructed to act as part of a deep level express tube, they could form only a small fraction of the total length of a new line. Subsequent studies indicated that greater benefit would be secured by building new lines on entirely new alignments, such as the Victoria Line and the Fleet Line serving areas without Underground lines as well as relieving existing lines, rather than duplicating an existing line by an express line that would be of real value only during peak hours.

White elephant

A campaign in the early 1960s to find new uses for the deep shelters achieved little. Suggestions that the Stockwell shelter might be used as a car park were rejected by the government, stating there was "still a likelihood of the shelters being needed in another war". In March 1962 the London County Council scotched rumours that the shelter at Clapham South would be opened to house London's 3.400 homeless people. "The plan was considered some months ago when the number of homeless rose sharply but there was never any firm suggestion that it should be used in this way," declared an LCC official.

Nothing happened in fact until the government finally changed its policy on deep shelters in 1975, as described in Chapter 19.

The Empire Windrush Legacy

Government expediency accidentally determines the nucleus of Black Britain

THE connection between black presence in Britain and subterranean London is both remarkable and at first sight unlikely. Its clarification calls for some background history first of all.

With the passage of time it's all too easy to forget the economic devastation that Britain faced in 1945. Together with the euphoria of peace came the urgent need for physical and economic reconstruction – and Britain needed all the help it could get. One source was in the West Indies, where high unemployment coincided with an acute shortage of labour in the 'mother country'. The British government advertised there for people to come and join the workforce rebuilding Britain as well as for solving workforce shortage in nursing and transport, and for some disillusioned Jamaicans this seemed an opportunity not to be missed. The first immigrants – several hundred skilled, unskilled and professional people including noted singers, students, pianists, boxers and a complete dance band – arrived from Jamaica in 1948 aboard the former troop ship *Empire Windrush*, which had called in at Kingston on its way to England from Australia.

The authorities were not well prepared for their arrival at Tilbury on 22nd June. Although the British Government had been discussing the possibility of using surplus colonial labour to meet demand, it was alarmed by such a large contingent. As British citizens, these people had the right to live and work in Britain, yet the welcome they received was not a friendly one; one of their first sights was 30 men carrying 'Keep Britain White' banners at Waterloo station. Marcus Lipton, Member of Parliament for Brixton offered a warmer welcome with the words "We want you to regard this country as your second home. I hope it will not be very long before each of you is provided for in a dignified fashion".

Shelter solution

An urgent consideration was to find accommodation for these people; after all, many of the people who sailed on the *Windrush* had nowhere to stay when they arrived in Britain. An ingenious solution came from Baron Baker, a Jamaican already living in London, who suggested to the Colonial Office that the Clapham South deep shelter be opened up and used as a temporary base for the new arrivals. His suggestion was accepted and the wartime shelter, which later became the Festival Hotel, now became home to 236 newly arrived Jamaicans. The remainder who had arrived on the *Windrush* stayed with friends or relatives whilst others lodged with friends or found rented accommodation in the face of considerable opposition from some local people.

A number of them have recounted their memories on websites, providing first-hand impressions of life in the shelter. Oswald 'Columbus' Dennison was one of them and told the BBC: "I went to the Clapham South shelter in London like everybody else who had nowhere else to go. We stayed there for two shillings a night. We always thought of England as the mother country – as a sort of school. Many of us thought we would come here to get a better education and to stay for about five years. But then some of us have ended staying for fifty."

On arrival he hit the headlines as the first of the *Windrush* passengers to find work. On 23rd June 1948 the *Daily Express* reported:

> Oswald M. Dennison – the first of 430 job-seeking Jamaicans to land at Tilbury yesterday morning from the trooper Empire Windrush – started a £4-a-week job last night. Wrapped in two warm blankets to keep warm, he settled in as a night watchman of the meals marquee in Clapham Common, SW, where 240 of the Jamaicans are staying in deep wartime shelters. All of them sat down there to their first meal on English soil: roast beef, potatoes, vegetables, Yorkshire pudding then suet pudding with currants and custard. A bed and three hot meals will cost them 6s.6d. a day. Most of the Jamaicans have about £5 to last them until they find work. Oswald Dennison, 35-year-old sign painter, got his job after making a speech of thanks to government officials. He called for three cheers for the Ministry of Labour and raised his Anthony Eden hat. Others clapped. Panamas, blue, pink, and biscuit trilbys and one bowler were waved.

Conditions in the shelter were acceptable to most of its new inhabitants. In a newspaper interview with journalist Chris Arnot, Edwin Ho from Guyana recalled: "It was comfortable. There was plenty of room and they gave us free meals," whilst Jamaican Tom Douce was impressed by the layout of the shelter, stating: "It was half-a-mile down and some of the guys were wary about getting in the lift. We were well looked after, though, given free food and bus tickets".

Community centre

The nearest labour exchange to the shelter happened to be in Brixton, which consequently but entirely accidentally became one of Britain's first West Indian communities, encouraged by Marcus Lipton's welcome. The Jamaicans were resourceful and determined people, working hard and pooling their money to buy houses of their own.

Consequently it was not long before a thriving and multi-racial community was created in the Brixton and Camberwell areas, although not all of the *Windrush* immigrants remained there. Others were offered work in the East and West Midlands by companies such as the Stanton Iron Works and Pirelli.

By 1960 around 250,000 West Indians (men, women and children) had come to Britain, many of them recruited actively by London Transport, the British Hotels and Restaurants Association, and the Ministry of Health; there are upwards of 500,000 today. With justification the arrival of the *Empire Windrush* has been said to have altogether changed the cultural, creative, educational, social and political outlook of British society – in short a pivotal point in modern history. The role of the shelters in this was entirely subordinate but nonetheless vital.

In July 1948 emergency accommodation for Jamaican immigrants was laid on at the spacious former air-raid shelter close by Clapham South Underground station. Meals were served from tents on Clapham Common. Kenneth Murray, Eric Dryndale and Aston Robinson had all arrived from Kingston.

[Hulton Archive]

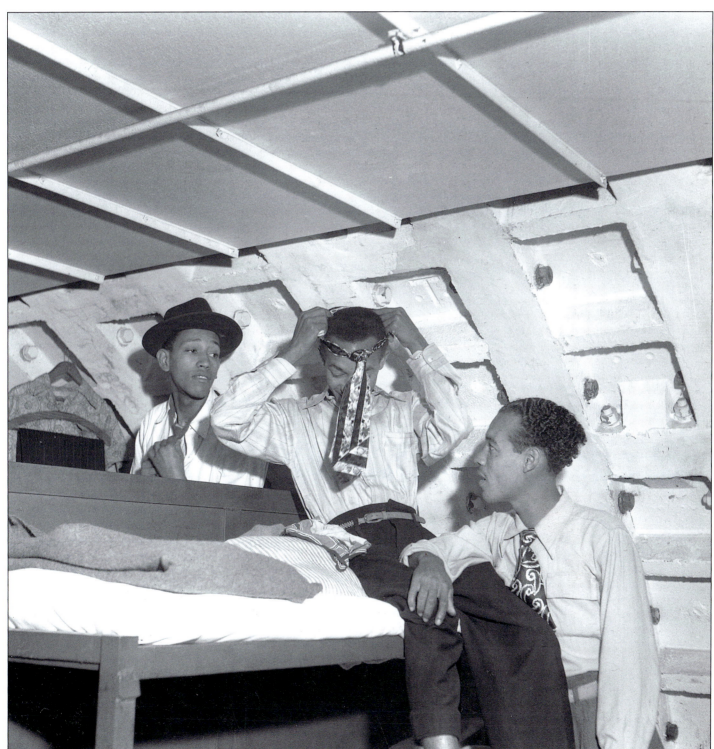

Station on the Hot Line

Chancery Lane takes on a new role

TODAY it is so easy to pick up a phone and dial (or more likely tap out) a number anywhere in this or another country and be connected almost instantly that it is easy to forget the previous way of obtaining trunk calls. Although subscriber trunk dialling or STD was first launched in Bristol in 1958, it took nearly 20 years more before it became available nationwide and not until 1971 did all parts of London have this facility (Ilford was the last area of London to be upgraded).

Before this trunk calls had to be made through the operator, who dialled trunk calls using lengthy and somewhat idiosyncratic dialling codes that took them as necessary through the various trunk switching centres around the country. Chief among these trunk exchanges (to which no subscribers were connected) was Kingsway, known to Post Office staff more generally as TZK (Trunk Zone Exchange Kingsway) or LTK (London Trunk Kingsway). Kingsway is not particularly close to the thoroughfare of that name but this conformed to an established Post Office procedure of giving important facilities names that had a geographical meaning but a deliberately inaccurate guide to their location. Kingsway was unusual in other ways too; unlike most telephone exchanges it was located 100ft underground in the former deep level shelter at Chancery Lane. This fact may well have been the inspiration for the choice of name 'Kingsway'; the exchange was built in a tunnel and not far away was the Kingsway Subway, still used until 1952 by electric trams.

Genesis

The beginning of the Kingsway story goes back to the inevitable *post mortem* discussions and appraisals of the performance of the Post Office telephone system during the war just ended. Vulnerabilities were recognised and led to an application to the Home Office in 1949 for "special accommodation for the important long-distance terminal apparatus which is the most vulnerable part of the Post Office system and the protection of which would be vital to the country's communications in time of war". Out of this were born broad-ranging plans for new hardened installations across the whole country (described in Appendix 3), of which Kingsway exchange and the London cable tunnels were only one particular element.

As far as London was concerned, the current terminal was Faraday House in the City and this was "not in the best position nor, indeed, sufficiently protected for its important function". Were this building to be damaged, long-distance communications would be seriously disrupted. The resulting plan was to divert some of Faraday's cables to another London terminal point having some protection located near the existing east-west Post Office cable tunnel and the only suitable location, said the Ministry of Works, was the extreme westerly section (both levels) of the south shelter of the Chancery Lane deep tube shelter. This was obviously of interest to all government departments and the Home Office indicated it was disposed to agree to this allocation. The Home Office concurred on 2nd June 1949 although any proposals to earmark further shelter accommodation for purposes other than operational Civil Defence activities would be resisted except in the most exceptional circumstances. Nonetheless it must have become obvious that 300 feet would be inadequate and the space allocated to the Post Office was doubled to 600ft in July 1949. The Post Office stated its requirements were "so fundamentally important . . . for a future war that we dare not risk any delay in the protection of this vital plant".

The original layout of the Chancery Lane shelter was of two parallel tubes with an intermediate floor to provide two levels in each tube, having simple lift and staircase shafts emerging in the old tube station at 38/39 Furnival Street, where bomb-damaged premises were demolished to make way (a temporary construction shaft had also been opened in the roadway at the corner of High Holborn and Furnival Street). A staircase also led down to the centre of the shelter from the Central Line station platforms.

After the site was taken over by the Post Office one of the first tasks was to extend the tunnel area by building four large-diameter lateral tubes under Staple Inn in the southern sector and it was probably at this time that the most southerly exit in Tooks Court was constructed. Another activity was the construction of a 9cwt goods lift in Furnival Street, allowing delivery of large items of apparatus by road. The alternative method, by rail to the platform of Chancery Lane station, would have disrupted train operations considerably. In any case the LPTB had already established in March 1942, in a letter from their chief legal adviser to the Ministry of Home Security, that, "on the termination of hostilities, the right of access to the shelters through the Board's properties now enjoyed by the Minister and his agents shall cease and access through their properties shall be solely at the discretion of the Board". The war was now long over.

Planning for the installation operations began in early 1950, with construction work starting a year later. The equipment contractor, Siemens Brothers Ltd, began its own planning and manufacture ready for the time when the full access to the new accommodation was to be ready, on 1st July 1952.

Following installation and commissioning the exchange opened to traffic on 30th October 1954, marking a significant milestone in the progress of inland trunk switching mechanisation in Britain.

Technically termed a non-director trunk tandem exchange, the Kingsway unit was designed to cater for a maximum of 5,000 trunk circuits and, although it was intended primarily as a 'through' or tandem unit, part of its capacity was also available for switching calls, referred to as terminal traffic, to and from the London group. In 1956 it gained importance becoming the London terminal of the first Transatlantic telephone cable, TAT1. This involved a complicated arrangement of equipment at three sites, with several hundred copper 'pairs' linking them – Kingsway itself, the International exchange in Wood Street and the Continental exchange in the Faraday building. Some notoriety was also gained since the then-famous 'hot line' that connected the United States and Russian presidents directly passed through the exchange and this was made a high point of guided tours for visitors.

A telephone city under London

That was the dramatic title of an article in the November 1969 issue of *Courier*, the newspaper for Post Office employees, and indeed it told a remarkable tale. Around the same time the Post Office had taken the press to see its subterranean domain, previously shrouded in the gloom of D Notices and the Official Secrets Act, and the marvels of this 12-mile tunnel network were revealed to the public in far more detail than odd remarks by Chapman Pincher had previously disclosed.

A city under the city – that is Kingsway trunk exchange, 100 feet beneath the Holborn area of London. Fully self-contained, Kingsway could seal itself off from the rest of London – and its 200 Post Office staff could go on working there in comfort and safety. The exchange is air-conditioned, has its own water supply from an artesian well, and emergency power from four diesel generators. Fuel tanks hold 22,000 gallons – enough to keep the generators going for six weeks.

Here is all the equipment needed for the automatic routeing of 6,600 trunk lines between London and telephone centres throughout the British Isles. Kingsway deals with 15 per cent of London's trunk traffic, handling about 6,000 calls at once, and carrying between 1.4 and two million calls every week. The exchange, which went into service in 1954, was on the secret list, until three years ago.

Safety is a religion at the exchange itself and – even more importantly – in the deep level tubes housing the cables that run into the trunk exchange. The whole system is wired to give immediate warning of fire or flood. Unlike the exchange, the cable tubes are not air-conditioned, and must be evacuated if there is a chance of the air in them becoming foul. The Meteorological Office supplies barometric pressure readings every 12 hours, and if the pressure falls below 1,000 millibars the engineer in charge of cable tube maintenance operates the 'clear-out' warning. Lights flash and hooters sound and everyone working in the tubes must leave immediately.

A two-man patrol walks quickly through the tunnels, to make sure no one is left behind. First-aid kits and stretchers are in plentiful supply, and there is oxygen breathing equipment on hand. The cable tubes are also evacuated after a Thames flood warning.

At Kingsway, the great bulkhead doors leading to the tubes are shut – and the underground city, along with its staff, is sealed off from the world.

What's it like to spend your working day – or night – in this underground city?

"I've worked here since the scheme opened 15 years ago," said Mr Ken Clark, executive engineer in charge of maintenance. After a while, you don't notice the noise of the tube trains rumbling above you."

Assistant Executive Engineer (AEE) Jim Barrett is another veteran underground man who enjoys the 'deep' life. Jim is one of four AEEs who man the trunk area fault control on a 24-hour rota. "Everything's at our fingertips," said Jim. "Phones and the Tannoy system keep us in touch with the staff. And our security board shows us, by a system of flashing

To accommodate Kingsway telephone exchange the deep shelter tunnels at Chancery Lane had to be extended. A 10ft diameter working shaft is being sunk through the gravel stratum to reach the tunnel workings in 1951.

[British Telecom]

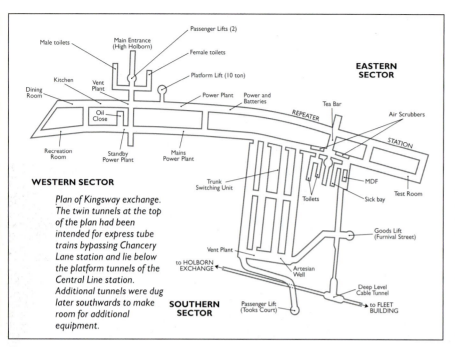

Plan of Kingsway exchange.
The twin tunnels at the top
of the plan had been
intended for express tube
trains bypassing Chancery
Lane station and lie below
the platform tunnels of the
Central Line station.
Additional tunnels were dug
later southwards to make
room for additional
equipment.

*Hardly any passers-by would
recognise this frontage on the
north side of High Holborn as
the one-time entrance to
Chancery Lane tube station.
Even fewer know that for
nearly 40 years the
inconspicuous twin doors at
the centre led down to a
secret telephone city 100ft
below ground.*

pumped along the pipes. "As for sewage – that has to be pumped up to the sewers."

Everything has been done to cut down any feeling of claustrophobia. The canteen has windows looking out on to colourful landscape paintings. Kingsway, built to withstand a siege, protects its citizens better than the walls of Troy. There have been no fatal accidents at Kingsway, nor in the cable tubes – no fires, no floods, no suffocation. Kingsway underground men live a healthier and a safer life than their colleagues 100 feet above their heads in choc-a-bloc London.

The description of Kingsway exchange as an underground town was not far off the mark, with its unique subterranean population and passageways named after the streets far above together with new names such as Third Avenue, By-Pass Alley and The Dog's Leg. Two parallel tunnels, each a quarter of a mile long and 16 feet wide, formed the heart of the exchange, housing much of the equipment. Altogether three miles of racking were installed, carrying 337 miles of switchboard cable, along with the 1.5 megawatt generator for standby power generation.

Kingsway exchange had other peculiarities too. Earlier it was stated that no subscribers were connected, but like most large exchanges it did have its own 'service PBX' for official telephones around the racks. This had the possibly unique accolade of having not one but two dialling codes, LTK in the London system and also the national code 0LTK (0585). The result was that you could reach its numbers by dialling either 01-LTK or 0LTK.

The strategic importance of the Kingsway trunk exchange declined after the introduction of subscriber trunk dialling (STD); the significant

lights, which doors are being opened between the exchange and the cable tube network."

Kingsway is almost an all-male community. There are just three women – the canteen staff, headed by Mrs Irene Spalding. In charge of the power plant is Ron Clayson, another underground veteran. Ron's staff of 33 engineers will change a light tube – or test one of the huge diesel generators. They also keep the very necessary pumps in good repair.

"The air is cleaned and cooled by water," explained Mr Clayson. "Water has to be constantly

growth in the number of long distance calls necessitated many new trunk switching centres to handle the additional traffic. A new switching and transmission plan for a new 'Transit' network was announced in 1960 and implemented in the late 1960s. This work coincided with the 'Sector Plan' for London, which aimed to decentralise the switching of trunk calls in London and supplemented the existing trunk switching centres with new 'sector switching centres' of new technology in the key central sector and in seven locations in outer London serving the suburban areas. A number of writers have noted some significance in the names chosen for some of Kingsway's replacements, Bastion, Citadel, Fortress, Rampart and Tower but this is probably more bravado than indication of supreme strategic significance, since other replacements were named at the same time after eminent scientists (naturally these new exchanges were also connected to the deep level network). Whatever the case may be, Kingsway was becoming more obsolete with each successive phase of trunk modernisation and in 1979 it was announced that the exchange would close within a year, its functions being transferred to Cavendish exchange in Houndsditch. The conversion of the trunk network to digital was the final nail in the coffin, and towards the end, only the Main Distribution Frame (MDF) was still in service, linking a few circuits between other sites.

The merit of Kingsway's secure central location ensured its survival for other purposes; during the early 1980s it provided a home for BT's London area group that serviced closed circuit television. Another part of these tunnels was used for the Kingsway Computer Centre (KYCC) between 1986 and 1990. This housed a secure backup for *Icarus*, (International Circuit Allocation Record Update System) located in central London, whilst another computer dealt with radiopaging. These functions came to an end in 1990, since when the sole use of Kingsway exchange has been for storage.

Newcomers arrive

To the public at large none of this activity was common knowledge, however. By the 1980s Kingsway exchange was no longer mentioned or discussed by BT, regardless of previous exposés by Peter Laurie, Duncan Campbell and others, and with good reason. For BT's staff had now been joined by government personnel. The latter established separate accommodation for themselves in the two easternmost of the four main tunnels in the southern sector, some time in the 1980s to judge by the fittings. This accords with BT gossip at the time of Kingway's 'invasion by men with scrambled egg on their cuffs' as one staffer described it and with the removal from the Headquarters telephone directory of the accommodation group covering Kingsway. Whatever the secrecy concealed then is now laid bare because the facilities have since been fully decommissioned and are no longer confidential.

The historical study group Subterranea Britannica made two visits to Kingsway during the 1990s and on the first foray (4th/5th August 1995) the door to this restricted area had its own bell push and spyhole; the accommodation was declared rather pointedly as being out of bounds. It was also marked as such on the orientation plan that was handed out. On the next visit (13th July 1996), however, members had total freedom to look around what was left of the facility.

Equally unremarkable in appearance is the rather dingy goods entrance to Kingsway exchange in Furnival Street. Replacing a previous pedestrian entrance here, its construction became essential after London Transport ceased allowing deliveries of heavy equipment by train.

During the 1980s a locked-off complex was established for central government use in the southern sector. This was widely believed to have been a temporary home for Pindar, a crisis management centre later moved to permanent premises under the Ministry of Defence Main Building in Whitehall.   [Keith Ward]

The heart of the new accommodation appeared to be a briefing room, with seating facing a screen at one end and a projection booth at the back; sleeping accommodation was also provided. According to an article in *New Statesman* (25th July 1985) this was the back-up site for the war control bunker known as *Pindar*, the primary site lying below the Ministry of Defence headquarters building in Whitehall. It is likely that Kingsway acted as temporary home for *Pindar* during construction of the Whitehall site and it is stated that the Tooks Court entrance (and modern passenger lift) to the Kingsway complex was provided to provide discreet and direct access to this special accommodation.

⌐ ENDNOTE ⌐

Kingsway's shaky legal foundations

When the Chancery Lane tube shelter was first built the surface sites required were requisitioned by the LPTB and subsequently transferred to the Ministry of Works, as at other shelter locations. Its subsequent takeover by the Post Office made the position more complex and the whole affair offers a fascinating illustration of the problems that occur when a facility is constructed under emergency powers. As an occupant of pre-existing facilities, the Post Office had initially no hindrance in

Typical aspect of large diameter tube at Kingsway. The site is no longer used operationally and nearly all communications equipment has been recovered.

[Keith Ward]

Creature comforts for the troglodyte denizens of Kingsway exchange were not overlooked, judging by the contemporary furnishings of this mess room! [Keith Ward]

Today the only operational equipment at Kingsway exchange is the main distribution frame (MDF), on which a few circuits are still cross-connected.
[Nick Catford]

establishing Kingsway exchange in the shelter tunnels at Chancery Lane. This position altered radically, however, with the approaching expiry of the emergency powers under which the shelters had been built. The independent operational nature of the telephone exchange lent it a status rather different from the remaining deep shelters, and whilst ownership of the latter was vested in the Ministry of Works by the Tube Shelters (London) Act, which vested ownership, Kingsway needed an act of its own, the Post Office Works Act of 1959, which vested ownership in the Post Office.

The provisions of the act were set out in the Post Office Works bill, which was debated in the 1958/59 session of parliament. The preamble of the bill stated that in the exercise of emergency powers the London Passenger Transport Board had constructed certain underground works situated partly in the Metropolitan Borough of Holborn and partly in the City of London and that the Postmaster-General had entered into occupation of those works and in the exercise of emergency powers had extended them. The same bill stated that in the exercise of emergency powers the Postmaster-General had constructed works in the City of Birmingham. In both cases the works were described as "a system of tunnels together with shafts and other means of access thereto from the surface and ancillary works".

The Bill had its second reading by the Lords on 20th January 1959 and was committed to a Select Committee. Petitions were deposited by five organisations, complaining that no indication of the depth of the works was given (withheld for security reasons), that no compensation was offered for any damage that might be incurred, or for reduced property values and arguing that surface owners should have unrestricted rights to develop their land.

One further complication surrounds the property at 31/33 High Holborn, which is now one of the two sole points of entry to Kingsway exchange (the other is the goods lift in Furnival Street). London Transport has ownership of the ground floor and basement of this building, which was then leased to the Post Office and later, British Telecom.

More Tubes Without Trains

The cable tunnels branch out

AT the same time as Kingsway exchange was conceived, plans were laid for protected cable tunnels at deep level to connect key telephone exchanges, a matter vital to national security at a time when the country faced the atomic bomb menace. Secrecy was absolute – until one day in September 1951 when the *Daily Express* placed the headline 'Secret Network of Tunnels' on its front page. The article listed accurately the four tunnels being dug for Kingsway exchange in Holborn, which a Post Office spokesman explained away as 'work in connection with defence' carried out underground for 'the maximum atom blast and radiation protection in the central London area'. Three days later a second article revealed that a shaft was being dug in connection with new tunnels under Whitehall, forcing a special Cabinet Office committee to consider how further leaks could be prevented, particularly over the next phase of the project 'Post Office Scheme 3245' involving a tunnel under Horseguards Parade and The Mall.

For this, Duncan Campbell notes in his book *War Plan UK*, the Trooping of the Colour ceremony had to be moved, while between 400 and 500 workmen toiled beginning in October 1951. A second meeting of the secret committee minuted:

> Details of the existing network of Post Office tunnels, with which the proposed new tunnels would be linked, had been published together with explanatory diagrams soon after the war. It would therefore be possible to guess with some accuracy at the possible direction of the new tunnels, even though they would not run (from A to B). But the information which it was most important to safeguard was the use to which some portions of these tunnels would be put, and this would not be obvious until the equipment engineers got to work . . . an astute journalist had only to ask one or two questions of different workmen to learn enough to piece together a fairly accurate picture of the tunnelling system.

Only about a third of these tunnels were in fact to contain Post Office equipment, the minute continued, although 'this would lend authenticity to the official version of the purpose of the tunnels'. The Post Office prepared a press release, explaining that the whole project was just a set of cable tunnels and referring to the need to protect 'vital communications' in the 'present defence situation' and the installation of 'terminal equipment associated with the cables'. Nothing further was published about the Whitehall tunnels though an article suggesting that the government was indeed building itself an atom-bomb-proof citadel appeared in the *Daily Worker* on 8th September 1951.

Meanwhile construction of the cable tunnels continued apace, with routes built in 1953–54 to Bethnal Green, Waterloo exchange and to Paddington and Maida Vale. Later tunnels, built starting in 1960, connected Fleet Building (Shoe Lane) to Trafalgar Square and Trafalgar Square to the new Post Office Tower. A project of 1966 provided additional capacity east of St Paul's, whilst the last tunnel to be bored provided a second connection from switching centres in the Waterloo exchange complex. According to Campbell, more than a thousand miles of cable ran by 1980 in these twelve miles of seven-foot diameter tunnels, which he described as 'impressive' and the deepest of any of London's underground networks.

The similarity between these cable tunnels and the tubes of the London Underground lies not only in the style of tunnelling but also in fascinating might-have-beens. Unfinished rail projects have their parallels among the cable tubes, notably two proposed routes, Waterloo–New Cross and Post Office HQ (St Martin's le Grand)–Bishopsgate, that were rejected on cost grounds in 1952. The heroic but never built Northern Line outreach of the London Underground to Bushey Heath has its counterpart in the cable tube extension along the Edgware Road from Cunningham out to Colindale that also never reached fruition.

Although for security reasons BT does not discuss these tunnels the description given by Campbell can be taken as accurate. Looking very similar to tube train tunnels, they house only cables, along with occasional large chambers in the vicinity of shafts or elsewhere, for loading coils, amplifiers, and other interconnections. Apart from Kingsway exchange itself there are no other underground switchrooms, workshops or dormitories and because access to the tunnels is restricted to the few people holding a 'deep level pass', they are not used as general walkways. There is no permanent presence in the tunnels, only occasional visits by maintenance and inspection staff (it's unlikely many new cables are installed now). The atmosphere is generally quiet except where tube trains pass overhead and although the tunnels are generally well ventilated, staff are instructed to leave by the nearest exit point if heavy storms are expected.

Access to the network is down shafts inside the adjacent exchanges, in exchange yards outside or, in a few cases, via shafts emerging into subways below the streets and pavements. Subways of this kind are at Bethnal Green, Waterloo, The Mall and Maida Vale. At major exchanges large lifts carry cable drums and other equipment down to the tunnels 80 to 100ft below but other staircases are extremely confined. When Duncan Campbell made his private 'Mole Tour' explorations in 1980 he saw at some sites small, specially-built electric trucks plugged into battery chargers that were used to haul cables and equipment through the tunnels.

Originally all deep level installations were highly secret, but a notable change of policy took place in 1967, when the tunnels were taken off the secret list and removed from the so-called D Notice list of subjects prohibited from media coverage. The press were shown round various parts of the system and various illustrated features followed. British Pathé was so impressed that it took its newsreel cameras down below twice, screening views of the tunnels below the Post Office Tower in March 1967 and a visit to the caverns of Kingsway exchange in May 1968. Both films can be viewed on the company's website at *www.britishpathe.com*.

Informative articles in the specialist press during 1971 and 1972 built on this new openness, describing the considerable new construction going on at the time. Most of this was in conjunction with the reorganisation of the London telephone system to provide significantly greater capacity, particularly for the growing number of trunk and international calls. The long-distance traffic in and out of London that had previously all passed through Kingsway or Faraday exchanges was now diverted to new 'Sector Switching Centres' built above ground and located at strategic points in the metropolis. Seven of these served the suburbs, whilst central London had five outgoing and five incoming trunk exchanges. The former were named after fortifications (Bastion, Citadel, Fortress, Rampart and Tower), the latter having a scientific theme (Cavendish, Faraday, Maxwell, Mercury and Varley) and all were connected to the deep level system with new tunnels built where necessary. The old Faraday and Kingsway exchange equipment was afterwards taken out of service.

The CBX scheme of the 1970s

Mention was made in Chapter 9 of Federal, the centralised branch exchange opened in 1940 to serve key government and service department personnel. Reports indicate that Federal moved around 1951 from its original location in the basement of the Old War Office building to the Broad Sanctuary site opposite Westminster Abbey, next to the Methodist Central Hall. The Broad Sanctuary citadel was built between 1950 and 1952 as a massive concrete blockhouse, three or four storeys deep. Designed to survive atomic bomb attack, it now lies covered by the Queen Elizabeth II International Conference Centre, opened in 1986. A report in the *New Statesman* for 20th June 1986 gives the full history of this structure, planned in 1949 as a shelter proof against the atomic bomb in the basement of a new Colonial Office yet to be constructed.

In the event, the Colonial Office was not built; only the citadel substructure was constructed. This measured 220ft in diameter with a 10ft concrete roof, and connected to the deep level cable tunnel system. While the bombsite above lay fallow – it was

the location for a temporary press communications centre for the 1953 Coronation and was later let to National Car Parks Ltd for parking – only a handful of people were aware that beneath this lay a massive citadel equipped with its own power and water supplies, air inlets and exhausts and electrical generators running 24 hours a day.

Federal moved once more, either around 1958 or during the 1960s (accounts vary), to the North Rotunda in Monck Street. With the introduction of all-figure numbering in 1966 the old alphabetical exchange names in London were withdrawn and replaced by new numeric codes. Federal was part of this scheme and the old FED code was replaced by 333, its direct numerical equivalent. The exchange lost this code along with its separate identity on 14th June 1971, when Federal was allocated a normal telephone number on 222 exchange, just like the switchboard of any other firm or organisation. The code 333 was revived for normal use by Mercury Communications Ltd during the 1990s.

The capacity of Federal was restricted and a proposal to replace it with an automatic system was suspended 'by Cabinet decision' in 1952. Consequently most government departments acquired their own manual switchboards (PMBXs) in the post-war years along with a criss-cross maze of private wire links. The growth of central government and rocketing number of telephone calls made plain that better facilities were needed. The solution, described in great detail in the Spring 1970 issue of the *Post Office Telecommunications Journal*, was to provide a new network of PABXs (automatic switchboards) to link government offices in the Whitehall area with one another and the Houses of Parliament. Its name was the CBX or Central Branch Exchange scheme (its name reflected the 'centralised private branch exchange' of 1939 mentioned in Chapter 9) and aimed to provide a flexible and cost-effective communications system that would cope with the rapid growth and frequent changes in location of staff and accommodation in the Whitehall area.

Some 45 manual branch exchanges were replaced by 15 shared PABX4 installations provided with direct dialling-in (the codes 210 to 219 were allocated) and connected to a tandem exchange known as Horseferry Tandem. This term 'tandem exchange' denotes an exchange to which no subscribers are connected; instead its function is for interchanging or re-routing calls intended for an exchange to which there is no direct route. For Whitehall offices it would be uneconomic to provide direct routes from each and every ministry to every other; between, say, the Department of Transport and the Ministry of Agriculture, Fisheries and Food there might not be enough calls to warrant provision of a direct circuit. Instead, calls from DTp to MAFF would go via the tandem, which has routes to and from every ministry exchange.

Phase One of the scheme opened in mid-1972. Horseferry Tandem exchange (location code YTAN) was built in the basement of the Rotundas,

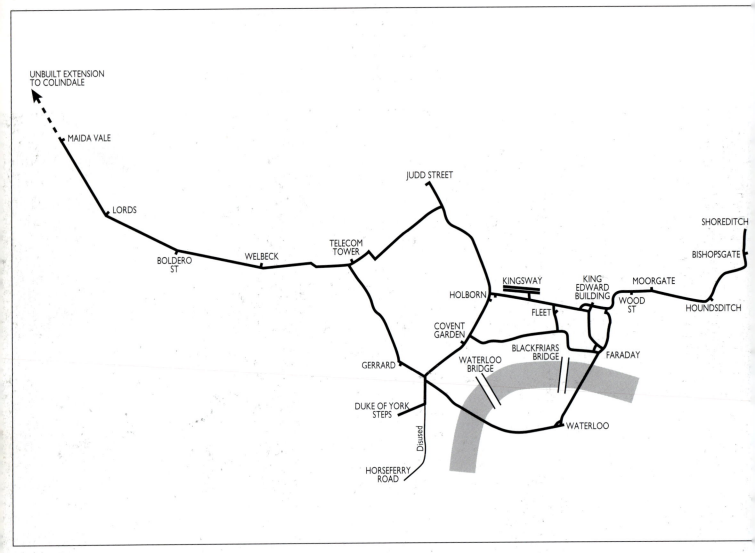

UNBUILT EXTENSION
TO COLINDALE

MAIDA VALE

LORDS

BOLDERO ST

WELBECK

TELECOM TOWER

JUDD STREET

HOLBORN

KINGSWAY

KING EDWARD BUILDING

MOORGATE

SHOREDITCH

BISHOPSGATE

WOOD ST

HOUNDSDITCH

FLEET

FARADAY

COVENT GARDEN

GERRARD

WATERLOO BRIDGE

BLACKFRIARS BRIDGE

DUKE OF YORK STEPS

Disused

WATERLOO

HORSEFERRY ROAD

London's alternative tube map, showing the deep level cable tunnels of British Telecom (interconnection between the two networks existed at Trafalgar Square and Bank stations and elsewhere). The Whitehall tunnel from Trafalgar Square to Horseferry Road was seldom shown on official plans and is now disused.

close to Horseferry Road, but is no longer sited here. Other equipment serving the Palace of Westminster and two other CBX 'areas' was placed underground in the Broad Sanctuary citadel. Other PABX locations listed in the article referred to include the Admiralty Citadel, the Adelphi, Whitehall Gardens, Almack House, Marsham Street, Waterloo Bridge House, Bridge Street, Cleland House and Great Westminster House.

From CBX to GTN

The success of the CBX scheme for rationalising government communications in the London area did not go un-noticed, and led to a comparable but more ambitious project to link all government buildings country-wide. The name given to this national system was GTN, the Government Telecommunications Network, which provides a low-cost national direct dialling system between sites using uniform short-form dialling codes that are standardised across the network. Today any publicly funded organisation can join the GTN, including government departments, local authorities, universities and the police. Private

sector companies can also be connected where they provide an executive function for government and the government determines that this will bring benefit to the public purse. GTN was established during the 1980s by British Telecom but since being awarded the GTN management contract in 1994, it has been run by Cable & Wireless Ltd. Today the GTN links more than 1,300 sites, from the largest offices right down to individual home workers, and is capable of delivering all the elements of modern voice communications.

Few observers would guess the strictly functional nature of this architectural adornment outside the Queen Elizabeth II International Conference Centre in Westminster. In fact it is an air vent, the only external evidence of an underground citadel constructed 35 years before the building that now covers it. At one time it housed the government's Federal telephone exchange and was connected to the deep level cable tunnel system.

London Calling

The BBC takes refuge in secret studios and strongholds

WITH this chapter our story develops another strand so without further ado " . . . we take you over to Broadcasting House."

The latter end of the 1930s was a period of considerable expansion for the BBC. Radio audiences had never been higher, whilst viewing numbers for its fledgling television service had reached 20,000 by the year 1939. This factor combined with preparations for war, kept the BBC's planning and installation teams extremely busy.

Pressure on facilities in London led to the opening of five new studios and recording rooms in a former skating rink at Maida Vale in 1935 but this

provided only temporary respite. A more radical solution was to extend Broadcasting House itself and in 1938 plans were unveiled for an architecturally impressive extension that would more than double the size of the building and provide new television studios conveniently located in central London. Dubbed 'London's New Radio City' and 'The Empire's Radio Centre', the proposed enlargement would have given Broadcasting House a far more balanced aspect than the cramped appearance it originally had (and still has to this day).

Site clearance was complete by the end of the year and contracts were let for excavating a huge 'tank' that would enclose five new underground studios and provide foundations for the new extension. Occupation of the entire building was scheduled for 1940, although in the event war broke out before construction work could begin. This grand new headquarters facility reflected the BBC's policy before the war, which had been to concentrate radio studio and control facilities at a small number of locations. This decision had to be reversed after the outbreak of war when the vulnerability to air raids was realised.

Contingency plans

In 1938 all public utilities and authorities embarked on air raid precaution measures and the BBC was no exception. *Radio Pictorial* magazine reported in May 1938 that preparations were well under way for gas-proofing the underground tunnels leading from

A glimpse of a London landmark that was never built. The Broadcasting House extension would have transformed the original truncated façade into a truly impressive headquarters building. The view is from Portland Place looking south-east.

The pecked lines in the aerial view show how far the radio and television centre of the future was to be expanded.

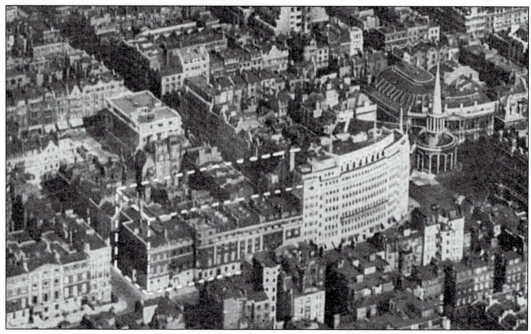

Broadcasting House where, three floors below ground, the air conditioning pumps were being made gas-proof. The artesian well in the basement of Broadcasting House, although sealed, could be opened within half an hour and this would provide the continuous supply of filtered water necessary for producing oxygen by chemical means in the gas plant. A supply of anti-gas tents had also been purchased. What benefit these facilities subsequently provided is not known. The tunnel referred to is probably the one that led to the building called Egton House (now demolished). In a separate measure the BBC undertook a policy of dispersing departments to safer venues around the country.

Going underground

At regional centres around the country subsidiary studio and control centres were provided in miniature a short distance away from the existing facilities. The same logic applied in London and in the search for protected underground accommodation, the BBC approached London Transport. Consideration was given first to the disused Drummond Street entrance to Euston station (Northern Line) in October 1940 but the BBC decided not to pursue this once a more radical scheme was conceived. Frank Pick, from 1933 to 1940 the Vice Chairman of London Transport, had taken a new post as Director General of the Ministry of Information (MoI) and in this role he wrote to his old colleague J.P. Thomas, recalled from retirement to take charge of tube shelter arrangements at London Transport. "A stroke of luck" is what he called the opportunity as the BBC now embraced a far more ambitious solution.

The BBC was now requesting the LPTB to drive two station-size tunnels northward from Oxford Circus towards Broadcasting House for studio and broadcasting purposes at its own expense. Pick could hardly contain his passion for the project since it could be tied in with the reconstruction of Oxford Circus station, "provided for free", and the MoI would support the scheme. For all of Pick's enthusiasm, this was not the opportunity that it appeared, since London Transport had firm proposals for improving Oxford Circus that did not involve rebuilding practically the entire station and shortly afterwards the BBC was informed that "any low level tunnels built for the BBC will have to be entirely separate from any interests of the LPTB".

Plans drawn up by London Transport envisaged a tunnel of 26ft internal diameter with accommodation on two floors. It would lie 75 to 80ft below ground, with access by an 18ft diameter shaft and a 12ft emergency shaft. The BBC decided that it should lie below the part of the Broadcasting House extension site that had not yet been excavated (Site No. 2) and on 30th December 1940 the BBC's Civil Engineer wrote that the proposal seemed "highly probable to go ahead".

Change of plan

The Treasury clearly had other ideas and following discussions with the MoI it was decided to abandon the tunnel scheme in favour of a first-stage development of the Broadcasting House extension for which basement retaining walls had already been built (Site No. 1). This decision was communicated to London Transport in May 1941. Work started soon afterwards, resulting in a 'complete broadcasting station in miniature' built underground at the rear of BH (as Broadcasting House is tagged in BBC circles) along Duchess Street.

Known as 'The Stronghold' and first revealed to the public at large in the *BBC Yearbook* for 1946, this underground structure contained studios, recording rooms, a control room and offices, all under the shield of a concrete roof 9ft 6in thick. There was also a generator room and a small canteen, all laid out on either side of a spine corridor with gas doors and staircases for access at either end.

Completed in November 1942 and linked by line and radio to transmitters at Brookman's Park and Daventry, the Stronghold was intended for emergency use only. Fortunately it was never needed, since although the main Broadcasting House was bombed on several occasions, it did not sustain damage serious enough to cause loss of programmes. The worst damage to Broadcasting House occurred on 15th October 1940, when a 500lb bomb landed in the music library, killing seven people. Bruce Belfrage, who was reading the nine o'clock news as the bomb exploded, paused briefly as he heard the noise and then finished the bulletin without stumbling. Several bombs subsequently left their mark on the outside of the building.

The Stronghold figured as a kind of last resort, along with Wood Norton (Evesham) in the BBC's planned scheme for evacuating studios. According to a document entitled 'Emergency Evacuation of London Premises' undated but almost certainly prepared in October 1942:

> The Stronghold and premises at Evesham are general reserves for all services. Within the limits of accommodation and facilities available, the Stronghold is a last reserve for any or all of the Corporation's services. It is also equipped so that Home News, News Talks and Presentation, could transfer to the Stronghold as soon as News Agency and Recording facilities were provided. (The Stronghold is reached through the gas-proof door, LG2, opposite the Lounge, on the lower-ground floor in the north-east corner of Broadcasting House. Keys are in the possession of the Duty Officer, Duty Room, B.23). Moves to Evesham or the Stronghold will be decided by the Director-General in the light of prevailing circumstances.

A total of 10,000 tons of concrete was used in the Stronghold's construction and it was designed from the outset to allow an extension of Broadcasting House to be built above later on. That said, it was an awkward structure to incorporate into later construction as the Stronghold is somewhat deeper than the lower ground level of Broadcasting House (one floor down from the ground floor and in fact

The Stronghold was a complete broadcasting centre in miniature built next to Broadcasting House during the war. In this view dated November 1945 the 9ft 6in-thick concrete roof (removed later to facilitate building the subsequent Broadcasting House extension) is clearly visible. The picture, looking north-east with Duchess Street on the left and Hallam Street on the right, shows protected air and exhaust vents, with a rectangular vent into the corridor. The protected porches have been removed but a temporary single-storey building is visible, along with the much deeper shored excavation for the basement of the abandoned pre-war extension scheme. It is just possible to make out the low-level door at the bottom of the staircase, facing into the excavation.   [BBC]

above the level of the basement studios) but above the level of the basement of the BH Extension as eventually constructed. Built into the Stronghold is a door with a staircase leading down and ending in a brick wall, intended to give access to the basement level of the Broadcasting House extension originally intended. The latter was finally opened in 1962, although not to the elegant designs of 1938 nor on exactly the same alignment. Currently the way into Stronghold is through the basement of the current extension building, although when originally constructed it stood on its own, outside the confines of Broadcasting House.

Working conditions in the Stronghold are not recorded, possibly because it saw little actual use during the war. One of the few who remembers the place is Roy Hayward, who worked as a Junior Maintenance Engineer (JME) in London Control Room (LCR) at Broadcasting House from 1942 to 1943. He recalls, "We were not brought into contact with the Stronghold at all and we were told it was to be the new, bomb-proof control room of the future. I do, however, remember that I used to park my bicycle in the entrance to the Stronghold alongside a few cars and motorcycles that were using the space for parking. This was on the east side of Broadcasting House in Hallam Street, where there was a sort of slope down from the road level into the depths. The slope was shut off by temporary doors or barricades several yards in from the road and I seem to recall a low wall beside the pavement enclosing the parking space in front of this slope. It was, of course, a building site and as such we were not told much about its purpose. I believe there was a large double-door entrance to BH next to the low wall that was used for the catering dept and other deliveries. It was

a tradesmen's entrance I suppose and used on one occasion I believe for admitting the King and Queen (or is that apocryphal make-believe?) Nobody I knew ever visited the Stronghold in my day and the place did not come up in conversation at all. We were reticent to enquire about things we did not understand as the war was on."

Incidentally, the Stronghold is the same protected accommodation that Peter Laurie described in *Beneath The City Streets* but mistakenly assumed to be at the Maida Vale studios.

Protected cables

The Post Office had an obvious role providing many essential lines and facilities to the Stronghold and to BH, both for internal communication and for taking broadcast programmes from the studio to the transmitters. It is reasonable, therefore, to assume that a cable route was provided at deep level for this purpose.

Rumours abound within the BBC of a tunnel connection to the Bakerloo Line of the London Underground, which runs so close that the rumble of trains is frequently heard in talk programmes on Radio Four. Searches of the BBC, BT and London Transport archives turned up nothing to confirm this speculation, but a letter in the BBC's *Prospero* magazine for retired staff in 2002 lent considerable support in favour of this contention. The letter's writer was Mr L.G. Smith who joined the BBC in 1929 and retired in 1972. He explained that in addition to a connection to the control room in Broadcasting House, the main outgoing cables from the Stronghold took a direct route (rather than passing through the control room in Broadcasting House) into the tube tunnel and away northwards to Maida Vale and to the Emergency News Headquarters (ENH) secreted in a private residence at Finchley, providing access into the main distribution network and transmitters. If BH had been rendered unusable then 'last ditch' government announcements would have been possible from the Stronghold to transmitters, he declared, and indeed the studios and other facilities in the Stronghold would have enabled the BBC to continue broadcasting a service of programmes.

It is still unclear whether the cable connection to the tube tunnels ran direct from the Stronghold or via the sub-basement of Broadcasting House but the former is more likely. Mr Smith understood a simple pipe connection was used and this would accord with the 12-inch bore steel pipe connections provided for cables from the War Office and Air Ministry buildings to the Whitehall cable tunnel system.

It is unlikely that the tube connection is still in use but its application was certainly foreseen during the Cold War. Treasury files at the Public Record Office discussing the BBC's planning to ensure broadcasts in the face of any future hostilities are one such place where this scheme is mentioned. The notes of a meeting held 12th March 1954 to discuss capital expenditure on civil defence include mention of financial provision to be made for "links between the BBC citadel in London and the Post Office deep-level cable system". A sidelight appears in a minute written 24th May 1954 by a BBC official: "While these [deep level cable] tunnels are not at a sufficient depth to safeguard against a hydrogen bomb exploding above, they would afford protection under other circumstances."

Four months later a BBC report to the Treasury set out 'the BBC Deep Level scheme' stating that plans had been made to connect the BBC Stronghold to the Post Office deep-level cable tunnels, involving the sinking of a shaft from the Stronghold to the Bakerloo Line at a cost of £56,000. Although not stated in the document, the cables would run southbound and connect with the Post Office network at Trafalgar Square. The BBC looked to the government for a decision and again sought advice the following year in view of the increased threat from the Soviet H-bomb. Although another note in the same file said the 'deep-level outlet scheme' had been abandoned in July 1955, this did not end the matter. A later document of 31st January 1957, relating to an internal Treasury review of the BBC's proposed civil defence expenditure plans for 1957/58, says under the heading Deep Level Outlet:

> There seems to be some mystery about this. This was, I believe, a scheme to connect the BBC stronghold with the GPO deep level communications system in London. The project was planned with the Post Office and was to be undertaken by them. It was originally expected to cost £36,000 (a figure of £20,000 has also been mentioned) but was abandoned in July 1955. We do not know why £5,000 was included as 1956–57 expenditure. Nothing has been spent up to 30th September 1956.

There is no factual evidence whether this new cable scheme was ever built. The BBC's written archives have not been able to trace any information and whilst British Telecom would know if it had laid cables in such a tunnel, it does not discuss matters relating to customers' private installations, meaning that the later history of the Deep Level Outlet remains an enigma.

More subterranean studios

Returning to World War II, the Stronghold was not the BBC's sole underground accommodation in central London. The growth of overseas broadcasting for presenting credible news reports and entertaining British forces abroad brought an urgent need for additional studio accommodation, preferably protected to avoid disruption by enemy bombing.

Among these studios were the Criterion Theatre (Piccadilly Circus), the Paris and Monseigneur news theatres (Waterloo Place at the bottom of Lower Regent Street and Marble Arch respectively) and a studio at Bush House belonging to the J. Walter Thompson advertising agency. All of these were underground and hence considered 'security areas'.

The Paris and Monseigneur studios were in sub-basements below ground level; the latter was used for programmes of the General Overseas Service such as *Marching On*. After Broadcasting House was bombed on 15th October 1940 the Criterion Theatre became the home of variety producer Cecil Madden – literally. After it was requisitioned by the BBC (all London theatres had been closed on government instructions), Madden and his Programme Assistant, Jill Allgood, not only worked there but also slept in the theatre. Her sleeping quarters were in a box next to the Royal Box, whilst her boss slept in the Upper Circle. Famous artistes who broadcast from the Criterion studios included Edmundo Ros and his band, also the singer Vera Lynn. It was also here that Petula Clark made her broadcasting debut. On the Saturday afternoon programme *It's All Yours* in October 1942 she was one of a party of children invited to record messages to relatives in the forces overseas. Although only nine years old, she asked to sing with the orchestra – and her wish was granted.

The Bush House studio of J. Walter Thompson had been opened in 1937 and was built specially for recording sponsored programmes broadcast on commercial stations such as Radio Luxembourg and Radio Normandy that sidestepped the BBC monopoly before the war broadcasting popular programming to Britain. It had been designed along the latest principles with no expense spared and was built below the building above a former basement swimming pool (its ceiling is a few feet below pavement level). The studio was acquired by the BBC in September 1940 and subsequently between January 1941 and March 1942 considerably more accommodation in Bush House (not all underground) was taken by the BBC. By the end of the war there were 15 studios in the building, which remained for sixty-odd years the hub of the BBC's World Service. The old JWT studio is known today as S16.

However, by far the most significant below-ground studio complex of the BBC during the war was at 200 Oxford Street, where the east block of Peter Robinson's department store was requisitioned in June 1941 for the BBC's overseas services (see endnote). Known operationally as the 'PR Building', the actual studios and control room were 50 feet below ground level in the basement, protected by heavy steel reinforcement applied to the floor and ceiling of the ground floor. Consid-

A central spine corridor runs the length of the Stronghold at Broadcasting House, with rooms on either side. Fluorescent striplights, seen in this recent photograph, are the only significant change to its fairly basic facilities.

[Roger Beckwith]

ered opinion has it that the studio had lines to Broadcasting House connected via the Central Line tube tunnels and Oxford Circus.

Creating a studio centre from scratch under war conditions was an immense challenge, but one to which BBC engineers responded with a degree of flexibility which managed to combine a utilitarian approach with a touch of imagination. L. G. Smith, mentioned above, was the engineer responsible for the planning and installation of the control room and studio equipment. He states:

> Before the war an installation of this size would have taken years rather than months since all equipment and interconnecting cables would have been individually designed. This was quite unacceptable in wartime. Many components were unobtainable; studio cubicle desks were made from office tables with plywood backs and sides. Microphone stands were derived from electric conduit components. Shortage of components was not the only problem; all circuits were lost when rats found their way into the microphone skirtings and bit through the lead covered cables to get at the wax inside. Nevertheless the whole installation, commenced in December 1941, was handed over for service for Overseas Programmes during May and June 1942.

For many reasons the PR Building was not an ideal location for broadcasting. Conditions were cramped, ventilation was poor and noise from passing trains was clearly audible on programmes. Pawley's official history of BBC engineering also mentions that the studios at 200 Oxford Street were so close to the tube tracks that the performers' ribbon microphones picked up a high-pitched hum caused by harmonics of rotary converter noise carried on the conductor rails.

One more underground (in both senses of the word) radio studio was that of ABSIE, the American Broadcasting Station in Europe. Operated under the auspices of the U.S. Office of War Information, this station went on air on 30th April 1944 as part of the Allied preparations for the invasion of Europe. Technical assistance was provided by the BBC, with a studio centre underneath Gaumont British offices at Film House, 142 Wardour Street in Soho. The station broadcast news, talk and music in many different European languages to promote the Allied message, initially to prepare the people of occupied Europe for liberation, then after D-Day to incite the foreign workers in Germany to sabotage the German war effort and finally, as the war neared its end, to urge the German people and armed forces to surrender.

ABSIE came to some prominence as the station that broadcast the remarkable 'lost' broadcasts in which the Glenn Miller Band broadcast in German to the Wehrmacht. The programmes were recorded at EMI's Abbey Road studios and introduced in German, with Miller himself reading from a phonetic script. Six half-hour programmes were recorded by the band and broadcast on Wednesdays starting 8th November 1944 as *Musik für die Wehrmacht* (Music for the Wehrmacht).

ENH identified

Mention was made of ENH, the BBC's wartime emergency news studio in Finchley. Its location was a private residence by the name of Kelvedon in Woodside Avenue, Finchley, N12. Houses in this road were not numbered in those days but a street directory indicates that *Kelvedon* was on the west side, the sixth house counting from the south end of the street. Roy Hayward (mentioned earlier) remembers and he recalls how he and his colleagues were required to take spending a night shift of four consecutive nights at ENH.

> Emergency News House was in the basement of a very anonymous looking but large Victorian house, set back from the road in its own splendid grounds at Woodside Park near Finchley in north London. It was rumoured that the house was 'allocated' to the Chief Engineer, Mr P. A. Florence, but I am not sure of this and I never saw anyone who lived in the house. It was permanently manned 24 hours a day by four engineers (following the four shifts A, B, C and D) and the same shift hour patterns.
>
> It was described to us as a place that could be used to continue broadcasting to the nation should BH become devastated by bombing. There were two studios, one of small 'news reader' size with a control cubicle underground in the basement, and another on the ground floor that was probably the drawing room of the house. It looked out over the garden through French doors and contained little furniture except for a middle-sized Challen baby grand piano. Underground in the basement was a control room – a long room with bays of jackfields and amplifiers carrying probably every network and programme service out of London. A small loudspeaker hung on the end wall and it was usually plugged during the night for us to hear Red Network being broadcast from 200 Oxford Street to America (I recall hearing Ed Murrow on several nights).
>
> There was an emergency electricity power and lighting Lister diesel generator that we were required to run up just before 06.00. I always thought that this time had been specially chosen to wake up the chief engineer upstairs and not before – but then we were very young! We were also required to do a full test on all the studio equipment and, on a nice early summer's morning after the test, I would put a mic out into the garden and relay to my shift brethren in LCR in the sub-basement of BH, the sounds of the dawn chorus. Other JMEs, more musically accomplished than me, would play that Baby Grand piano quietly!
>
> There was also another ENH located in the basement of a block of expensive flats in Grosvenor Square, diagonally across the square from the American Embassy. This was a single, unattended studio. It was always tested about 05.30 about once a month. The Senior Control Room Engineer would give one of the JMEs the keys to the entrance of the block of flats and the studio door, which was two floors down in the lift. The studio would be

This artistic lettering leaves no doubt about the Stronghold's date of construction
[Roger Beckwith]

already plugged at the 'Lines incoming' bay in LCR to a bay position and all the routine testing of the mic, the mic leads, the plug in the wall, the clock, the lights and the TD/7 record turntable (Teddy Bear's Picnic, the BBC's standard test record, was in the rack) would be done and, before switching off the power, a ring on the internal telephone to test it and to correct the clock time if necessary and finally check that all was well with the test. Then it would be a rush to catch the 73 bus along Oxford Street to Oxford Circus and report back to the SCRE to hand in the keys and sign that the studio had been tested. I can only remember doing this about three times in the three years I was in LCR. Perhaps it was taken out of service eventually. Then again we JMEs were not supposed to know everything that was happening – there was a war going on!

Old plans for a new war

Consideration of broadcasting under wartime conditions did not cease with the end of hostilities in 1945, as the advent of the Cold War soon proved. The result was the Wartime Broadcasting System (WTBS) scheme. Devised by the government in conjunction with the BBC, this new scheme was intended to maintain a radio service for informing the public during national emergency. The BBC report *Home Sound Broadcasting in War* dated July 1957 clarifies that the nucleus would remain in London, operating from the Stronghold until it becomes untenable or the seat of government leaves London. WTBS was thus seen to form an integral part of the government's civil defence strategy and in the event of hostilities would provide a single national programme of news and information during the transition to war period and post-attack.

ENDNOTES

London's New Radio City – a contemporary description of the unbuilt Broadcasting House extension

Excavation of the Portland Place site upon which Broadcasting House will be extended to more than double its current size is to begin in early 1939. More than a million cubic yards of earth will be removed and the depth to which the building will go – 54ft below pavement level – will be lower than the vaults of the Bank of England. Broadcasting House is probably London's deepest building. So large will be the volume of the pit, from which the superstructure will ultimately rise that it would have a capacity of nearly ten million gallons of water.

The architects are Messrs Val. Myer and Watson-Hart, FFRIBA, and Messrs. Wimperis, Simpson & Guthrie, FFRIBA, in association with Mr M. T. Tudsbery, MInstCE, the Civil Engineer to the Corporation. Messrs Higgs and Hill Ltd have been awarded the contract for the excavation and for the erection of retaining walls around the site, which has already been cleared. The work will be complete by about the middle of next year. Soon afterwards work will begin on the construction of the new building, which it is hoped will be ready for occupation by the end of 1940. This work will be the subject of a later contract.

The first stage of the present work will be the opening of a trench around the site, some thirty feet wide and fifty-four feet deep, in which self-supporting retaining walls will be constructed to withstand all external pressure. Asphalt will face these walls and will be returned, beneath them, and laid over the whole of the site. Five feet of 'loading concrete' will be superimposed upon it. The main structure, therefore, will virtually be built into a huge 'tank'.

The lower part of the tank will be below the standing level of subsoil water, a fact which will demand special measures to ensure that the asphalt seal is perfect at the junction of the new 'tank" with that of the existing building, to compensate for settlement when the weight of the new building comes to be taken upon the foundations. The site area at ground floor level is 20,950 square feet, compared with 17,390 square feet of the existing building.

The elevation – one of five schemes submitted – has been approved by the Royal Fine Art Commission. The architectural treatment of the extension will continue and amplify that of the existing facade to Portland Place, the two portions of the building forming a complete architectural entity that will be both dignified and in harmony with its surroundings.

Five underground studios will be incorporated in the extension, and, in order to eliminate all possible risk of extraneous noise, each will be constructed as a separate shell, floated and isolated from the building itself. A General Purposes studio will be 80ft long, 54ft wide and 30ft high. Three Dramatic studios, an 'Effects' studio and a number of rehearsal rooms are also being provided.

Above ground-floor level the extension is designed as an office building, with rather more accommodation than Broadcasting House has at present. A Control Room suite will be situated on the seventh floor and this will be in addition to the present Control Room. On the sixth floor will be a Staff Rest Room, while a restaurant with accommodation for nearly three hundred people is to be built on the top (eighth) floor. A light court will occupy the centre of the extension above first floor level; the building itself will have a maximum height of approximately 110 feet.

Department stores as offices

Earlier in this chapter it was noted that the BBC took over part of the Peter Robinson department store for office and studio accommodation. In fact the building also served as overflow accommodation for COSSAC, mentioned in Chapter 6. This was not a unique arrangement, either. The Air Ministry occupied part of the Harvey Nichols building, whilst the India Office took part of the Peter Jones department store. The U.S. Headquarters Air Service command occupied part of the John Lewis building.

Tunnel Vision

Farsighted facilities below ground for trains and trams

TRANSPORT facilities played a vital role in winning the war and it is only natural that the mechanisms that supported the unimpeded operation of these undertakings earn some mention in this book. Chapter 8 has already told the story of the deep-level accommodation at Down Street tube station that was constructed in anticipation of hostilities and later shared by the Railway Executive Committee and the Prime Minister 'for the duration'. The railway companies also used other underground facilities for ensuring the smooth running of trains and interesting tales can be told of London's tramway subway stations too.

Preparedness pays off

As part of their general 'preparedness' exercises during the late 1930s the four main line railway companies took strategic steps to ensure their continued functioning in war time. A joint body with the understated name of the Air Raid Committee considered how best to ensure the survival of operating staff under air attack and how best to keep the railway running in these conditions.

Dispersal of headquarters departments from London was part of this exercise and as a result, facilities were duplicated in country houses outside London, whilst safer locations were also found for the control offices so vital to directing and regulating traffic flows (these also reported to the Railway Executive Committee's overall movement control built in the old Down Street tube station, described in Chapter 8). In addition whole trains were assembled to create mobile offices, complete with manual telephone exchanges, ready for

To counter the risk of disruption from bombing all four main line railways relocated some of their headquarters office functions to places in the Home Counties outside the capital. Three of them chose country mansions, whilst the Southern took over the Deepdene Hotel near Dorking for its emergency HQ. Throughout the Second World War experts here planned the special trains for H.M. Forces including the evacuation of Dunkirk and the D-Day landing.

[Southern Railway publicity photograph]

dispersal across the system in case bombing destroyed important buildings, and expensive (if not exactly extensive) measures were taken to provide standby radio communication facilities if Post Office and railway trunk telephone lines were put out of use. To a large extent these additional means of last resort were not required but major use was made of the dispersed offices and underground control rooms.

Southern story

The Southern Railway chose for its emergency headquarters the former Deepdene Hotel near Dorking, with subsidiary locations at a mansion named Sitka in Southill Road, Chislehurst (close to Elmstead Woods station) and in part of the locomotive works at Brighton. Part of the Deepdene establishment was underground; *War On The Line*, the official Southern Railway war history says, "It has in its grounds a cave dug in the face of a hill, which was developed into a catacomb full of tables and telephones so that work could be carried on whatever happened overhead". Further detail can be found in the 22nd June 1945 issue of the *Railway Gazette*, which states:

Because of the natural protection resulting from these caves being surrounded on three sides, they were eminently suitable to house the telephone exchange serving the Southern Railway Headquarters, and for accommodating the key staff engaged in the control of traffic movements in emergency. As a safety precaution, a spiral staircase ascending through an escape shaft was provided to permit of exit in the event of either of the two normal exits being blocked. At their deepest point underground the caves are 60 ft below the surface. Above those rooms protected by a lesser depth of earth a concrete burster slab was provided to minimise the possibility of a bomb piercing the caves. The switchboard is a 'three-position' installation with Post Office lines, extensions serving the headquarters staff in the hotel, and direct lines to the headquarters of the various divisional traffic and engineering officers. The switchboard is open continuously through the twenty-four hours.

The night staff of the Operating, Motive Power, Chief Mechanical Engineer, and Chief Electrical Engineer's Departments worked in the caves, which accommodated a total of 30 clerks. In addition, the night officer was located in the caves so that he was in immediate contact with all the staff working there. Among the accommodation is included a meeting room suitable for any conferences which might have to be held under emergency conditions. The caves are equipped throughout with a ventilating plant, and the temperature of the air is regulated by radiators as it enters the rooms. Among the special features of the caves is the

exhibition of diagrams of all important junctions on the Southern Railway, thus enabling the staff to have immediate access to all information necessary to enable them to make emergency or alternative arrangements for any diversions of traffic necessitated by damage caused by enemy action. Each of the rooms is fitted with a radio receiving set for the reception, under emergency conditions, of any important Government announcements which might have been broadcast.

The caves just mentioned in casual terms were in fact a magnificent 18th century shell-encrusted grotto of a calibre rivalling the more famous examples at Stourhead, Goodwood and Goldney. The wall treatment changed abruptly from elaborate shell patterns to wartime concrete. The emergency staircase exit was topped with a classic witch's hat conical bomb deflector, a surprising feature in dense woodland.

Photos of Deepdene can be found in that magazine, in the Southern Railway's war history *War On The Line* and also in the book *Guildford to Redhill* (published 1989), which adds that the building and grounds had been purchased by the SR in 1938 for its wartime headquarters; use as railway offices ceased in 1966, when the staff were transferred to Southern House at Croydon. Deepdene was demolished in 1968. The Subterranea Britannica website reveals that the underground control centre, which housed an underground telephone exchange, consisted of a series of tunnels driven into the steep hillside to the rear of the house. There were three entrances plus a fourth emergency exit accessed from the hillside 50 feet above via a spiral staircase.

In addition to this overall headquarters location the Southern Railway established Divisional sub-offices at

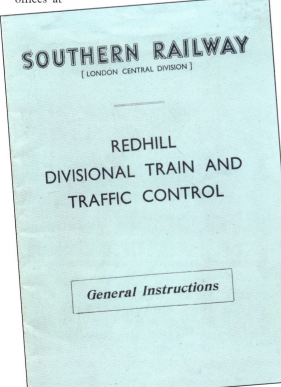

Woking, Redhill and Orpington, each with its reinforced underground chamber for the control staff. These HQ and Divisional control offices were kept busy taking executive decisions as to which trains had priority, allocating scarce motive power, rolling stock and staff resources and so on. They were provided with dedicated Control telephones to every signal cabin in their Division and to other strategic locations such as other control offices, main motive power depots, electrical control rooms and so on. Woking had separate desks for nine controllers and this figure is probably typical for the other offices. The building itself was a shallow buried affair, with two air-locked entrances. The control room itself was around 12ft across and 35 to 40ft long. Parallel to it were four smaller rooms containing telephone apparatus, ventilation plant, electrical control apparatus and an electrical substation.

Top: Control room in the caves of the SR headquarters at Deepdene before more elaborate communications equipment was installed in late 1942. At the deepest point the caves are 60ft below the surface. [Railway Gazette]

Above: Sleeping quarters for Deepdene's night officer with telephones for immediate contact. [Railway Gazette]

Left: Working instructions gave no clue to the underground location of divisional Control offices.

The protected above-ground railway control office at Bletchley (a similar structure stood at Willesden Junction but both were demolished long ago). The structure on top is a 'strong point' for last-ditch defence.

[LMSR publicity photograph]

Northern and western lines

The LMS Railway had a small emergency control room in tube tunnels underneath Euston station but its main wartime headquarters were at The Grove, a country mansion set in a park of 300 acres near Watford, Herts. Chief officers occupied the main house, with clerical staff accommodated in 32 wooden hutments in the grounds; the remains of the latter and the underground air raid shelters were still visible in the 1970s when the facilities had become a staff training college for British Railways. Its wartime control offices, such as those at Bletchley and Willesden Junction, were heavily protected but not placed underground.

The London & North Eastern Railway built hardened control offices at Gerrards Cross (GC lines), Knebworth (GN lines) and Shenfield (GE lines), also at Bawtry near Doncaster and Godley near Manchester. A country mansion, The Hoo, at Whitwell (near Hitchin, Herts.), served as wartime headquarters for the Chief General Manager of the LNE Railway.

Finally the Great Western Railway built an underground control centre 84ft below Paddington station in London. Although its location was not published for security reasons, it was in space belonging there to the Post Office Railway. It was dismantled soon after the war was over. Other underground control centres were built at Exeter, Plymouth, Bristol, Newport, Cardiff, Swansea, Gloucester, Worcester, Birmingham and Chester. Each was equipped with an air filtration plant and telephone exchange. The GWR company's general offices were dispersed to a number of locations in Berkshire, including Beenham Grange (near Aldermaston station), a number of new steel and brick buildings close to Aldermaston station and country houses in nearby villages. None of these country sites was below ground, however.

Communications considerations

Vital to the effective operation of these emergency headquarters and control rooms was the provision of telephone, telegraph and teleprinter facilities on a colossal scale, made all the harder by the shortage of materials and manpower and because most of the locations were not on railway land. Whilst the railways have always had the right to 'self provide' telecommunications apparatus and lines on their own land, the Post Office actively pursued its monopoly everywhere else. An undated Post Office memo written after the war was over reflects despondently that in the heat of the battle it was not always successful in exercising this monopoly. At Beenham Grange (Aldermaston) the GWR 'agreed to P.O. provision and maintenance on the position being explained' but the installation of the Southern's PBX at Dorking came to notice 'too late to take the appropriate steps' and was conditionally allowed to continue. The LNER was allowed 'exceptionally' to provide its own switchboard at Whitwell 'in view of the urgency of the requirement and the pressure under which the Department (the G.P.O.) was working at the time.' For the LMS 'search has been made but the relative papers cannot be located'. Despite the pique of the Post Office, the railways continued as normal doing their own thing, particularly at a time when the Post Office had virtually no spare men or apparatus!

Line communications were of course subject to disruption by enemy action and although the railways petitioned for the right to operate 'wireless' (radio) circuits as a back-up, the Post Office (as regulator of the airwaves) considered this unnecessary as the railways could use standby P.O. lines or despatch riders. After strong representations from the Railway Executive Committee the railways obtained in July 1940 what had been previously denied them, namely a small reserve of wireless apparatus. A hundred sets were allotted to the companies but since their effective range was only 50 miles, they would not cover the whole country. Around half of them were installed for mobile use on road vehicles or in rail parcels vans, whilst the remainder were installed at permanent locations. Not all of these were close to railway control rooms; poor reception conditions often made this impracticable, which meant the radio stations had to be linked to control offices by telephone and dispatch service. A policy laid down by the Postmaster General and the War Office ruled out speech transmission, except for the few words that established contact; operational messages were to be sent in a mixture of plain text and cipher using Morse code. The system was used only a few times under true emergency conditions but performed adequately then, whilst at other times staff practised their competence by transmitting routine messages.

An interesting sidelight on communications can be found in a secret War Office instruction of 20th May 1940, which authorized military officers to use railway telephone facilities 'in grave emergency'. The instruction gives a list of all railway headquarters and control office locations and how these can be connected through the Railway Executive Committee switchboard by private wire (dedicated circuit or tie-line) to the War Office.

Post-war policies

The end of hostilities in 1945 removed the need for protected control rooms and at Deepdene at least the equipment was soon relocated above ground in 1945. This policy was reversed twice subsequently. In the 'serious' Cold War period of the 1950s plans for underground facilities were made once more, only to be undone later, when mobile control trains were seen as the way forward, with work on the concrete blockhouses halted. In his work *Struggle for Survival* Steve Fox states:

> In the early 1950s, the British Railways planned to build 37 purpose built hardened controls with walls five feet thick as part of their 'due functioning' preparations. In practice, money was short and only one was actually completed. By the early 1960s, the idea had been abandoned in favour of using the peacetime control system with railway liaison officers at regional and county controls supplemented by Mobile Emergency Controls to take over if the peacetime Divisional controls could not function. Two such emergency controls each consisting of four coaches were proposed for each British Railways region. Detailed planning started in 1961 but in the tradition of civil defence work they were not operational until 1967. They were all scrapped by 1980 having largely been forgotten for many years. One perhaps apocryphal story tells of one such set of coaches marooned inside its sealed shed for many years after the track connecting it to the main line had been taken up. As with many plans for many organisations the railways also ran into problems with emergency communications, notably how they would be paid for.

The re-assessment just mentioned in fact came in 1962/63, when the fixed control installations were abandoned and their equipment transferred to mobile emergency control offices built into trains stabled at strategic locations. By that time only a few of the concrete surface bunkers for use in the event of nuclear attack had been built, one being at Bricket Wood. The building, now used for storage by a local builder's merchant, was located next to the station on the Watford to St Albans line (this unlikely location was chosen apparently because of the proximity of trunk telephone lines, the same reason that the massive concrete Thames North emergency standby electrical control centre of the National Grid (now demolished) was built nearby at How Wood).

Another protected railway control office finished before the change in policy was at Knebworth alongside the East Coast main line in Hertfordshire (now flattened). At Shenfield (Essex) only the foundations were completed. The site remains with the steel reinforcement rods protruding, just as it was left in 1957.

Tramway tales

Like several other facilities described in this book, the Kingsway Tram Subway has led more than one life. It started – and ended – life as part of London's transport infrastructure but also performed some unconnected and less well-known roles in between. It was also the role model for a second tram subway

that, had it come to pass, would have been closely connected with the Northern Line tube improvements in south London.

The Kingsway Subway is a remarkable survivor and dates back to 1906. Running below ground from the Victoria Embankment, around the Aldwych and along Kingsway, it emerges in Southampton Row a little south of the junction with High Holborn. The southern portal is an arch below one of the arches of Waterloo Bridge, whilst access at the northern end is via a steeply inclined ramp in the middle of the road (both entry portals can still be seen today and the rails of the tram tracks are still clearly visible in the northern approach ramp). The subway's dimensions are 16ft 6in high and 20ft wide; it lies at a depth of 30ft and is three-fifths of a mile long.

Inside the tunnel, tramway stations with platforms not dissimilar to tube stations were

A tram ascending the slope at the northern entrance of the Kingsway tram subway in the early 1930s. The ornate lamp columns and the two-aspect colour light signal that controlled trams entering the tunnel have long since disappeared but the ramp and tracks remain, more than 50 years after trams last ran here and probably the last place in central London where tramlines are still visible.

The glazed bricks, island platform and tram tracks are still evident in this present day photograph of Holborn station. In the background is the cabin of the former GLC flood control centre, dwarfed by the tall ceiling that once accommodated double deck trams. [Nick Catford]

provided at Aldwych and Holborn, approached by steps from road islands in the centre of Kingsway. Aldwych was just south of where the northern exit of the Strand Underpass comes to the surface today, whereas the entrance to Holborn station was outside the tube station at a spot marked by a radio antenna tower today. The subway was provided for the exclusive use of trams (other vehicles were prohibited) and opened in 1906. Between 1930 and 1931 the subway was enlarged to take double-deck trams and continued in use until the last tram ran through the subway on 5th April 1952. Further information, track plans and many photos can be found in an excellent booklet entitled *London's Tramway Subway*, which many readers will find extremely interesting.

The subsequent history of the subway is less well documented. Part was reputedly used as a store for

gas masks and in the coronation year of 1953 it served as parking area for 120 reserve buses. A proposal for permanent use as film studios was turned down on account of fire risks, although the subway was used to represent a railway tunnel during the making of the film *Bhowani Junction* in 1955. In that same year London Transport invited applications for the use of the tunnel as a store for non-inflammable goods, and finally leased it in October 1957 to S. G. Young & Co. of Blackfriars as a store for machine parts. A number of visits were arranged for tramway enthusiasts after this, during which it was noted that telephones in the inspectors' room at Holborn were still connected.

New uses

Following this, in June 1958, the London County Council expressed interest in taking over the subway to mitigate the traffic jams that then frequently extended across Waterloo Bridge. Part of the subway, from the north side of Waterloo Bridge to just north of the Aldwych, was converted for use by cars and single deck buses to avoid the congested road junctions between the Strand and Kingsway and around the Aldwych. Known as the Strand Underpass, it was opened on 21st January 1964 by Lord Morrison (whose original notion it was to use it for relieving traffic congestion). The new road tunnel was constructed as a box within the former tram subway leaving a narrow passage outside the box on one side of the ramp leading down from Lancaster Place. This passageway, which contains wires and cabling, emerges into the wider storage area at the Waterloo Bridge portal. The underpass also had the distinction of being the last place in central London – to our knowledge – to retain the pre-Continental style of pictorial road signs, long after they had been replaced everywhere else.

There were schemes also for the northern end of the subway. A scheme for redeveloping Holborn unveiled in January 1963 by the mayor of Holborn was conceived by the architect R. A. Cook; it proposed an underground subway with shops in the old tram tunnel. It was not proceeded with, however, and it lay dormant until 1975 when it was home to the Greater London Council's London Flood Control headquarters (its closure in 1985 followed the opening of a new control room at the Thames Barrier site). It was contained in a pair of portable cabins just inside the northern portal of the subway, on the western side. The control centre was manned at times of flood threat, including over at least one Christmas period, and much of the debris left after one Christmas party remained long after the event. All this activity was out of sight of the public and the only evidence on the surface was a conspicuous tower supporting VHF radio antennas and a television receiving aerial. Another use of the centre took place during the fire brigade strike of 1977 when army fire personnel and 'Green Goddess' fire engines were controlled from a temporary underground command post here at Holborn.

According to researcher Duncan Campbell it was no coincidence that the army's own flood control centre was then housed at the disused British Museum tube station nearby. In *War Plan UK* he said that in the event of peacetime flooding of London, the London district military command would operate from here rather than the wartime AFHQ 5 armed forces headquarters at Beaconsfield.

After 1984 the sole use of this part of the subway was for the storage of street signs and road materials by the London Borough of Camden, in the far north end of the tunnel. When visited by members of Subterranea Britannica in 1996 and 2003, this section of the subway, including Holborn station, was found to be in good condition with the twin tram tracks intact throughout. Strand station was demolished during the construction of the

Strand Underpass, although traces of it are still visible beneath the up ramp. The portable cabin for the flood control centre was still in place, stripped of all fixtures and fittings. The southern end of the subway, fronting on the Embankment, is used for storage.

The Croydon Tramlink of 1950

If the construction of deep tube shelters along the route of the Northern Line during World War II bolstered hopes that pre-war schemes for increasing the capacity of the 'misery line' would soon come to fruition, they did not last long. Chapter 13 told of the rapidly waning enthusiasm for this proposal but it was not the only suggestion for improving travel conditions south of the Thames. In 1950 the Tramway Development Council revealed an equally radical plan, arguably more revolutionary than those planned Northern Line improvements or the Croydon Tramlink scheme opened 50 years later.

Laid before the public was a plan for a rapid transit tramway running at surface level and below ground along a corridor from Purley and Croydon to a major new transport interchange at Kennington Oval. Here the 'rail coaches' would interconnect with Northern Line tube trains to the City and West End, also with a future extension of the rapid transit line to Victoria, Marble Arch and Paddington.

The 1950 scheme anticipated Tramlink in almost every respect. The line would create reserved tracks for street running, with tunnels and flyovers to avoid traffic pinch points. Stopping places would be spaced further apart than with other modes of street transport, provided with small platforms and shelters for use in adverse weather. More elaborate stations would be provided at rail interchange points, including a substantial underground tram station in central Brixton where Acre Lane and Coldharbour Lane cross Brixton Road and Brixton Hill. An interchange station in cutting below street level was to give interchange at Oval tube station.

Twin-coach trams would be made up of long single-deck carriages (rail coaches) with a high power-to-weight ratio and rapid acceleration. Plenty of space would be provided for standing passengers, whilst resilient rubber wheels would reduce noise. Grass and flower borders would help make the reserved track sections more attractive and neat fencing would ensure pedestrians did not stray into the path of high-speed trams. A more elaborate development of this scheme covering more of south London appeared in *The Modern Tramway* for July 1950.

Regrettably none of this came to pass. In this era of austerity there was simply no money for major new capital investment, whilst the scheme also suffered the handicap of not emanating from London Transport itself. Nonetheless its technical conception was first class, as proved by the subsequent Croydon Tramlink, and to this day the Brighton Road corridor in south London still desperately needs transport improvement.

The Structures Today

A brief status report

THIS chapter brings up to date what has so far been a largely historical account and sets out the fate of the facilities and structures described so far. In one form or another many of them remain in use, although their bombproof protection capabilities are long surpassed. Although the best citadels of World War II (Curzon Street House, Montagu House Annexe, etc.) had been built to withstand a direct hit by 500lb S.A.P. (semi armour-piercing) bomb, just a decade and a half later the power of the H-bomb made a mockery of this, as a report of 1954 for prime minister Winston Churchill demonstrated. Written by William Penney, director of the Atomic Weapons Research Establishment at Aldermaston, it stated that a five-megaton H-bomb dropped on London would produce a fireball two miles across plus a crater three-quarters of a mile wide and 150 feet deep. The 'undemolishable' Admiralty Citadel would be crushed at a distance of one mile, houses would be wrecked three miles away and badly damaged at seven miles; within a radius of two miles all habitations would catch fire.

Paddock

The Paddock bunker at Dollis Hill was used as laboratory accommodation by the Post Office until the early 1950s and then fell into disuse (it provided makeshift sleeping quarters for staff who missed the last bus home though). During the 1960s it was refurbished and restored to use as office accommodation for the expanding Post Office research station. At this time one of the men installing new fluorescent lighting came upon a coat hanger marked Winston Churchill but considered it a legpull and gave it away. By 1970 the bomb-resistant doors on the escape routes were giving cause for concern and when one jammed, the order was given to remove them. As they were cut up on the spot, one was found to contain a letter concealed by a Guard Commander of the Middlesex Regiment in which he speculated when it might be found, guessing 100 years later. He was wrong by 75 years!

In the early 1970s a visitor noted some tatty furniture and other bits and pieces remaining but little paperwork, probably due to the damp. The curator of the Cabinet War Rooms later went up to reclaim whatever he could. The actual research station establishment that occupied the Dollis Hill complex moved to Martlesham Heath in Suffolk in 1975 (now named Adastral Park by British Telecom). A derelict site remained, and by 1999 the

Thanks to annual 'Open House' showings, the one-time reserve War Cabinet War Room at Dollis Hill, codenamed Paddock, now receives far more visitors than in its heyday. A party of intrepid explorers are seen inspecting the solid construction of the bunker, led by Nick Catford of the study group Subterranea Britannica.
[Charles Brookson]

main buildings had been demolished and replaced with up-market town houses. The entire site now belongs to the Network Housing Association, which is in charge of development. So far as the Paddock bunker is concerned, it too is derelict, having been stripped out partially. The entire ventilation plant remains intact as does the standby generator, some GPO racks and a few signs on the walls indicating location, floor and so on. The bunker itself is on two levels, subsequently coded Floor 27 and Floor 28 (rumours of another 26 floors below ground are fantasy!). The lower of these floors became flooded in part to a depth of a foot once the pumps had been switched off but is now dry again. The two main corridors are about 120ft long with numerous rooms on both sides.

Reportedly the planning permission insisted on the retention of the bunker, so it was left untouched with two access points retained. One is an unobtrusive steel door in a wall between two houses (actually in someone's front garden) and the other beside the road in a brick blockhouse that also houses a small electricity sub-station. A loophole or embrasure is still visible in the wall. Lighting has been installed in the underground section and public access is normally made available on London's 'Open House' days held annually in September. Entry on these occasions is down a spiral staircase from the door between the two houses mentioned above.

Station Z and Insurance Party Building

The surface buildings of Station Z at Wealdstone, constructed in the standard Ministry of Works 'Georgian' style in red brick with tall sash windows, were demolished during the mid-1990s together with the adjoining HMSO printing works to make way for a new industrial development. A landmark on top of the building was a standard Home Office lattice tower bristling with radio antennas; this was a reminder of its use during the 1980s as a repair base and special projects workshop for the Home Office directorate of telecommunications when it was known as their London Region Building. The lower of the two basements was permanently flooded at this time. Not far away, in Cricklewood, the Admiralty's Insurance Party building still stands, now used as a carpet warehouse, although *Secret London* states it was brought back into use in 1982 for the Falklands War.

Deep shelters

The deep shelters are all still in being, used mainly for secure archiving. A long period of inactivity (care and maintenance) ended in a change of policy in 1975. This saw the government endeavouring to recoup some of its investment by leasing all the shelters (except Kingsway, which was then still actively in use as a telephone exchange) to commercial tenants. The Property Services Agency placed advertisements in London and national papers worded: 'Former Tube Shelters in Central London to be Let'. Leases on the seven shelters,

each having a floor space of 94,000 sq feet (8,900 sq metres), and 'the highest security' were offered for 'commercial or other uses'. Duncan Campbell notes that a clause in the proposed lease reserved the government's right to resume occupation if the need arose.

Uses for these properties took some time to materialise. Camden Town was used as a set for the *Doctor Who* and *Blake's Seven* television programmes. A more permanent tenancy came in 1977 when the data storage company Security Archives Ltd (founded in 1976 and renamed Recall Total Information Management in 1999), took possession of the deep shelter at Belsize Park, later leasing also Camden Town and Goodge Street (in 1986). The first two are now operated by Abbot Data, whilst branding has been removed on the signs at Goodge Street. Subsequently Clapham Common was let at various times to Data Management Services Ltd and Britannia Data Management, whilst Clapham North remained vacant.

The *Evening Standard* reported on 6th November 1978 a plan to use Goodge Street as a document store for the British Library but no more was heard. From 1980 to 1994 the National Sound Archive, now part of the British Library, did, however, keep all security copies in the Belsize Park shelter. Other occupants of this deep archive included prominent merchant banks, solicitors, accountants and North Sea oil companies. The Goodge Street shelter was subsequently christened 'The Eisenhower Centre' by its new tenants and was commissioned for use by them in June 1986.

The east entrance in Chenies Street of 'The Eisenhower Centre', as the Goodge Street shelter is now called. The cream paint with red stripes is now fading rapidly and arguably looks worse than surface buildings at other sites that have been allowed to weather naturally. Note the war memorial 'trapped' inside the security fence.

[Nick Catford]

Afterwards options were taken on two shelters at Stockwell and Clapham South. Goodge Street, with its location convenient for the media companies of Soho and Fitzrovia that cluster around the Telecom Tower, soon found itself a major archive for security copies of video tapes, films

Many deep shelter shaftheads have been defaced by graffiti but at Stockwell imaginative murals have turned a potential eyesore into an artistic feature. [Jonathan James]

and audio masters belonging to record firms, Channel Four Television and a variety of independent production companies. More than 1.5 million video tapes were stored there by 1989, with access provided to clients 24 hours a day, 365 days a year. Protecting this empire were an air conditioning plant, halon gas fire suppression systems, fire doors, dust filtration equipment along with humidity and temperature controls. Smoking, eating or drinking down below meant instant dismissal for staff, such was the strictness of control. Subsequently Security Archives quit its shelters and Britannia Data Management relocated to new premises at Earls Colne, near Colchester.

A Parliamentary question in December 1997 was doubtless intended to be serious, even if it sounds faintly comic.

> MR. HANCOCK: To ask the Secretary of State for Defence if the Clapham Deep Shelter still exists.

The reply, dated 19th December and written in the name of the Chancellor of the Duchy of Lancaster, stated:

> Seven Deep Tube Shelters are now managed by Property Advisers to the Civil Estate, PACE. There are three tube shelters at Clapham; they are at Clapham North, Clapham South and Clapham Common. The last two are let for storage, the first is vacant. PACE are at the moment in the process of disposing of all seven Deep Tube Shelters. We have conducted an informal tender and hope shortly to conclude a sale.

Following this, all the shelters but Chancery Lane (which is still in the hands of British Telecom) were put up for sale by estate agents Lambert Smith Hampton in 1998. This time they were purchased by London Transport. The annual report and accounts for 1997/98 announced that the seven shelters had been purchased during the year "to assist with the

upgrading of the Northern Line". An informed interpretation of this rather ambiguous statement is that it refers to minor building works at stations involving electrical improvements and staff accommodation. Where needed, these could be provided in the former shelters, avoiding the need for new tunnelling, and the modernisation of Camden Town station is one location where this might happen. In addition, London Transport now benefits from any rental income provided by companies using the shelters for archive storage.

Goodge Street was seen to be bustling on a television filming visit in February 2000, much of the accommodation being given over to archiving audio and video tape. All the 4,000 remaining bunks have been removed and every available space is occupied by Dexion racking (it appeared completely full). All the side tunnels (toilets, warden's quarters, kitchens and first aid room) have been converted into private 'vaults' for personal storage by commercial organisations and extremely well-to-do individuals. The connection to the tube station has been bricked off. All the canteens (including the 'long bar' with bar stools) have gone. The Lamson pneumatic tube terminals have been partly dismantled and the tubes removed. The 1950 to 1955-era graffiti drawn by National Service squaddies are intact. Most interestingly the vault in Zone 10 leading to the drop to the BT cable tunnel was locked, had no identification on the door (unlike the other vaults) and was expunged from their plans, yet they must have a covenant with BT to allow emergency access/escape.

At Clapham North, the Bedford Road access has been cleared and the station staff park their cars there. Internally the shelters are reasonably clean, although the paint is peeling off most of the metalwork. All toilet facilities have been removed. Some of the lighting on the spiral stairs has failed and around a third of the shelter lighting is out. The main public entrance on Clapham High Street next to the station is bricked up.

A technician working in Clapham Common station noted that the power supply to the deep shelters was fed from slate switchboards and via ducts in the cavernous inverts below the platforms there. He remembers viewing the boards and knife switches with interest as they were marked 'Govt Tunnel No. 1, No. 2, No. 3 and No.4,' although long since disconnected.

Chancery Lane (Kingsway exchange) was not bought by London Transport and is awaiting clearance, ready for intended disposal. The site was first offered for sale by British Telecom in 1996 but successive attempts to sell the underground accommodation as a shelter for the homeless failed. Notice was given in November 2000 of the intention to demolish the surface buildings at Kingsway's rear entrance in Took's Court and a year later this work began. In early January 2002 the 10ft walls and roof were putting up a keen fight to the demolition contractors but succumbed in time. To minimise disturbance to people in nearby offices, acoustic shielding was provided and a mechanical digger used rather than pneumatic drills. The shaft was to be capped once the area had been dug out to form the basement of the new building taking its place.

For the Southwark Borough Council shelter no use was ever found after the war and work began in November 1959 to reinstate the tunnels to their former state, ready for handing back to London Transport. All structures above floor level of the tunnels were demolished and waterproof concrete plugs constructed in the access passages. The work was completed in June 1960 and no trace of the entrance portals remains now.

Former tube stations

The surface buildings of the tube station at Brompton Road still stand and although the frontage of the building was removed in the early months of 1972 for road widening, the side profile is still clearly visible in Cottage Place. The remaining building is owned by the Ministry of Defence, maintained by the Territorial Army and used by the University Air Squadron and the University of London Naval Unit. Many features remain at track level; this section is owned by London Underground and access between the two sections is barred. Visits by the public are disallowed on grounds of safety and security and the potential danger was proven a few years ago when someone attending an air squadron function plunged to his death down one of the lift shafts. Conducted tours of the facilities have been arranged in the past but it is understood that current health and safety regulations make further trips unlikely (instead a 'virtual tour' is offered on the LT Museum website and indeed on the websites of a number of other enterprising individuals – see *Sources of Information* at end of book).

At Down Street the building remains at street level as well as some sub-surface features. A visit by one of the authors revealed that although the offices in the lower subway remained intact in 1986, including the historically most interesting committee room, the whole lot has now been swept away and the subway returned to a long, bare, empty subway. There was foul-smelling penetration in the bathrooms in the upper subway, and the whole of the platform level offices had been painted a uniform battleship grey. An interlocking machine room for the signal department has replaced the staff dormitory. Passengers hoping to spot the station from passing trains do so only with great difficulty since the platforms have been bricked off. The station does, however, retain two entries in the London Transport internal telephone directory, being provided with telephone there for the interlocking room and maintenance use. The temporary signals were removed when the station's use as a shelter was no longer required.

At surface level nothing remains of British Museum station; the booking hall and offices above were demolished to facilitate redevelopment in 1989. Clearance of shelter fittings began on 10th August 1945 and in 1947 the shelter was dismantled completely. The walls separating the station area from the running lines were taken down and the surface building and basement restored to their former state for reoccupation. A few poster notices remain as evidence of its wartime use. According to Duncan Campbell the station building was being used in 1982 as an administrative office for the Scots Guards, with a potential use in time of flooding by the London District Military Command. Building work at the surface has cut access to track level and the former lift and staircase shafts are stated to have been filled with concrete as part of the foundations for the new office building that has replaced the original surface entrance to the station. It is notable (and not coincidental) that the Army's operations centre was to have been close by the GLC's flood centre in the Kingsway Subway (mentioned in Chapter 18). The premises fronting the street pavement were adapted for retail use, latterly photographic and clothing shops, also a café.

At Post Office all that remains is a ventilation shaft in the middle of a road island, all other features having been swept away for redevelopment many years ago. Nearby is British Telecom's headquarters building, the BT Centre, which was built on the site of the old Central Telegraph Office that had been badly damaged during the war. Construction started in 1980 and the building opened in 1984. A shaft from the deep level stands on the site but it is understood this is capped, without any connection from the tunnels to the building. At planning stage it was envisaged that the building would have its own entrance to the sub-surface booking hall of St Paul's station but this was cancelled on cost grounds.

South Kensington blockhouse

After the war the bunker was sealed and remained so until 1970, when the land was required for an extension to the Natural History Museum (which incorporates the old Geological Museum). Because of the difficulty in demolishing the building, it was incorporated into the new extension with further storeys added above the roof and another building added to the front of the bunker (the use of explosives was vetoed and the alternative of chipping away at the bunker would have resulted in many months' delay and huge expenditure). The rear wall was clad in brick in line with the rest of the new extension and is no longer recognisable. Construction around the bunker took three years and was completed in October 1975. Official opening of this east or Palaeontology wing finally came in May 1977.

During the new development the original entrance tunnel was removed, with the area between the old Geological Museum and the new extension becoming a service road. The bunker, known today as the War Room, is now accessed at either end by stairs in the new extension. Its present use is by the museum's palaeontology department and two large rooms, running the length of the bunker are now stacked with movable shelving containing boxes of human bones excavated from sites around the country. The bunker also provides vibration-free conditions for microscopy work, and a plant room serving the whole museum is also here.

Deep tunnels

British Telecom's deep level cable tunnels are not something that the company discusses but they are still very much in use. Unlike the 'mothballed' Post Office Railway, there are no plans to cease using the cable tunnels although BT has stated that it is unlikely that new tunnels will be built (*POEEJ*, October 1981). During the 1990s the company allowed organised visits to Kingsway exchange on several occasions after its closure, but the tunnels themselves are totally out of bounds and will remain so. The company tried, unsuccessfully, to interest the Shelter charity in using the Kingsway facility as lodgings for the homeless, but there are problems relating to asbestos removal and water ingress, so its future remains problematic. Major road works carried out in High Holborn on behalf of BT during early 2003 were not connected with the exchange, as some observers thought. A broad concrete raft protecting the pneumatic dispatch parcels railway, first built in the second half of the 19th century and now used as a conduit for telephone cables, was disintegrating and starting to subside. This was not the first time the tunnel had caused problems; back in December 1933 a gas explosion inside it blasted through almost half a mile of solid tarmac reducing the thoroughfare into a twisted trail of rubble.

As far as the Whitehall tunnel is concerned, it was stated with contention a few years ago that this was disused and totally impassable. On the other hand the authors of the book *London Under London* indicate that the first part of the tunnel under Whitehall is in good preservation but the extension to the Rotundas is damp-ridden and had in fact flooded in March 1983. It was not pumped out for three weeks as no government department was prepared to accept responsibility. If an unconfirmed report in the *Sunday Telegraph* of 30th April 2000 is correct, then the tunnel has been refurbished and turned into high-security offices for the government, although exact details have been shrouded in secrecy, even from civil servants, ministers and MPs. Work was expected to take nine months to complete, with new tiling and fire doors installed along the walls of the tunnel. In small offices opening onto the tunnel every 200 yards workmen were installing computers and video surveillance cameras. As no official denial or confirmation followed the publication of this story readers must put their own interpretation on it.

Cabinet Office Briefing Room

In the Cabinet Office basement and linked to the construction described above, is a construction of recent times named COBRA. This facility is described in the press as 'the Government's national emergency management room beneath the Cabinet office in Whitehall' and fulfilling the same role as the White House situation room in the US capital. It is opened at times of crisis such as the Stansted hijacking and fuel crisis in 2000, the foot-and-mouth outbreak and World Trade Centre outrage of 2001; also the firemen's dispute of 2002. The initials embody the name Cabinet Office Briefing Room A and the same name is given to the special committee that meets there (amusingly another government COBRA acronym is the Co-Ordinated Briefing and Rebuttals Advice knowledge management system of the DTI, a derivation that some might find equally apt for the other COBRA!). According to *The Guardian* (8th February 2001), the team comprises members of the government's civil contingencies unit, activated (by radio pager) to co-ordinate security emergencies. COBRA is made up of senior civil servants from the home office, the foreign office and the transport department as well as MI6, MI5, and Scotland Yard's anti-terrorist branch, and is chaired by a senior Home Office official.

The location itself is described by Sir Peter de la Billiere in his autobiography *Looking for Trouble* as 'an undistinguished rectangular room without windows, up to twenty-five people sat round a long table, with nothing to distract them but a battery of television sets mounted above head level and, on one end wall, a digital clock with small flaps, one of which tumbled down with a snap every time a minute ticked by,' equipped additionally with two bullet-proof doors according to Rachel Sylvester in *The Independent* (4th April 1999).

Cabinet War Room

After the facility was closed on 18th August 1945 the lights were dowsed and the doors locked, with everything left intact and undisturbed until an announcement in Parliament in 1948 ensured their preservation as an historic site. Because no cleaners' passes were issued, apparently through bureaucratic error, the place afterwards became so filthy that when re-use was mooted during the Suez crisis of 1956, its potential occupants took one look and thought better of it.

In recent times restricted public access was possible, although few were even aware of the existence of this previously top secret installation. A change came in 1981 when the Prime Minister, Margaret Thatcher, decided that the site deserved greater recognition and should be opened to the public. Over the next three years the Imperial War Museum and the Department of the Environment arranged for the careful preservation and restoration of the complex, also adapting the place for visitors.

The facility is now open to the public daily, with entry at Clive Steps, King Charles Street, SW1 (telephone enquiries 020 7930 6961). A £7.5 million project will treble the size of the existing museum and create public access to rooms hidden for nearly 60 years. During 2003 some rooms inaccessible for 55 years were opened, including the Churchills' private kitchen, dining room and Mrs Churchill's bedroom, using original furniture found in rooms that had been used for storage.

Telephone Network (GTN) we mentioned earlier in this book. The equipment racks and MDF were on the lowest level with the switchboard room above and offices on the top level. There was also an administrative centre here.

During the 1970s the South Rotunda became the Civil Service sports and social club, offering a wide range of facilities including cricket nets, a boxing ring, snooker, karate, judo, theatre/cinema, table tennis, rifle range, disco and numerous bars. This remained in use until the 1990s, as did a suite of rooms in the South Rotunda that was refurbished as a control centre for emergency situations arising in any Government offices in Westminster or in the

A civil service volunteer records hypothetical nuclear strikes on a wall chart at an air raid training school, deep underground in central London. That's the official caption for this photograph, dated June 1961, when the North Rotunda location could not be revealed for security reasons. [Hulton Archive]

Rotundas and Horseferry Citadel

Strategic use of the Rotundas declined after hostilities ended in 1945, with the buildings allocated to a number of government departments. The South Rotunda was first used by the Air Ministry as a hostel, then as office space for the RAF Film Unit in July 1946 and the Ministry of Information the following year. Another newcomer in 1947 was a section of the Government Communications Bureau, relocated from Broadway Buildings in Westminster, and in 1951 the Air Commodore Director of Weapons moved in.

Twelve years after the site had been requisitioned, the government finally acquired the entire site from the North Thames Gas Board in 1952 to build new office accommodation. A new four-storey building was erected after the remains of the steel-framed building were demolished, retaining the citadel below. The Rotundas were also saved as they were considered to be proof against the atomic bomb and by the late 1950s the North Rotunda had a role as the central government war room network. In 1962 it featured under the code name Chaplin as communications centre for the nuclear war exercise known as Fallex62. Another facility here was a Royal Observer Corps air raid training school, which remained in use into the 1960s. In the 1960s the North Rotunda became home to Federal telephone exchange and subsequently to the Horseferry Tandem, the central switching point in the Government

rotundas themselves. Around 1990 an access way was cut from the South Rotunda into the former gas company control room known as the Crescent Room; this was to accommodate the government's regional control centre RGHQ 6.1, which moved here from Crowborough in 1992.

Until demolition in 2003 the basement level of the South Rotunda also contained the plant room for the two buildings with a large air scrubber (unused for years because of the risk of Legionnaire's disease) and three big generators. One of the last uses of the North Rotunda was by British Telecom in 2001 for the removal of asbestos after cleaning their tunnel network.

A visit by Subterranea Britannica members in February 1999 passed through one part of the North Rotunda where their guide indicated that MI5 had listened into telephone intercepts. There was enough floor area to accommodate a few dozen staff and these rooms had been cleared with particular thoroughness. Most of the others left some clue as to their function, but here all the observers could see were the marks left by desks on the floor.

Between 1963 and 1971 a vast office block was built above (and incorporating) the Rotundas for use as government offices for what became the Department of the Environment. Designed by the architect Eric Bedford in association with Robert Atkinson and Partners, the structure was built to provide 450,000 sq ft of office space for some 3,600

Watch it come down! A northward glimpse along Monck Street shows the DoE Office block that was built above the Rotundas and Horseferry Citadel shrouded just before demolition. Part of the Citadel is nearest to the camera.

civil servants. The ground floors rested on stilts surmounting the original three citadels, whilst above them towered three slabs 200ft high. Five connecting wings projected to Marsham Street, where the entrance was. The complex was the largest single office building project in London before Canary Wharf in Docklands and in its day reflected the bold aspirations of its time, as did other monolithic structures such as the Post Office Tower (also designed by Eric Bedford) and Centre Point. As architectural fashions change, building styles are re-assessed and what was once considered exuberant is now seen as brutal or even grotesque. The Marsham Street Towers' days were already numbered when the Department of the Environment vacated them, moving to pastures new at Eland House, Victoria. Two years later in 2000 it was reported that the site had a value of around £200 million.

Although the offices were refurbished to provide a temporary home for the Home Office while its main site at Queen Anne's Gate was being renovated, they were declared unfit for further use and an 18-month deconstruction process began in late 2001 ready for redevelopment of the site – towers, rotundas and all. In early 2003 demolition work was at an advanced stage in preparation for a new £310 million headquarters block for the Home Office. On 11th March the *Daily Mail* reported,

> They've demolished the three 200ft towers in Marsham Street, Westminster, built during the 1960s, that housed the old Department of the Environment, but the old nuclear-proof bunker underneath is intact. "All the drills are bouncing off the three-foot-thick wall," says my source. "They are going to have to blow it up."

The bunker was by no means nuclear-proof. Another observer stated the company responsible for the demolition, Brown & Mason, had started to use explosives on the South Rotunda, also that it had taken almost as long to demolish half of the South Rotunda as it took to remove the Podium structures and the South Tower above. In fact only the upper portion of the Rotundas and Citadel are being removed; the lowest levels are not being demolished but filled with concrete to form a base for the new building on the site. One side of the Citadel building or 'Blockhouse' is to be retained as a retaining wall.

Other citadels

Unlike the Rotundas next door, the Horseferry Citadel retained some significance after 1945. Official information is thin on the ground, but it appears that the Citadel served as the central hub of the Regional War Room network, possibly only until the Central Government War Room was opened at Broad Sanctuary. The Horseferry citadel was in effect the government's central emergency headquarters, although the coming of the hydrogen bomb saw the Regional War Rooms replaced by Regional Seats of Government (RSG) in the 1960s, with a replacement central HQ at Corsham in Wiltshire. It resumed a significant role in the 1980s and 1990s, when it housed a naval communications centre and operations room that saw active service in both the Falklands Conflict and the first Gulf War.

The underground citadel at Broad Sanctuary was refurbished between 1979 and 1982 by the contractors Mowlem at a cost of £4.5 million, under conditions of high security. An article in the *New Statesman* of 20th June 1986 suggested this had become a phone tapping centre for GCHQ.

In theory the Admiralty citadel should have been demolished at the end of hostilities; a personal assurance had been given to King George VI to this effect since the building trespassed on a Royal Park. Ministry of Works correspondence in August and September 1958 noted that its demolition was physically impossible and only an Act of Parliament could legitimise its retention. On the other hand the cost of providing its communications and other specialist facilities elsewhere in a protected form would be very expensive. These, another document explained, included all the line terminations, cross-Channel and inland, housed in the Victoria and Trafalgar exchanges and under the Citadel, also the Lamson tube system used for speedy circulation of messages throughout the Admiralty. "Until the GPO and Admiralty can provide alternative facilities, the Citadel must remain," states a letter. Since that time the building has been awarded Grade II* listing by English Heritage and is now very much part of the landscape.

Curzon Street House housed several official departments during the war and immediately afterwards the War Department Prisoners of War Information Bureau. By 1974 the Department of Education was in occupation, followed by the Registry, Administration and Technical services departments of domestic Security Intelligence Service (MI5) from 1978 to 1995. It was demolished in 1996.

The Faraday Citadel and the telephone exchange inside it closed on 28th July 1989. Up to that time Citadel exchange handled outgoing subscriber trunk dialling calls from London using 4000-type Strowger apparatus installed in 1961.

Central Line extension

To allow work to begin completing the construction of the new railway, London Transport requested all local authorities to clear and vacate their air raid shelters by August 1945, later extended to October. Once this was achieved contractors then had the task of removing the concrete floors that obstructed tracklaying, and at Liverpool Street and Bethnal Green alone this task produced 10,000 cubic yards of debris. In July 1946 the spiral emergency staircase at the Carlton Square shaft was removed for scrap and the superstructure demolished. The ventilation fan, switchgear and water tank were saved for re-use.

Now marooned in the centre of a giant roundabout below the North Circular Road is this fan and pump house at Redbridge. During World War II it was one of the few outward signs of the Plessey factory that produced aircraft and communications components that helped win the conflict for Britain. Fresh paint shows it is still very much in use for Central Line trains.

[Duncan Hawkins]

A remarkable survivor of the wartime underground Plessey factory at Ilford is the still standing shafthead building on the south side of Eastern Avenue opposite Danehurst Gardens (photo on page 115). At Redbridge another shaft still emerges in the middle of the roundabout, where the new North Circular Road crosses Eastern Avenue. The shaft provides access to the pump room underground.

BBC studios

The Stronghold, together with its steel blast doors and the words 'BBC AD 1942' cast into the concrete of its approach ramp, survives and is now used by Radio Engineering Services for workshops and storage. Over the years the Stronghold has seen a number of alterations. At the end of the war its roof was partly removed to allow a car park to be built above it and subsequently the Broadcasting House extension has covered the remainder. Its use as a fallback studio location was over by the 1960s, when alternative reserve studio locations were provided should Broadcasting House have to be evacuated, and there are now no studio facilities in the Stronghold. The entire block surrounding Broadcasting House is due for redevelopment and this work may include the destruction of Stronghold.

Emergency News Headquarters, also known as Emergency News House (ENH), was located at a private residence in Woodside Avenue, Finchley, N12. According to local gossip, it had never been used in earnest and its wartime use was completely forgotten until its basement was uncovered during building work. Its site is now covered by newer housing.

The Monseigneur Marble Arch, one of about fifteen news theatres belonging to the J. Davis circuit, reopened again after the war and was later sold with the others to the Jacey group. The Paris studio, in Waterloo Place at the bottom of Lower Regent Street, was retained by the BBC. Many famous radio shows were recorded here before it finally closed in January 1994, including *Week Ending* and *The Hitchhikers' Guide to the Galaxy*.

The Peter Robinson building was sold after the war to clothing retailer C&A Ltd, becoming their flagship store and head office until the company ceased trading in Britain during 2001. The studios 'below stairs' were nonetheless retained by the BBC until the World Service moved to Bush House, vacating 200 Oxford Street in November 1957 (when this part of the building became a shop). Currently (spring 2003) it is an empty building with the ground floor gutted. Its façade still has dirty patches where the illuminated oval C&A signs were previously fitted.

Brent Building

Although earmarked for a vital role in defence communications, the building ended up becoming something of a white elephant and saw a number of subsidiary uses. Between 1949 and 1974 it housed the Post Office's radiotelephony terminal for overseas service under the name Brent Radio Telephony Terminal. This served the overseas (International) exchange, which opened in the Monarch ATE building on 24th November 1947.

By 1952, the Brent Building was home to the Gladstone Repeater Station L/GLA/B, the London Radio Telephone Terminal L/RTT, an MCVF Telegraph Terminal known as L/TSN and the London North Telegraph Auto. Switching centre (TASS) JXN. Then in 1976, when expansion of the ILTMS (International Leased Telegraph Message Service, later named Primex) was necessary, the accommodation was upgraded and pressed into service for this. This use ceased around 1982 although the building had a stay of execution, being used from 1986 to 1991 by London Payphones as a maintenance and customer care training centre, as well as base for the payphone modernisation programme. Nothing exists of the building, the site now being an overflow car park for the Brent Cross Shopping Centre.

St Paul's grid control centre

Sudbury House and the other structures of Paternoster Square erected in the 1960s have now been swept away in favour of a new 15,000 square-metre redevelopment by the Mitsubishi Estate Company, with office buildings, retail outlets and leisure accommodation as well as a new London Stock Exchange. Construction began in 2001 and completion is due by March 2004. So far as the old control centre is concerned, the brick ventilation shaft at the junction of Newgate Street and King Edward Street is now the sole visible reminder of the control centre. Road realignment means the former lift shafts are now entirely covered. Below ground some recent building works at landing level of the lift shafts have created additional electrical switchrooms and a communications equipment room. In the pit of one of the lift shafts is a very narrow spiral staircase leading to a subway painted in cream and green (or possibly blue) with a black dividing band running horizontally throughout, all flooded to a depth of a foot or more.

Kingsway Subway

The northern end of the former tram subway was sold in November 2003 to a commercial organisation that requested anonymity until its plans for developing the structure were ready for publication. The isolated southern end remains in use for storage.

Railway and electrical control rooms

A number of the wartime underground railway control rooms survive to some degree. After the surface buildings of Deepdene House were demolished, a modern office block was built on the site, occupied since 1990 as the headquarters of Kuoni Travel. A fire started just inside one of the entrance tunnels in 1997 by local children led to the discovery that the whole network of tunnels was heavily contaminated with asbestos. Following a survey of the tunnels all four entrances were sealed. In June 1999, a photographic survey was made by Nick Catford of Subterranea Britannica, with a detailed report posted on his website. Remains of the ventilation plant and ducting were found, along with rusting telephone racks and against one wall the remains of three floor standing switchboards. In the woods to the south of the site are three parallel lines of anti-tank pimples (dragon's teeth). Following this survey the concrete block wall across the emergency exit was made secure again and the company has made it clear that further requests for access will not be granted.

Part of the underground Control office at Orpington was used as a staff social club until the 1960s and is in reasonable condition. One of the rooms still contains many of its original desks, tables and shelves, albeit now in poor condition. The gas tight door from the bottom of the stairs is lying on the floor. There is some wording on the inside of the door *Air Lock – Upon receipt of the purple or red gas warning close all steel doors when entering or leaving the shelter. The first door must be closed before opening the second.* Behind one of the gas tight doors is a wooden rifle rack for six rifles that would have been used by the Home Guard. At the top of a short flight of steps is another gas tight door forming an air lock. Beyond this is the bricked up second entrance. All internal wooden doors have

been removed but some of them are leaning against a wall. The similar facility at Woking was already derelict and vandalised by 1981, whilst part of the Redhill office is used for storage by the permanent way engineering staff, who occupy a building above the bunker (the other underground rooms are flooded to a depth of 10 inches).

At Shenfield the World War II control block-house is still in use as office accommodation for a company called Spall Sports in Alexander Lane. The new owners, who have occupied the structure since 1972, have thoughtfully restored the blast shutters on the windows. As noted in Chapter 18, the mobile control trains are no more and by the time they finally came to be disposed of during the 1980s, both the rolling stock and the communications equipment inside were museum pieces. One carriage of this kind (from Craven Arms) is preserved on the Dean Forest Railway.

Of the eight blockhouse-style emergency Grid Control Centre rooms of the Central Electricity Generating Board, two were in the London region. Thames North, located at How Wood, near Bricket Wood, has since been demolished for a housing estate. It acted as back-up for Redbourn GCC, which was at Cumberland House, Redbourn. Thames South still stands in Imberhorne Lane, Felbridge, Sussex; it was built as the back-up for East Grinstead GCC.

Ventilation Tower for the Goodge Street deep level shelter, photographed in 2002. It is sited opposite Torrington Place.

Tales of Mystery – and Imagination

Fallacies and facts exposed

'NEVER believe anything until it has been officially denied.' So said writer and political activist Claud Cockburn, and he may well have been right. But although many elements of postwar political and security history are indeed open to dispute and denial, the subject matter of this book is not in contention, simply because it has not been discussed in detail before. Indeed, one of the reasons why a book of this depth (apologies for the pun!) has not been published before is obscurity – obscurity of the subject itself and of archival material relating to it.

Security is another factor; at the time of their construction many of the facilities described here were state secrets. Since then the passage of time, changing attitudes, the so-called peace dividend and other altered priorities have all forced a reassessment of the subject.

After the end of hostilities in 1945 the climate of opinion altered and in an outpouring of relief many of these wartime secrets were described openly in books and pamphlets with the general enthusiasm that pervaded all publications of the 'It Can Now Be Revealed' variety. Ironically the Cold War that followed soon afterwards brought with it the need for secrecy again.

Since then policy on openness has vacillated with the seasons. The Post Office invited the press to visit its system of deep level tunnels in 1968 and earned considerable news coverage in the process. Arranged visits to the underground Kingsway exchange were welcomed at the time too. Further press publicity was sought (and achieved) for extensions to the tunnels in the early 1970s but by 1980 this had all changed. The existence of the tunnels was now acknowledged but not discussed, enabling revelations such as Duncan Campbell's 'Mole Tour' in New Statesman to create a stir for the media as a whole and deep embarrassment for the Post Office, soon to become British Telecom. Interestingly, he was not charged with trespass, mainly because the Post Office claimed to the Press that the incident never took place and indeed could not have happened – and therefore didn't!

Peter Laurie's previous articles for the *Sunday Times* and his book *Beneath The City Streets* had already created a climate of public interest in 'secret subjects', and Duncan Campbell's *War Plan UK* together with a steady output of other revelations in *New Scientist* and *Computing* helped fan an emerging interest.

New ethos for a new era?

The admission in the 1990s that the Cold War was over spawned renewed media and public interest into 'secret' underground artefacts, which in turn swelled membership of the group Subterranea Britannica and its Cold War studies offshoot RSG, the Research Study Group. A number of excellent books, websites and bunker museums followed and our subject emerged at last from obscurity.

Bogus bunkers

With the new age of enlightenment came new fantasies. Peter Laurie generously acknowledged that some of his book was based on inspired guesswork – and to be fair, pretty intelligent guesswork backed up by meticulous research into books and papers then available for scrutiny. Other writers, however, have allowed the mystery and secrecy of the subject to lead them into wild speculation. Extracts from one individual's website illustrates this point nicely . . .

> . . . a series of tunnels . . . provide communications and access to a number of Government buildings in Westminster. One . . . has a number of branches and there is a rumour that one of these leads directly or indirectly to Buckingham Palace. The reason being that the Royal Family could use this to escape to Charing Cross and thus by tube to a main-line railway station and safety in the country.

It's a nice idea but probably belongs alongside the rumours that Buckingham Palace has its own private station on the Victoria Line of the Underground (itself constructed decades before its public opening), the fabled strategic reserve of steam locomotives mothballed in a tunnel near Malvern and the captured UFOs that the RAF has secreted underground at Rudloe Manor in Wiltshire. Also entirely mistaken is the allegation that Curzon Street House had a tunnel to Buckingham Palace so that the Royal Family could head to this citadel in safety were the palace ever bombed. Anecdotes about the use of the main Whitehall tunnel as a private escape route by Margaret Thatcher are also probably mistaken; these refer more likely to the so-called 'Queen's Tunnel' that connects Pindar (under MoD main building) and Downing Street.

Flight of fancy

The Whitehall tunnels have a number of spurs leading to individual buildings but what has not been explained is a separate tunnel that according to Andrew Duncan's *Secret London* "burrows its way in the Pall Mall direction and apparently has an exit at the Duke of York's Steps, where there is a door with a doorbell next to it". He states that behind this door is a vestibule from which another door leads possibly into the tunnel and that you can see the vestibule by peering through a louvred window in the men's lavatory in the Institute of Contemporary Arts (ICA), entered from the Mall. He then speculates there is another tunnel connecting the Duke of York's Steps with Buckingham Palace, constructed before or during the Second World War, to enable the Royal Family to make a quick get-away via Charing Cross tube station and Paddington mainline station to Bristol and so to Canada.

Intriguing but a flight of fancy nonetheless. The mysterious door provides no more than access to the ICA's boiler room whilst the window in the gents' loo provides ventilation for the same facility. It has no connection whatsoever to BT's cable tunnel, which is a separate affair ending in a wet sub-surface chamber beneath the roadway of Pall Mall. The cable route goes no further and whilst its purpose is anybody's guess, the Admiralty Citadel directly across the road might be its destination.

A tenuous connection with surreptitious subways does exist, however, in that close at hand is the Secret Intelligence Service's former Y Section headquarters, at 2 Carlton Gardens. Starting in 1948 agents of the SIS (with technical assistance from the Post Office special investigations unit at Dollis Hill) dug tunnels under Vienna to tap Russian military signals cables and the messages intercepts were transcribed and translated at this location.

More myths?

One oft-retold tale is of narrow-gauge trains trund-ling variously along the Post Office cable tunnels or deep in the bowels of Whitehall. The first allegation is easily dismissed; although battery-operated tugs are used to haul lengths of cable along the tunnels, these run on rubber wheels and not on rails. The so-called rails some people imagine they have seen in photographs of the tunnels are in fact steps or divisions in the concrete floorway.

Tales of an elaborate underground meeting room decorated in medieval style as part of the 'Maggie Bunker' could conceivably have some foundation in truth, but are more simply dismissed as spirited confabulation. There is no doubt, however, over King Henry VIII's Wine Cellar, a vaulted brick undercroft with octagonal stone piers built in 1530 and now a Grade I listed structure. It originally formed part of the Great Chamber of Henry VIII's Whitehall Palace and stood in the way of the present Ministry of Defence Main Building in Whitehall. When this was constructed in 1950 the cellar was removed bodily and re-established lower down at basement level. Andrew Duncan describes the work involved as a challenging but impeccably executed engineering feat. "First, the entire structure was cut away at foundation level and a concrete band inserted under its walls. Then it was placed on rollers – all 1,000 tons of it – and carefully rolled to one side. A large pit, 10 feet west of the original site and about

This telephone cable chamber under Pall Mall near the Duke of York's Steps is no flight of fancy, but the notion that it's located along a walking passage from Buckingham Palace to Trafalgar Square is pure fantasy. It's a dead end with nothing more than a 24-way cable duct and puddles.

[British Telecom]

18 feet deep, was then dug and the cellar was rolled back and lowered into it. The new building was then constructed over it. Throughout the whole of this lengthy and delicate operation, no damage was done to the cellar and no new cracks appeared anywhere in its walls or roof."

Another 'fact' of dubious substance is the allegation that the Cabinet War Room and the Goodge Street North deep shelter were linked by a Lamson pneumatic despatch tube for transporting documents. Whilst both locations had their own local tubes, it is difficult to imagine how they could have been interconnected without monumental engineering effort, under war conditions or not. The Lamson company's archives do not reach back this far but discussion with the company's 'more mature' engineers leads them to consider such a link between the buildings highly unlikely. Examination of the connection from Goodge Street North into the deep level telephone cable tunnel revealed no Lamson tubes passing through the bulkhead. There was (and may still be) an extensive pneumatic tube network along Whitehall linking all the Government Offices with a central exchange in the basement of the War Office. There were also connections to the Post Office's central London telegraph tube system that had its hub at the Central Telegraph Office, St Martin's le Grand. There was also a proposal to re-route the Whitehall pneumatic tubes into the Whitehall cable tunnel, which was not proceeded with (within the life of the PRO file available for inspection).

Lastly an alleged emergency exit from the southern extension of the Whitehall cable tunnel into the basement of the present Westminster Hospital mentioned by some authors is mistaken and entirely apocryphal. To begin, the tunnel ended halfway between the two Rotundas and went no further south. In any case, when the tunnel was first built the Westminster Hospital was still located in Broad Sanctuary (exactly where the Queen Elizabeth II Conference Centre stands today) and one of the working shafts was dug at this spot.

It is only fair to note as well that some of the allegations previously dismissed in some quarters as wild rantings have been validated. These include the deep level outlet at Broadcasting House, the secret cellar in Ealing and the installation in a secret underground factory at Corsham of escalators intended originally for St Paul's and Holborn tube stations on the Central and Piccadilly Lines.

The dangers of misrepresentation

Throughout this book we have tried to avoid embellishing reality in the way some press stories have done. Many so-called 'government citadels' are nothing of the sort. Many facilities were built in protected underground accommodation but served functional purposes, such as providing survivable communications facilities. They were not bolt-holes that any old civil servants could commandeer for shelter in time of need, simply because there was no food and bed provision for supernumerary individuals.

There are myths now gaining currency, such as the suggestion that in the event of nuclear war the prime minister would rapidly abandon Downing Street for the bunker at Kelvedon Hatch, or that the cable tunnels beneath Whitehall could serve as convenient day-to-day pedestrian routes between ministry buildings while war raged above. These melodramatic tales may make good journalism but they don't fit the facts. Worse, they can confuse and mislead even intelligent readers, as the author Oliver Rackham sums up so well:

Pseudo-history has no connection with the real world and is made up of factoids. A factoid looks like a fact, is respected as a fact and has all the properties of a fact except that it is not true. Pseudo-history is not killed by publishing real history . . . new factoids are even now being devised. It wins ground at the expense of real history.

Pneumatic tube systems supplied by the Lamson Engineering company served several government departments during and after World War II. One system using conventional 4-inch diameter tubes connected the War Cabinet Offices with 10 Downing Street, the Home Office, the Foreign Office, the Colonial Office, the India Office and the Treasury. A more specialised affair, shown here, allowed box files to be sent through 13 x 5-inch tubes and served all upper floors of the War Office main building, the Montagu Underground Fortress, Quarter Master General House and Metropole. During the war the station shown handled more than 400 carriers a day, equivalent to 50,000 papers weighing three tons. [John Liffen]

Narrow gauge trains in Post Office cable tunnels cannot be dismissed as a complete myth because they were indeed used during the construction phase of these works.
[British Telecom]

Tunnels once completed do not contain railway tracks although 'trains' of a kind are used to haul cables to places where they are needed. Here a driver demonstrates his Harbilt battery cable tug to a Post Office photographer.
[British Telecom]

London's Deep Level Shelters in Detail

Summary of locations, with entrances and opening dates

'New Tube Shelter' sites completed

Belsize Park

Entrances

at the end of a drive alongside 210 Haverstock Hill beside tennis courts (north) and corner of Haverstock Hill and Downside Crescent (south).

Sections named

Amhurst, Baden-Powell, Cook, Dampier, Frobisher, Godley, Hudson, Jameson, Kimberley, Livingstone, Milner, Phillips, Rhodes, Scott, Vancouver, Wolfe (explorers).

Transferred to the management committee

7th December 1942 (first half), 18th October 1943 (second half).

Opened to public

23rd July 1944, closed 21st October 1944 owing to lack of use and remaining users moved to Camden Town. Transferred from Ministry of Home Security to Ministry of Works on 1st October 1945.

Used

as document storage by Board of Trade, Foreign Office, Ministry of Health, National Debt Office, Passport Office and War Department after the war until June 1951.

Camden Town

Entrances

at Buck Street (north), Stanmore Place off Underhill Street, also known as Underhill Passage (south).

Sections named

Allenby, Bruce, Clive, Dalhousie, French, Gordon, Haig, Kitchener, Lawrence, Marlborough, Napier, Outram, Plumer, Roberts, Townshend, Wellington (military generals).

Transferred to the management committee

30th November 1942 (first half), 22nd February 1943 (second half).

Opened to public

16th July 1944, closed 7th May 1945. Transferred from Ministry of Home Security to Ministry of Works on 1st October 1945.

Used

by War Office as weekend hostel for 2,000 British and Dominion troops from September 1943, as leave hostel from June 1945 (vacated September 1947). Also for document storage by Assistance Board, Board of Trade, India Office, Ministry of Food, Ministry of Labour, Ministry of Transport, Passport & Permit Office and

Public Record Office from November 1947 to February 1952.

Chancery Lane

Access

via frontage and lift shaft of old station at 31–33 High Holborn (north), plus goods lift in Furnival Street (east) and 1980s personnel entrance in Tooks Court (south). A staircase shaft located in the roadway of High Holborn between Brooke Street and Furnival Street appears on a sketch plan and is mentioned in a progress report of 20th February 1941 as follows: "One shaft just starting in main road. Other shaft is finished as the old lift shaft was used and it was only necessary to excavate a further 30ft. The cross tunnel here is completed and work has started in the shelter tunnel." The most probable explanation is that the shaft stopped in a sub-surface chamber 15ft down and was intended to connect with a stair shaft in the south pavement of High Holborn. Instead a horizontal pedestrian tunnel may have been dug sideways to the Furnival Street shaft, where there was probably a pillbox entrance during the war. Subsequently small 9cwt goods lifts were provided at the surface entrances at 31/33 High Holborn and 38/39 Furnival Street.

Sections named

Addison, Balfour, Cromwell, Disraeli, Eldon, Fairfax, Gladstone, Hastings, Lawrence, Melbourne, Northcote, Onslow, Pitt, Russell, Salisbury, Walpole (political leaders).

Transferred to the management committee

30th November 1942 (first half), 22nd February 1943 (second half).

Equipped

as working and sleeping accommodation for key government staff in early 1944 but used by ISRB only.

Unoccupied

as at 3rd May 1945, vacated two days later.

Used

as military hostel from 28th November 1942, for accommodating female members of the Services from 3rd January 1944, by ISRB in early 1944, for document storage by Public Record Office in June 1945, officially transferred from Ministry of Home Security to Ministry of Works on 1st October 1945. Handed over to GPO on 1st July 1952, opened as Kingsway telephone exchange on 30th October 1954, used for storage only from 1990 onwards.

Clapham Common

Entrances

Carpenters Cottages, behind hoardings on Clapham High Street at its junction with Carpenters Place (north), behind hoardings at the junction of Clapham High Street and Clapham Park Road, (south).

Sections named

Armstrong, Brunel, Crompton, Denny, Fairbairn, Greathead, Hawksley, McAdam, Napier, Parsons, Royce, Stephenson, Trevithick, Unwin, Watt, Yarrow (engineers).

Transferred to the management committee

30th November 1942 (first half), 22nd February 1943 (second half).

Equipped

as reserve working and sleeping accommodation for key government staff following decision of March 1944. Half was earmarked for the War Office and occupation commenced in June 1944.

Unoccupied

as at 3rd May 1945.

Used

as hostel for American troops during 1943, by Admiralty and Principal Probate Office for storage of records from July 1945 to 1951, officially transferred from Ministry of Home Security to Ministry of Works on 1st October 1945.

Closed entirely

on 3rd October 1952.

Clapham North

Entrances

at 400 Clapham Road, on the west side opposite 383 Clapham Road and beside Russell Pickering House (north) and in York Terrace yard behind Clapham North between Bedford Road and Clapham High Street (south).

Sections named

Arnold, Burns, Carlyle, Dickens, Emerson, Fielding, Hardy, Johnson, Kipling, Lyttons, Milton, Pepys, Ruskin, Shakespeare, Tennyson, Wordsworth (writers).

Transferred to the management committee

30th November 1942.

Opened for sheltering

by NFS male personnel on 12th May 1943.

Opened to public

13th July 1944, closed 21st October 1944 owing to lack of use and users moved to Clapham South. Transferred from Ministry of Home Security to Ministry of Works on 1st October 1945.

Used

as document storage by Board of Trade and Public Record Office until August 1951 and as naval billet during 1953 Coronation.

Clapham South

Entrances

on Clapham Common at the junction of Clapham Common South Side, Nightingale Lane and The Avenue (north) and at 4/6 Balham Hill on the west side opposite Gaskarth Road (south).

Sections named

Anson, Beatty, Collingwood, Drake, Evans, Freemantle, Grenville, Hardy, Inglefield, Jellicoe, Keppel, Ley, Madden, Nelson, Oldham, Parry (naval commanders).

Transferred to the management committee

5th June 1942.

Opened to public

19th July 1944, closed 7th May 1945 (northern section and entrance closed 21st October 1944). Transferred from Ministry of Home Security to Ministry of Works on 1st October 1945.

Used by War Office

as weekend troop accommodation from 1943, as leave hostel from June 1945, as armed forces troop billets in June (only) 1946; hostel for Jamaican immigrants in 1948; Festival Hotel in 1951; troop billet for funeral of King George VI in 1952; for Coronation visitors in 1953.

Goodge Street

Entrances

at Chenies Street at junction of North Crescent (south), Whitefield Gardens next to Tottenham Court Road west side (adjoining the American Church, and opposite junction with Torrington Place (north).

Sections named

Ayrton, Boyle, Eddington, Faraday, Jenner, Kelvin, Newton, Priestley (scientists).

Transferred to the management committee

30th November 1942 (half only), ready for occupation 19th March 1943 (second half).

Used by U.S and British Forces

beginning nominally on 31st March 1943 (vacated by the Americans on 29th May 1945), also used for sheltering by NFS female personnel beginning on 12th May 1943, closed entirely on 3rd January 1944 when users moved to Chancery Lane. Transferred from Ministry of Home Security to Ministry of Works on 1st October 1945.

Used as document storage

by Admiralty, Charity Commission, Colonial Office, Commonwealth Relations Office, Foreign Office, Ministry of Food, Public Record Office and War Office for storage until June 1951. The London District Assembly Centre occupied half of the accommodation as armed forces hostel from 1947 until fire of 1956.

Stockwell

Entrances

at island in junction of South Lambeth Road and Clapham Road (north) and behind lock-up garages in Studley Road (south).

Sections named

Armitage, Blake, Constable, Dicksee, Etty, Flaxman, Gainsborough, Hogarth, Kent, Lawrence, Millais, Poynter, Reynolds, Turner, Vanbrugh, Wren (architects and painters)

Transferred to the management committee

30th November 1942 (first half), 22nd February 1943 (second half).

Opened

to public 9th July 1944, closed 7th May 1945 (southern section and entrance closed 21st October 1944). Transferred from Ministry of Home Security to Ministry of Works on 1st October 1945.

Used

by British troops as hostel from 23rd January 1943, by 4,000 U.S. troops for weekend accommodation from September 1943, as British leave hostel from June 1945, by museums, Public Record Office and India Office for storage from 1947 until May 1951.

Administrative centre

Compound in 4/6 Balham Hill SW12, next to the south entrance of the Clapham South shelter.

Resident engineer's office

386 Clapham Road, SW9, near Clapham North shelter.

'New Tube Shelter' sites begun but not completed

Bethnal Green

(abandoned, ingress of water)

Halfway between Bethnal Green and Liverpool Street (ingress of water)

Oval

(abandoned, ingress of water)

Entrances planned at 2–6 Clapham Road (entrance around the corner in Ashmole Place, formerly Church Street), road triangle where ventilation shaft stands (junction of Kennington Park Road and Camberwell New Road).

St Paul's (Post Office)

(abandoned, objections from Cathedral authorities)

Entrances planned at Paternoster Square (west), Panyer Alley (east). Modern street plans show neither of these locations. Paternoster Square was totally destroyed by bombing during the war and no longer exists in its pre-war form but stood to the east of Warwick Lane. Panyer Alley exists today as the walkway behind the main entrance to St Paul's tube station on the south side of Newgate Street; before the station was rebuilt it was a narrow walkway lined with houses, connecting Newgate Street and Paternoster Row.

'New Tube Shelter' sites rejected and not constructed

Leicester Square

(difficulty of access for sinking shafts)

Mornington Crescent

(difficulty of access for sinking shafts)

Warren Street

(unsuitability of subsoil)

Shelters adapted from incomplete Central Line tunnels and stations

Bethnal Green station

Entrance

from street at present location. Emergency exit by shaft into Carlton Square.

Opened to public

11th September 1940, closed owing to flood risk the next day and reopened on 5th October. Closed following major accident on 3rd March 1943.

Administered

by Metropolitan Borough of Bethnal Green.

Gainsborough tunnel

Entrance

by temporary staircases from the south side of the bridge where Gainsborough Road crossed the railway cutting.

Opened to public

1940, closed 7th May 1945.

Administered by Leyton Borough Council.

Gants Hill shelter

Entrance

by six roadside staircases still in use today as station entrances. Shelterers used the public pedestrian subways only, not the booking hall.

Opened to public

1940 (probably). Noted in use on 25th August 1944 but closed some time before May 1945.

Administered by Ilford Corporation.

Liverpool Street siding tunnels

Entrance

down timber ramp into tunnel entrance at east end of present westbound platform of Liverpool Street station (Central Line).

Opened to public

June 1940, closed shortly before May 1945.

Administered by City of London Corporation.

Redbridge station

Entrance
from surface structure close to location of
present station.

Opened to public
1940, closed shortly before 6th February 1941.

Administered by Ilford Corporation.

West Ham tunnel

Entrance
via footbridge from the west end of William
Street, near Stratford station, and along
walkway between railway tracks that led into the
tube tunnel. Emergency exit by shaft into
Queen Street.

Opened to public
September 1940, closed 21st May 1945.

Administered by County Borough of West Ham.

Westdown tunnel

Entrance
along footpaths across the railway depot from
High Road Leyton and from Westdown Road,
then by footbridge over the railway with steps
down to the tunnel mouth from there.
Emergency exit by shaft into Queen Street.

Opened to public
September 1940, closed 18th May 1945.

Administered by Leyton Borough Council.

Shelters adapted from disused Central Line stations

British Museum

Entrance
at former station entrance in High Holborn.

Opened to public
September 1941, closed 7th May 1945.

Administered
by Metropolitan Borough of Holborn.

Chancery Lane

Entrance
at original station entrance, 33 High Holborn.

Opened to public
September 1940 (probably), closed November
1940.

Administered
by Metropolitan Borough of Holborn.
Shelter adapted from disused Northern Line tunnel.

Borough tunnel

Entrances at the following locations:
Marlborough Yard (now Marlborough
Playground), a short distance behind number
116 Borough High Street.
St Margaret's Court (between 62 and 64
Borough High Street), approximately behind
number 60 Borough High Street.

75–85 Borough High Street (called George
House).
Adjacent to 9 London Bridge Street, down a
flight of steps from street level, roughly opposite
the later British Telecom building and present
hotel.
143 Borough High Street, nos. 141 and nos.
145–149.
Adjacent to St George the Martyr's Church,
Borough High Street (entrance was in the
garden beside the church on the Tabard Street
side).
Opened to public 24th June 1940, closed 7th
May 1945.

Administered
by Southwark Borough Council.

Shelter adapted from closed Piccadilly Line branch

Aldwych

Entrance
at Aldwych station.

Opened to public
22nd September 1940, closed 7th May 1945.

Administered
by Westminster City Council.

Plessey tunnel factory

Access shafts
at Whipps Cross Road, Cambridge Park, west
end of Wanstead station site, Nutter Lane,
Redbridge substation, Danehurst Gardens, east
end of Gants Hill. There were separate shafts
for ventilation (not all permanent) at Selsdon
Road, Nutter Lane, in allotments beside the
River Roding fields, Redbridge Cottages,
Eastern Avenue central reservation at Ellesmere
Gardens, Beehive Lane and Middleton
Gardens beyond Gants Hill. A shaft on the
north side of Eastern Avenue opposite the
junction with The Drive gave access to the
'Ellesmere' electrical substation.

Personnel access
was provided at all station sites and possibly
also via the access shafts at Cambridge Park
and Danehurst Gardens.

Production
was organised as follows.
Wanstead station was used for Breeze assembly
work, with machining carried out in the tunnels
on either side. Redbridge station made Coffman
starters and Pesco aircraft pumps were made in
the tunnels nearby. The Gants Hill tunnels were
used for coil winding and an automatic machine
shop. West of Wanstead radio and radar work
went on, almost as a separate operation.

All spelling as in original documents.

Appendix 2

Bunkum Bunkers

The secret shelters that don't exist

Two of the planned deep shelters, St Paul's and the Oval, have attracted considerable attention and speculation because some writers are simply not prepared to accept that their construction was abandoned. Instead they prefer to believe that work was continued surreptitiously to produce bolt-holes of the utmost secrecy. Research in the Public Record Office and London Transport archives eliminates all doubt whatsoever.

Suspect shelter?

The basis of the conspiracy theories lies in some apparent contradictions in history books. In his book *Beneath The City Streets* Peter Laurie remarks: "Jackson and Croome say the work at St Paul's was abandoned for fear of damaging the cathedral but O'Brien says only that 'considerable delay was experienced'. Both descriptions conceal the building of something under … St Paul's rather different from a public shelter."

Several writers mention the discovery of an Act of Parliament that prevented underground works in the vicinity of the cathedral; this is not strictly true and in any case, the objections that caused the shelter site to be abandoned did not specifically mention any such edict. The statute in question, the City of London (St Paul's Preservation) Act, defines a prescribed area near St Paul's where development below prescribed depths is controlled. This act was passed in 1935, which incidentally explains why there was no hindrance to the construction and opening of the Central Line tube railway at this point back in 1900. This also disposes of another so-called anomaly, why there was opposition to building a deep shelter here but none to the construction of the new booking hall for St Paul's station (opened in January 1939). The explanation is simple: the new booking hall lay only just below the road surface level, whereas the greater depth of the planned tube shelter was sufficient to give concern.

Spring 1941 saw signs of confusion and a report dated 30th May 1941 declares:

> The question of the future of the site at St Paul's station is still under discussion. The Cathedral authorities have objected to the proximity of the tunnelling and its possible effects on the foundations of the Cathedral. The proposal was that the shelter tunnels were to be on the Cathedral side of the existing railway. The siting of the tunnels on the other side of the railway is being investigated, and an early report is expected. No work had been carried out on the shafts, although the sites had been selected and requisitioned. Should it be impossible to construct the shelters at St Paul's, a station further west on the same line will be selected.

A few days later, on 6th June 1941, a London Transport memo from the engineer in charge of the works stated that all negotiations for building a Home Office tunnel shelter at the site were now in abeyance owing to the opposition of the St Paul's Cathedral authorities. The whole subject would have to be re-opened if and when the objection was overcome, which never came to pass, as a later report states:

> Work has not yet been started at St Paul's station. At first it was difficult to find sites for the shafts, until the raids in April destroyed buildings in the neighbourhood. Later the Dean and Chapter of St Paul's expressed fears as to the effect of the projected work on the safety of the cathedral foundations, and it is now proposed to abandon that site. The expense at St Paul's is negligible. The abandonment of St Paul's (one station out of ten) means a saving of £270,000.

The scheme was officially abandoned in August 1941, with no construction work having been undertaken. Property required for the western entrance to the shelter in Newgate Street, Three Tuns Passage and Paternoster Square was de-requisitioned on 19th August 1941. These sites had been earmarked for compulsory acquisition to sink construction shafts but plans on file are marked 'site abandoned, no requisitions served'. A letter from London Transport to the Ministry of Home Security clarified on 25th August 1941, "I am now informed that it has been definitely decided to abandon the site at St Paul's." The last word lies in a letter from the Secretary of London Transport to the Town Clerk of the Corporation of London dated 15th September, stating: "It has been decided to relinquish this site."

As regards the eastern entrance, the engineers' plan (Halcrow D.S. 19) shows a shaft in the roadway where Newgate Street and Cheapside meet in front of what is 3 Cheapside today. It is likely this would have stopped in a sub surface chamber, with a horizontal pedestrian tunnel from there on to a stair shaft nearby, away from the road.

Soggy site

There is overwhelming written evidence that nothing came of the deep shelter planned at the Oval either, although much more had been completed before work was abandoned. Situation reports tell of problems early on.

> One shaft has reached 40 rings. Sinking has not yet started at the other site but the gantry has been erected. (20th February 1941)

> Shaft 1 is nearly down. There is water trouble here and work has temporarily stopped until the final level of the shelter tunnel is settled. Pumping is

necessary to keep water down. Shaft 2 (is) about 35 feet down. The men here are working in water, which is being kept down by pumps. They believe that after one more ring (20 inches) they will be through the water-bearing stratum. (19th March 1941)

The shafts have been sunk and 125 linear feet of 12ft diameter cross-passages have been excavated. 45 linear feet (2%) of 16ft 6in diameter shelter tunnels have been excavated. (27th May 1941)

An undated report of later that summer declares:

Considerable difficulty has been experienced owing to the presence of water at one of the workings at the Oval station and it is evident that tunnelling from the shaft concerned would require to be carried out in caissons. This is both protracted and expensive, and it is proposed to abandon that half of the Oval site. Whilst a certain amount of expense has already been incurred at the Oval, the saving at the Oval is put at about £100,000.

The proposed action was taken in August and the workers were transferred to Camden Town, as completion there was deemed to have higher priority. The writer of the report just quoted continued that the abandonment of the Oval and St Paul's sites would involve the sacrifice of shelter for around 12,000 people but accommodation for that number could be obtained at a much cheaper cost by lengthening the remaining tunnels by 100ft at either or both ends and also by extending the tunnels at Clapham North and Clapham Common to link the stations. Work continued on the other half but at the end of November it was decided to abandon this as well and to make no attempt to provide means of communication between the tunnels and station platforms.

A London Transport memo of 27th July 1942 confirms the reason for the abandonment was the presence of unexpected quantities of water in the subsoil. After the works were abandoned the shaft was sealed off with a massive bombproof plug and an access gallery with an entrance gallery in Church Street (now Ashmole Place) had been completed to give access to the works constructed for pumping and maintenance purposes. Another memo on 22nd September states there was a permanent (electricity) supply for pumping purposes. A further note dated 1st October explained that all but the top 12ft of the 90ft southern shaft was filled with clay and rubble and the remainder plugged with concrete. The side entrance to the shaft 5ft below the ground in Ashmole Place was also filled with concrete.

The situation was confirmed to the Ministry of Home Security by London Transport's solicitor on 13th October 1942, saying, "You will recollect that a shaft was sunk adjoining Oval station and the works were abandoned owing to technical difficulties." The letter added that the circuit supplied by the South London Electricity Supply Corporation was for the operation of pumps to keep the (southern) shaft free from water and would be required until some further steps were taken.

That was not the end of the woes at the Oval, however, as a letter from London Transport to the Ministry of Home Security spelled out on 31st August 1943. Despite the presence of not only a shaft and subterranean passage but also the transformer and switchboard supplying current to the pumps installed in the disused shaft, a mistake had been made in de-requisitioning land at Nos. 2, 4 and 6 Clapham Road. Problems remained still as a butcher's shop and a house on the site had been demolished without adequate compensation; settlement payments were not made until early 1947 and mid-1948 respectively despite press criticism.

By 1947 the responsible body was the Ministry of Works, which was told on 20th August that all land requisitioned for the planned shelter at the Oval had been relinquished except that the government retained an easement for the shafts and the entrance manhole thereto. Negotiations were pending for filling up the shaft and manhole so as to avoid a heavy maintenance charge for periodical pumping (at the north entrance on the triangle site). By November 1951 it was realised that the cost of filling in the remainder of the works would exceed the cost of constructing a new shaft there (for ventilating the existing station) and the ministry agreed to the British Transport Commission (to which London Transport was responsible) acquiring and using a portion of the northerly shaft so long as the BTC filled in and made good the rest. To this London Transport agreed.

Going Down

For the many readers who have not worked 'down below' or had the opportunity to visit a deep level cable tunnel, this graphic description by a former BT engineer will provide the next best thing to an actual visit:

During my time as a telephone engineer I have been into some strange and interesting places. One of the interesting ones occurred when I repaired a telephone underground. I was asked one afternoon if I knew about the Deep Level Tunnel. Everyone knew about it but nobody was *supposed* to know about it!

The tunnel was dug during the war to provide a safe route for trunk and junction cables to avoid destruction by enemy action and because of this they were supposed to be secret. The entrance from the exchange was via a basement room, the entry to which was kept locked and alarmed. In the centre of the floor was a round iron grating probably 15–20 feet in diameter, through which a great number of lead-covered cables disappeared, and to one side protruded an almost vertical iron ladder. The lights were switched on and standing on the grating you could look down this shaft and see similar gratings with ladders disappearing into the depths. With toolbag in hand I descended the first ladder to the next platform, again of steel grating and then onto a second ladder. As I went down I passed about ten of these platforms until the bottom was reached. My guess at the time was that if the rungs were spaced about one foot apart then the shaft was about 100 ft deep. At the bottom was a steel door that led into a sort of airlock chamber, as at this point the tunnel network is provided with air pumped down to keep it dry.

Once into the cable tunnel, one branch led away to the Post Office Tower, but as I was told to go towards Covent Garden I took the other tunnel. These tunnels were constructed of iron segments exactly like the underground railway tunnels and were about twelve feet in diameter with cable supported on iron bearers on each side of the central walk way. The tunnel is lit by electric lamps that are switched on in sections of about fifty yards or so. Progress is made by switching on the next section and switching off the previous section.

After some distance I came to a junction in the tunnel above which a signpost pointed to the direction which each tunnel led. Turning left I continued towards Covent Garden, I remember looking back and seeing a pinpoint of light away in the distance and realised I was not alone in the tunnel. The lights went on and off, growing brighter as the person came nearer, until I was able to see who it was. He was an Engineer Cleaner who patrolled the tunnels to report any problems with the air condition, lights and so on. We passed the time of day and while I checked the wall telephone, he continued on his way, the lights now growing fainter. My destination was reached when the tunnel widened out into a large chamber about twenty or so feet in diameter. In the middle were rows of large drums with cables entering them. These were loading coils and were necessary to keep the impedance of the cable to zero and prevent faint transmission. The telephone was on the wall in this chamber and after repairing the fault, I set off back the way I had come. I soon began to realise how deep I was, since at one point I could hear the tube trains rumbling overhead. I may be wrong, but I think that the Piccadilly Line here is one of the deepest, so I must assume that I was actually below this. I have been told by other engineers that when they have been working down there in the night when the trains were stopped that they could hear the London Transport engineers in their respective tunnel and our engineers would hammer on the iron tunnel segments and speculate if they had frightened the railway engineers above. Maybe this gave rise to tunnel ghost stories!

Arriving back at the bottom of the shaft it was a long climb back to the surface, but well worth an experience that few engineers have had. When digital exchanges had taken over from the old mechanical ones, I was again called on to go underground again. This time I had to check the concentrator end of an ISDN system. There was quite a to-do about this as I had not got the necessary security clearance and so had to have special dispensation to do the job. I arrived at an exchange in central London and went to the basement where I was met by the security people. Accompanied, I was led to a lift and whilst I am a slim person and so was my minder, we only just got into the lift with the test sets. If we had been larger people I am not sure what would have happened. At the bottom we walked a short distance in a small tunnel and then passed into a larger main tunnel. I remember passing a distribution frame and other equipment until we came to the remote System X concentrator. What a strange sight the racks for the whole concentrator were, in one long straight line . . . My equipment was at one end and a good walk away at the other end was the VDU terminal that I had to use to interrogate the fault. I did some necessary checks and then said I think I need to go to the MDF (main distribution frame).

"Bring all your gear" was the advice from the minder; "It's a long walk back". He then asked, "Will you be long?"

I asked him why. He said, "Well, because the doors are locked at 5 o'clock and not opened until 8 in the morning, so you could be here all night!"

"That's OK by me if your boss is willing to pay the overtime", I replied. By this time I had completed all I could do and so was allowed to surface again. A strange place to work in when you are used to an oblong room; all the equipment racks were stretched into long lines to fit into the tunnel.

Reflections on Security

For many years virtually everything described in this book was 'secret', protected either by the Official Secrets Act, by D Notices (voluntary non-disclosure orders agreed by the press) or by institutional security that revealed information only to those with the 'need to know'. So long as national security was at stake no right-thinking person would have disagreed with this policy of secrecy. With the ending of the Cold War and the coming of the 'peace dividend', these issues of national security appeared no longer to apply, meaning any reluctance to talk about these subjects could lie only in company confidentiality.

Since then new forces of terrorism have arisen and communications facilities have become a potential target once more. As mentioned already, the subject of this book is entirely historical, with no reference to facilities of strategic importance today. All the same, we have practised a degree of self-censorship and avoided providing detailed information on access routes to underground facilities.

Of course the effectiveness of secrecy is always debatable and how well these secrets were protected in the past is a matter for conjecture. The public at large may well have been ignorant of them but can the same be said of foreign intelligence agencies? The success of one attempt at secrecy can perhaps be judged from the reminiscence of a retired senior BT engineer Donald Wray, published in the *RSS Newsletter* (Dollis Hill and Martlesham Research Stations). The year of the event described is not given but it cannot be later than the mid-1960s.

When we learned that a party of Russians was coming to visit the TV Network Switching Centre at Museum Exchange (the great virile P.O. Tower had yet to be erected on top of it), there was something like panic in Bill Newman's office. Bill was in charge of the NSC and of all the TV links coming into it. A large map of the London cable network was displayed on the office wall. Clearly this was too sensitive an item to remain on view so it was ripped off, leaving a large rectangle of clean cream paint on an otherwise uninterrupted surface of London filth; the final touch was the four little strips of flaked plaster where the Sellotape had been.

We discussed TV transmissions and switching quite amiably with the Russians (via their interpreter of course) and learned they were going to establish something similar in Moscow. Then Bill said – unwisely in my opinion – "I'm sorry we haven't a map of the London cable network to show you but we have just sent it back to the Drawing Office to be brought up to date."

"No problem," replied the interpreter quite blandly; "we saw a copy in the Embassy before we set out this morning."

Security is of course a source of great fascination for most people and the reason why spy films and novels are so popular. Official secrets were well protected in this country, both by the stringent provisions of the Official Secrets Act and the careful scrutiny of government files before they are made available for public inspection at the Public Record Office (PRO). Documents created by government departments are usually 'closed' (in other words unavailable for viewing) for thirty years but occasionally records may be closed for longer than thirty years. These are known as 'extended closures' and are usually released after either fifty or seventy five years, although under the Open Government Initiative files can now be opened early with approval from the Lord Chancellor.

Many files were inspected at the PRO while researching this book and it was interesting to see the mixed open and closed status of files covering some subject areas. Annoying as it was to discover some files closed, this was compensated by the valuable material we found in the open files. One file has the intriguing title *Finsbury: Emergency committee chairman's irregular action in connection with deep shelters*, but to discover the nature of the indiscretion committed we shall have to wait until 2017!

The only area where the writers encountered a total block was in the archives of British Telecom, whose policy was to allow no access at all to files concerning its deep level tunnel system. Information in this book on this subject has therefore been drawn exclusively from already published sources.

Is this the end of London's secret subterranea? By no means! There are literally hundreds of files in the Public Record Office that remain to be examined, even setting aside those currently classified as 'closed'. Nonetheless the authors hope this book will satisfy readers' initial curiosity and if it stimulates further research and interest we cannot ask for more.

A.A.	anti-aircraft (as in A.A. Command)
AAOR	anti-aircraft operations room
ack-ack	anti-aircraft (from the military phonetic alphabet for the letter 'A')
AEF	Allied Expeditionary Force
A.I.D.	Air Inspection Department
A.R.P.	air raid precautions
barrage balloon	extremely large inflated balloon, tethered to the ground by steel cables flown above urban areas, gun emplacements and other important sites. The cables deterred attacks by low-flying aircraft, which could not fly through them, and also allowed the balloons to be winched up or down for refilling or moving to another location.
battery	a group of heavy guns or rocket projectors together with their crews, accommodation, stores, radar equipment and so on
BBC	British Broadcasting Corporation
BT	British Telecom (formerly the telecommunications business of the Post Office)
BTC	British Transport Commission (1948–62)
Buzz-bomb	see V1
CD	Civil Defence
CEGB	Central Electricity Generating Board
COSSAC	Chief of Staff to Supreme Allied Commander (AEF department responsible for planning the Normandy invasion 1943/44)
Doodlebug	see V1
DTS	deep tunnel shelter
ETOUSA	European Theatre of Operations, US Army (tasked with building up the American forces in Great Britain and then supporting them with logistics and administrative services). It replaced USAFBI.
Flying bomb	see V1
GCC	Grid Control Centre (of the CEGB)
GCHQ	Government Communications Headquarters
GLC	Greater London Council (successor in 1974 to the LCC)
GPO	General Post Office (predecessor of both British Telecom and the postal business of the Post Office)
GWR	Great Western Railway
H.E.	high explosive
hp	horse power

HMSO	Her (or His if before 1952) Majesty's Stationery Office
INREBU	Inter Services Research Bureau (actually its telegraphic address)
IPOEE	Institution of Post Office Electrical Engineers
ISRB	Inter Services Research Bureau (cover name for the research and development section of Special Operations Executive)
LCC	London County Council (later Greater London Council, then Greater London Authority)
LCDR	London Civil Defence Region
LMSR	London Midland & Scottish Railway (1923–47)
LNER	London & North Eastern Railway (1923–47)
LPTB	London Passenger Transport Board (1933–47)
LRT	London Regional Transport (1984)
LT	London Transport (1970–84; used also as a short title successively by the LPTB, LTE, LTB, LTE again and LRT)
LTAF	London Transport Aircraft Factory (Chiswick)
LTB	London Transport Board (1963–69)
LTE	London Transport Executive (1948–62)
MAP	Ministry of Aircraft Production
MDF	main distribution frame, on which telephone cables are terminated
MoD	Ministry of Defence
MoHS	Ministry of Home Security
MoT	Ministry of Transport
MoW	Ministry of Works
NFS	National Fire Service
NTS	New Tube Shelters
PABX	private automatic branch exchange (business telephone system in which extensions dial one another)
PMBX	private manual branch exchange (business telephone system where a switchboard operator handles internal calls)
POEEJ	Post Office Electrical Engineers' Journal
P-Plane	pilotless plane, see V1
Q.M.G.	Quartermaster-General
PRO	Public Record Office now National Archives (located at Kew)
RAF	Royal Air Force
RTA	Regional Technical Adviser (LCDR)

SHAEF	Supreme Headquarters Allied Expeditionary Forces (inter-allied organisation that replaced ETOUSA)
SOE	Special Operations Executive, an offshoot of MI6 set up initially to help the Resistance in German-occupied countries
SR	Southern Railway (1923–47)
STC	Standard Telephones & Cables Ltd
U.S.	United States
USAFBI	United States Army Forces in the British Isles
VDU	visual display unit (computer terminal)
VE Day	The day when victory in Europe was secured (8th May 1945)
V1	German V (for *Vergeltung*, i.e. vengeance) weapon – a pilotless aeroplane and warhead combination, effectively a flying bomb
VIP	very important person
VJ Day	The day on which Japan surrendered (14th August 1945)
WWW	World Wide Web (Internet)
YMCA	Young Men's Christian Association
YWCA	Young Women's Christian Association (the YMCA and YWCA ran clubs and hostels)

Names of Bodies

A number of government departments and ministries changed name or status during the period covered by this study. The Board of Works became the Ministry of Works and Buildings in 1940, then in 1943 the Ministry of Works. After the war it became the Ministry of Public Building and Works. In 1970 it was merged with the Ministries of Transport and of Housing and Local Government to form the Department of the Environment. In turn the Department of the Environment, Transport and the Regions (DETR) was formed in 1997 by a merger of the Departments of Environment and Transport. The Ministry of Transport (known as the Ministry of War Transport from 1941 until the end of the war) existed until 1970, when it was merged into the newly constituted Department of the Environment, the transport function then being returned to a re-constituted Department of Transport in 1976.

The Ministry of Defence in its present form is a fusion of former ministries: from 1946 to 1964 there were, as well as the MoD itself, five Departments of State doing what the unified MoD does now: the Admiralty, the War Office, the Air Ministry, the Ministry of Aviation and the Ministry of Defence itself. In 1964 the first three and the MoD were amalgamated, and the defence functions of the Ministry of Aviation Supply (as it had by then become) were absorbed in 1971, when the MoD took over responsibility for supplying military aircraft and guided weapons.

The Special Operations Executive (SOE) had responsibility for training and controlling secret agents dropped into occupied Europe committing sabotage but not espionage. It had a research and development section under the cover name of the Inter Services Research Bureau. MI8, also called the Radio Security Service, was a branch of military intelligence responsible for monitoring enemy command broadcasts.

The activities of the main line railways and London Transport were transferred from peacetime to wartime conditions on 1st September 1939, when the government took over their control (but not their ownership). A Railway Executive Committee (1939–1946) was appointed by the Minister of Transport to be his agents controlling the railways on a day-to-day basis. Four main line railway companies had existed since 1923, the London, Midland and Scottish Railway (LMS), the London and North Eastern Railway (LNER), the Southern Railway (SR) and the Great Western Railway (GWR). The Transport Act of 1947 caused these four railways to be nationalised, being absorbed into British Railways as of 1st January 1948. Both British Railways and the London Transport Executive (which replaced the LPTB) came under the direction of the British Transport Commission, which in turn was abolished under the 1962 Transport Act, when British Railways and London Transport became separate Boards answering directly to the Ministry of Transport.

The main supplier of gas in London until nationalisation in 1949 was the Gas Light & Coke Company. It then became the North Thames Gas Board, one of twelve area Gas Boards that operated until 1973, when the British Gas Corporation was established and the area Gas Boards became Regions. The assets of the Corporation were transferred to British Gas plc in August 1986, then owned solely by the government. In November 1986 shares in British Gas plc were offered for sale on the stock market, with trading starting in December. Just over ten years later in February 1997 British Gas was 'demerged' into BG plc and Centrica. In December 1999 BG plc completed a financial restructuring, with a new parent company, BG Group plc, engaged in the development, management and supply of existing and emerging gas markets around the world. October 2000 saw BG Group plc complete the demerger of Lattice Group plc into two separate companies, British Gas and Scottish Gas, providing gas and electricity supply in England, Scotland and Wales for homes and businesses. At the same time Lattice group plc and National Grid plc merged to become one company, National Grid Transco plc, the UK's largest utility.

Civil Defence

Civil Defence is defined by the Civil Defence Act 1948 as 'any measure not amounting to actual combat for affording defence against any form of hostile attack by a foreign power or for depriving any form of attack by a foreign power of the whole or part of its effect, whether the measures are taken before, at or after the time of attack'.

Crossbow

The term 'Crossbow' can take on different shades of meaning according to the context in which it is used. It was first used as the cover or codename of the Committee on the Maintenance of the Machinery of Government under Rocket Bombardment, set up under Sir Findlater Stewart. This followed rumours reaching Britain in 1942 that Germany was developing rocket weapons at Peenemünde on the Baltic Coast. These came to be known as V missiles – vengeance weapons or *Vergeltungswaffen* in German. To examine the reports and rumours and to advise the government how to counter the forthcoming attacks, the War Cabinet established the Crossbow Committee. By extension, attack by enemy missiles of this kind was termed Crossbow, used as a handy cover name to avoid causing widespread panic by revealing the true nature of the threat.

Ironically the lessons of Crossbow, when the Allied attempt to counter German V1 and V2 operations became the dominant focus shaping airpower employment during the critical spring and summer months of 1944, were soon forgotten. A paper by Lt. Col. Mark Kipphut of the US Air Force, *Theater Missile Defense, Reflections for the Future*, remarks that during the Gulf War its planners did not learn Crossbow's lessons, when most of the challenges faced in World War II resurfaced during efforts to suppress Scud missiles. As he says, "Rather than properly studying history to gain a rich appreciation of the subtleties of war, we ransack the history record in search of principles that guarantee success. This 'cookie-cutter' approach typically leads to dogmatic application, not strong doctrinal thought."

Deep Shelters

In official files several different names are given to these and they tend to be used indiscriminately. To clarify, the most commonly used names are *Deep Shelters*, *Deep Level Shelters*, *Home Office Tunnel Shelters* (after the war) and *New Tube Shelters* (during the war).

Construction Terms

Citadel accommodation, in its specific World War II meaning, defines working space or shelter considered to be bombproof. It can take the form of a steel-framed building or a structure buried underground. In case of above-ground buildings, the steel frame was intended to absorb the shock of a direct hit and thus survive, along with the people inside. Shafts (giving access to tunnels below) were not normally dug directly over the line of a main tunnel; the connection was made instead by a short *lateral* tunnel or *adit*. A *cap* over a shaft is a slab of sufficient strength to protect the shaft even in the face of a direct hit by high explosive, whilst a *burster slab* is a slab of concrete buried below ground, intended to force a bomb to detonate at that point without penetrating further. For security purposes tunnels were divided into sections by obstructions called *bulkheads*; these could take the form of stout movable doors or a physical barrier wall through which essential cables would be passed in circular openings (glands or conduits). An *embrasure* is a shaped opening in a parapet or casemate wall that allows artillery to fire through the parapet or wall.

A *trench shelter* is a simple form of air raid shelter constructed just below ground level. It is made by excavating a trench that is lined with concrete, roofed over with concrete slabs and finally covered with a raised earth mound. Shelters of this kind can still be seen in public parks all over the country.

Single storey *Horsa Hut* buildings were a familiar sight during the 1940s, '50s and '60s, with a few still remaining. Made of concrete sections, brick infill and metal window frames, they had corrugated asbestos roofs and were installed as British Restaurants during the war and as additional classrooms and canteens in schools afterwards. The name is said to mean 'huts on raising school age' but this may be a subsequent coining. The *Maycrete* hut is one of the most instantly recognisable of all wartime prefabricated buildings, with rendered walls and buttresses, asbestos roof and metal window frames. With a wide variety of sizes and applications, they were used on virtually every airfield, also at gun emplacements and after the war as temporary housing in the Netherlands (where some cherished developments survive). *Nissen*, *Quonset* and *Romney Huts* are frequently confused and these names tend to be (mis) used interchangeably. All three are constructed from a row of semi-circular steel ribs covered with corrugated sheet metal, designed as a cheap, lightweight, portable structure that could be put up by untrained people. The Nissen Hut is the oldest design, dating to the First World War, developed for the British army by the Canadian army officer and mining engineer Capt. Peter Norman Nissen. Romney Buildings, named after the Kentish firm that developed them, are a larger civilian version of the same thing. So also are Quonset Huts, developed in 1941 for the U.S. Navy by the George A. Fuller construction company in New York. The name comes from the location of the production facility, near Quonset, Rhode Island.

Jubilee track (also known as Decauville track) is temporary railway track laid by a contractor during the building of a railway or other civil engineering or construction enterprise. It is very light and designed to be carried and laid by hand directly on the ground. The track is suited for hand pulled carts or very small locomotives and is easily disassembled and transported. Finally, a *Bostwick* (trade name) gate can be either a folding lattice gate that contracts like lazy-tongs or else a fireproof metal door of zigzag segments that can be folded up out of the way like a concertina. Generally the first meaning is implied, unless described as fireproof.

Security Designations

On some of the documents consulted the British term 'Secret' corresponds to the U.S. term 'Confidential'. The British classification 'Most Secret' has the same meaning as U.S. 'Top Secret'.

Bombing and the Blitz

The Blitz began effectively on 25th August 1940, when the first German bombs were dropped on London. The first real air raid took place on 7th September and bombing continued until 10th May 1941, which was the last major raid on London. Occasional attacks followed for three years until January 1944, when heavy bombing returned to London. The 'Little Blitz', as it was called, lasted from 21st January to 8th April 1944 and although not as bad as in 1940, it was bad enough. German V1 flying bombs began to hit London, beginning on 12th January 1944 and these continued until the end of August, when British troops destroyed the launching sites in northern France. The first V2 arrived on 8th September 1944 and these rockets remained a menace until attacks finally ceased at the end of March 1945.

Right The initial official response to the use of tube stations for shelter.

WAR EMERGENCY

UNDERGROUND STATIONS MUST NOT BE USED AS AIR RAID SHELTERS

———

The public are informed that in order to operate the Railways for essential movement, Underground Stations cannot be used as air raid shelters. In any event a number of stations would have to be cleared for safety in certain contingencies

UNDERGROUND

Sources of Information

Using footnotes to cite the source of every piece of information used in this book is not a realistic option, so instead a comprehensive resource list is provided.

Books consulted

Bancroft, Peter: **The Railway to King William Street and Southwark Deep Tunnel Air-Raid Shelter.** *Self-published*, 1981. Detailed study of the civic shelter tunnels constructed in Southwark.

Bancroft, Peter: **London Transport Records at the Public Record Office** (part one). *Nebulous Books*, 1996.

Barty-King, Hugh: **Girdle Round The Earth.** *Heinemann*, 1979. Official history of Cable & Wireless Ltd.

Bell, R.: **History of the British Railways During the War, 1939–1945.** *Railway Gazette*, 1946. The official war history.

Bragg, Michael: **RDF1: The Location of Aircraft by Radar Methods 1935–1945.** *Hawkhead Publishing*, 2002. Remote GCI radar display at Brompton Road.

Bruce, J. Graeme and Croome, Desmond F.: **The Twopenny Tube.** *Capital Transport Publishing*, 1996. Includes Plessey factory in tube tunnels.

Campbell, Duncan: **War Plan UK.** *Burnett Books*, 1982. Detailed discussion of deep level tunnels and shelters.

Clayton, Antony: **Subterranean City.** *Historical Publications*, 2000. Subtitled *Beneath the Streets of London*, this book provides a comprehensive survey of natural and man-made features of London.

Cocroft, Wayne and Thomas, Roger: **Cold War Architecture – Building for Nuclear Confrontation.** *English Heritage*, 2003. Plans and photos of deep level telephone exchanges.

Connor, J.E.: **London's Disused Underground Stations.** *Capital Transport Publishing*, 2001. Extremely comprehensive survey of closed station features.

Connor, J.E.: **Abandoned Stations on London's Underground.** *Connor & Butler Ltd*, 2000. Pictorial survey of closed station features.

Darwin, Bernard: **War On The Line, The Story of the Southern Railway in War-Time.** *Southern Railway*, 1946 [also reprint by the Middleton Press, 1993].

De la Billiere, Sir Peter: **Looking For Trouble.** *HarperCollins*, 1994. This autobiography mentions COBRA.

Dunbar, C.S. and others: **London's Tramway Subway.** Booklet of articles on the Kingsway Subway reprinted from *Modern Tramway* magazine, *Light Railway Transport League, no date but circa* 1976.

Duncan, Andrew: **Secret London.** *New Holland*, 1995. Readable tourist guide to London's unusual places, with brief mention of cable tunnels and government citadels.

Fox, Steve: **Control Chain.** *Published privately*, 1999. Traces the development of government war headquarters in Britain from the birth of the A-bomb to 1968. Details from the author at steve@foxfox.freeserve.co.uk

Fox, Steve: **Plan for Survival.** *Published privately*, 2000. Continues the story of war preparations from 1971 to the end of the Cold War in 1993. Details from the author at steve@foxfox.freeserve.co.uk

Gillham, John C: **The Waterloo & City Railway.** *Oakwood Press*, 2001. Chapter 28 mentions the laying of Post Office telephone cables along the railway tunnel.

Graves, Charles: **London Transport At War 1939–45.** *Almark Publishing*, 1974 (first published in 1947 as *London Transport Carried On*). Construction of deep level shelters (page 58) and mobilisation plans for Black and Yellow Moves on pp 79/80.

Graves, Charles: **The Thin Red Lines.** *Standard Art Book Company Ltd*, no date but circa 1947. The war history of Cable & Wireless Ltd.

Gregg, John: **The Shelter of the Tubes.** *Capital Transport Publishing*, 2001. Comprehensive survey of arrangements for sheltering civilians in tube stations during World War II.

Gunby, Norman: **A Potted History of Ilford.** *Self-published*, 1997. Includes wartime history of the Plessey Company.

Harris, Brig. L.H.: **Signal Venture.** *Gale & Polden*, 1951. Military signals operations during World War II.

Hay, Ian: **The Post Office Went To War.** *HMSO*, 1946. War record of the Post Office.

Horne, M.A.C.: **The Central Line.** *Douglas Rose*, 1987. Includes Plessey factory in tube tunnels.

Horne, M.A.C. and Bayman, R.: **The Northern Line.** *Capital Transport Publishing*, 1999. Includes wartime contingencies and brief mention of deep shelters.

Horne, M.A.C.: **The Jubilee Line.** *Capital Transport Publishing*, 2000. Discussion of pre- and post-war plans for new lines.

Horne, M.A.C.: **The Victoria Line.** *Douglas Rose*, 1988. Includes discussion of pre-war plans for new lines.

Jackson Alan A. and Croome, Desmond F: **Rails Through The Clay – A History of London's Tube Railways.** Second edition, 1993 *Capital Transport Publishing*. Plans for new tube railways, construction of the shelters etc.

John, Evan: **Timetable For Victory.** *The British Railways*, no date but around 1947. Wartime history, including telecommunications.

Kohan C.M.: **History of the Second World War: Works and Buildings.** *HMSO*, 1952. Includes London Ring Main exchange.

Laurie, Peter: **Beneath The City Streets.** *Allen Lane*, 1970. Deep level tunnels (this is the first book on the subject, written before many records had been declassified; parts of this book are stated by the author to be speculative).

Lee, Charles E.: **The Central Line.** *London Transport*, 1974. Includes Plessey factory in tube tunnels.

London Transport: **War Time Deep Tunnel Shelters.** Undated internal report (in London's Transport Museum resource centre).

McCamley, N.J.: **Cold War Secret Nuclear Bunkers.** *Leo Cooper*, 2002. Covers government and local authority control centres in and outside London (and much, much more).

McCamley, N.J.: **Saving Britain's Art Treasures**. *Leo Cooper*, 2003. Storage of art treasures in tube tunnels.

McCamley, N.J.: **Secret Underground Cities**. *Leo Cooper*, 1998. Subterranean storage and factory sites in the West of England, mentioning diversion of escalators from London tube stations.

McLachlan, Donald: **Room 39 – Naval Intelligence in Action 1939–45.** *Weidenfeld & Nicholson*, 1968. Contains several references to life in the Admiralty Citadel.

Marks, Leo: **Between Silk And Cyanide – A Codemaker's War, 1941–1945.** *HarperCollins*, 1998. Graphic memoir of his experiences as head of communications at the Special Operations Executive (SOE), with mention at the end of the book of the Curzon Street House bunker.

Menear, Laurence: **London's Underground Stations – A Social and Architectural Study.** 1983, *Midas Books*. Comprehensive survey of station architecture.

Messrs. Tecton, Architects: **Planned A.R.P.** *Architectural Press*, 1939. Practical study of air attack protection and policy based on the experience of the Metropolitan Borough of Finsbury.

Report of the Chief Medical Officer of the Ministry of Health on the State of the Public Health during six years of war. 1946, *His Majesty's Stationery Office*. Section on New Tube Shelters.

Ministry of Home Security Deep Tunnel Air Raid Shelters, in *The Engineer*, 27th November and 4th and 11th December 1942, also reproduced as an offprint in a single brochure. Detailed technical description of the construction and specification of the shelters.

No author given: **Improving London's Transport.** *Railway Gazette*, 1946. Comprehensive survey of the New Works Plan constructions.

No author given: **Lloyd's Under Fire.** *Lloyd's of London*, 1945. Covers civil defence work in deep shelters with photographs of the Goodge Street shelter in use.

Nock, O.S.: **Britain's Railways At War.** *Ian Allan*, 1971.

O'Brien, T.H.: **History of the Second World War: Civil Defence.** *HMSO*, 1955.

Pawley, Edward: **BBC Engineering 1922–1972.** *BBC Publications*, 1972. Contains further information on the Broadcasting House

'Stronghold' and video for gunnery control.

Pennick, Nigel: **Bunkers Under London,** *Valknut Productions*, 1988. Easily the most comprehensive study of London's bunkers but not without elements of speculation.

Pennick, Nigel: **Tunnels Under London,** *Electric Traction Publications*, 1981. Covers London's bunkers and citadels to a degree.

Ramsey, Winston G.: **The Blitz Then and Now, volume 2.** *After The Battle*, 1988. Detailed material on Paddock, also general coverage of shelter policy in London.

Ramsey, Winston G.: **East End Then and Now, volume 3.** *After The Battle*, 1998. Detailed material on the Bethnal Green disaster and the Plessey factory, also general coverage of deep shelters in London and bunkers in Berlin.

Reckitt, D.N.: **Diary of Anti-Aircraft Defence 1938–1944.** *Arthur H. Stockwell Ltd*, 1990. Recollections of Brompton Road AAOR.

Reekie, Douglas: **These Were The Nerves – The story of the electric cable and wire industry of Great Britain during the years of war.** *Insulated Conductors Export Group*, no date but circa 1946.

Ritchie, Berry: **Into the Sunrise.** *James & James*, 1989. History of the Plessey company.

Simkins, Peter: **Cabinet War Rooms.** *Imperial War Museum*, 1983. Comprehensive description of the accommodation and its entire pre-history.

Smith, Michael: **Station X: The Codebreakers of Bletchley Park.** *Channel 4 Books*, 1998. Companion book to the television series on wartime codebreaking. Mentions MI8 at Devonshire House.

Stafford, David: **Spies Beneath Berlin.** *John Murray*, 2002. Covers phone tapping operations under Vienna.

Stanway, L.C.: **Mails Under London.** *Association of Essex Philatelic Societies*, 2000. Covers all aspects of the Post Office Railway.

Stationery Office: **Tragedy at Bethnal Green – Report on an inquiry into the accident at Bethnal Green Tube Station Shelter.** *HMSO*, 1999.

Thomas, S. Evelyn: **Practical Guide to A.R.P.** distributed by *James Askew & Son*, 1939.

Thompson, George Raynor and Harris, Dixie R.: **The Signal Corps, volumes 2 and 3 (United States Army in World War II).** *Office of the Chief of Military History, U.S. Army*, 1966. U.S. Signal Corps operations in Britain.

Trench, R. and Hillman E.: **London Under London.** *John Murray*, 1993. A fascinating and readable book not without some factual inaccuracies.

Valentine, K.J.: **Willesden at War, Volume Two – The Secret Citadels of WW2.** *The Maurice Press*, 1995. The meticulous text is backed up by detailed references to official papers and also details the false trails and cover-ups used (successfully) after the war that have ensured this 'Now It Can Be Told' story has remained largely secret until now.

Warner, Philip: **The Vital Link – The Story of the Royal Signals 1945–1985.** *Leo Cooper*, 1989.

The role of the War Office citadel during the Suez Crisis.

West, Nigel: **GCHQ – The Secret Wireless War 1900–86.** *Weidenfeld and Nicolson,* 1986. The standard work on the subject of official communications interception by the British government.

Wicks, Ben: **Waiting for the All Clear.** *Bloomsbury Publishing,* 1990. Includes deep shelters.

Wood, Robert: **A World In Your Ear.** *Macmillan London Ltd,* 1979. Includes establishment of Group H radio stations.

Wright, Peter: **Spycatcher – The Candid Autobiography of a Senior Intelligence Officer.** *Viking Penguin Inc.,* 1987. Includes use of deep shelter as a counterespionage base.

···

Articles in periodicals

Barron, D.A.: **Post Office Cabling in the Mersey Tunnel.** *POEEJ,* July 1939 (Vol. 32), p.79.

Beaumont, E.B.M. and others: **The Provision of Communications for the Coronation of Her Majesty Queen Elizabeth II.** *POEEJ,* July 1953, pp.71–78.

Boryer, W.F.: **Holborn Cable Tunnel.** *Post Office Magazine,* December 1947.

Boryer, W.F.: **Some Features of Deep Level Tunnelling in London. Part 1 – Driving Bore Tubes and Tunnels.** *POEEJ* January 1947 (Vol.39), p. 146.

Boryer, W.F.: **Some Features of Deep Level Tunnelling in London. Part 2 – Engineering Services.** *POEEJ,* April 1947 (Vol.40), p.14.

Campbell, Duncan: **A Christmas party for the moles.** *New Statesman,* 19th December 1980, pp.4/5; **New Whitehall Bunker.** *New Statesman,* 25th July 1985, p.6; **Bugs in the Basement.** *New Statesman,* 20th June 1986, p.8.

Connor, J.E.: **Looking at Post Office.** *London Railway Record,* October 1999.

Connor, J.E.: **Recalling British Museum.** *London Railway Record,* January 1999.

Darvill, Robert: **Wartime on the Central Line, The Narrow Gauge** *(journal of the Narrow Gauge Railway Society).* Autumn 1986, pp.16/17.

Epps, H.F.: **Safeguarding Telecommunications in Wartime.** *POEEJ,* January 1946 (Vol.38), p.127.

Farrell, F.K.: **A Future for London's Tramways.** *The Modern Tramway,* July 1950, pp.145–148, 157–158.

Graves, Ralph: **A.R.P. at the BBC.** *Radio Pictorial,* 6th May 1938, pp.7, 39.

Groves, G.L.: **Tunnel Linings.** *Journal of the Institution of Civil Engineers,* March 1943, pp.29–64.

Groves, G.L.: **The Ilford Tube.** *Journal of the Institution of Civil Engineers,* March 1946, pp.6–49.

Harbottle, R.H.: **Provision of Line Communications for the Fighting Services during the War.** *IPOEE paper,* 1946.

Harper, R.: **Protection Against Thames Flooding.** *POEEJ,* October 1980 (Vol.73), p.185.

Harper, R.: **Tunnelling into History.** *POEEJ,*

October 1977 (Vol.70), p.199.

Haville, P.J.: **New telephone network for Whitehall area.** *Post Office Telecommunications Journal,* Spring 1970, pp.24–26.

Hollinghurst, F. and Sowton C.: **Resumé of VHF Point-to-Point Communications** in *POEEJ,* volume 94, part IIIA (1947), pp.126/127 (London ring-main radio scheme).

Kynaston, P.: **An Undiscovered World Beneath Our Feet.** *Forum,* the newspaper of the Manchester Civic Society, December 1997.

Lack, Jessica: **The Hush-Hush Catastrophe.** *The Guardian Weekend magazine,* 15th February 2002, pp.34–41 (Bethnal Green disaster).

Lamb, W.H.: **Underground at Oxford Circus.** *Post Office Telecommunications Journal,* Spring 1967, p.42.

Lamb, W.H.: **The London Cable-Tube System.** *POEEJ,* April 1970 (Vol.63), p. 14. Also produced as an IPOEEJ printed paper, with greater detail and a plan of the tunnels.

Lamb, W.H.: **London's Telephone Cable Tunnels.** *Electrical Review,* 2nd July 1971, p.18.

Lomas, Del: **Deep Level Underground 'Tube' Shelters.** *Underground News,* May 1979, pp.95–99.

McGregor, J.E.: **War Office Pneumatic Tube Centre,** *POEEJ,* April 1926, pp.4–16.

No author given: **A Rapid-Transit Line for South London.** *The London Passenger,* March 1950, pp.61–64, also published as a separate leaflet.

No author given: **Further Extension of LPTB Central Line.** *Modern Transport,* 13th December 1947, p.11.

No author given: **Proposed High-speed Tube Railways.** *Railway Magazine,* January 1919, pp.56–57.

No author given: **Kearney high-speed railway.** *Railway Magazine,* July 1920, p.68.

No author given: **Kearney Tubes as Air Raid Shelters.** *Railway Gazette,* 14th July 1939.

No author given: **A telephone city under London.** *Courier (PO staff newspaper),* November 1969.

No author given: **Tunnelling Under Manchester.** *Tunnels & Tunnelling,* May 1972, pp.200–201 and September 1974, pp.30–33.

No author given: **Anchor in the news.** *Telecom Today (BT staff newspaper),* March 1983, p.9.

No author given: **This is it – the hush-hush nerve centre.** *Birmingham Evening Mail,* 11th October 1968.

No author given: **No secrets at exchange now – it's obsolete.** *Birmingham Post,* 12th October 1968.

No author given: **Air Raid.** *Picture Post,* 17th August 1940, pp.9–29.

No author given: **Deep-Level Shelters.** *Railway Gazette,* 14th July 1944, pp.29, 40–42, 45.

No author given: **The air raid warning system.** *Practical Mechanics,* November 1941, pp.36–37.

No author given: **New London recording studio.** *Practical Mechanics,* September 1937, pp.683–684.

No author given: **Troglodytes of 1944: Some**

aspects of Life in London's deep shelters. *Illustrated London News*, 29th July 1944, p.133.

No author given: **Underground control rooms**. *Railway Gazette*, 18th October 1940, p.414 and 21st March 1941, p.330, also **Deepdene** 22nd June 1945.

No author given: **The Story of Deepdene**. *Southern Railway Magazine*, February 1940, pp.40–43, also **The Control in the Caves**. July 1945, p.105.

No author given: **Broadcasting House extension** articles in *Wireless World*, 13th January 1938, p.39 and *Practical and Amateur Wireless*, 24th December 1938, p.385.

No author given: **Plessey tunnel factory**. *Railway Gazette*, 1st March 1946, pp.210 and 226; *London Transport Magazine*, December 1947, p.6.

No author given: **Horseferry Road Citadel** and details of engineering services, *The Times*, 4th January 1948.

No author given: **Plessey's Underground Factory**. *Underground News*, November 2003, pp.496–506.

No author given: **Paddock London Bunker, Caves and Tunnels in South East England, Part 15**, *Chelsea Spelaeological Society Records*, Volume 27, 2001, pp.27–31. Description and floor plans.

Partridge, F.V. and Grant, C.G.: **London Trunk Kingsway Exchange**. *POEEJ*, July 1955 (Vol.48), p.87.

Pendegrass, J.J.: **Keybridge House Tunnel**. *POEEJ*, April 1978 (Vol.71), p.34.

Prescott, J.: **The New St Paul's Tube Station**. *POEEJ*, January 1939 (Vol.31), p.301.

Ramsey, Winston G.: **The Secret Underground Railway Executive H.Q.** *After The Battle*, issue 12, 1976.

Special correspondent: **Railway Control Secrets – Safe Quarters for Mr Churchill**. *The Times*, 15th January 1946.

Tomlinson, Martin: **Whitehall At War**. *Nexus* (*student magazine of the Polytechnic of Central London*), Spring 1977.

Turley, T.G.: **Cabling Problems in Subways and Tunnels**. *IPOEE* Printed Paper No.187, 1945.

Various authors: **The London Sector Plan**. *POEEJ*, reprint of articles in April 1974 issue.

Various authors: **Trunk Transit Switching**. *POEEJ*, reprint of articles in October 1967 issue.

Ward, W.C.: **Holes in the Ground**. *IPOEE* Printed Paper No.223, 1963.

Williams, Clifford: **Supreme Headquarters for D-Day**. *After The Battle*, issue 84.

Wilson, Geoffrey: **Brompton's Railways**. *London Railway Record*, April 1999.

Winkworth, D.W.: **War Report – Wireless in Railway Operation**. *British Railways Illustrated*, April 1999, pp.298–302.

IPOEE is the Institution of Post Office Electrical Engineers and **POEEJ** is the *Post Office Electrical Engineers' Journal*.

Underground News is the bulletin of the London Underground Railway Society.

Other documentary sources

BBC: Studio & Equipment Committee minutes 1942–46 (Munroe Archive, by courtesy of Michael Bennett-Levy).

BT: The Telecomms Contribution to Winning the War (British Telecom D-Day travelling exhibition, 1994).

London Transport Archives, London:
A110/001, 002, 005, 006.
A111/005, 007, 009.
A115/005.
LT12/389/02.
LT234/21 – 401/2A.

London's Transport Museum, London:

A Factory in a Railway Tunnel (draft article for the technical press, September 1945).

A Short History of the Plessey Tunnel Factory 1941–42 (no date).

Report on maximum capacity of train services, New York and London (July 1936).

National Archives (Public Record Office), Kew:

Admiralty – ADM 1/26961.

Air Ministry – AIR 2/9856.

Atomic Weapons Research Establishment – ES 3/57.

Board and Ministry of Works – WORK 12/455; 20/144; 28/37; 28/40; 28/58; 28/60; 28/61; 1281/45.

British Transport Commission and British Railways Board – AN 2/729 section 1081; 13/164; 207/354.

Cabinet Office – CAB 21/773; 21/1066.

Metropolitan Police – MEPO 2/6354; 2/8406.

Ministry of Health – MH 76/577.

Ministry of Housing & Local Government – HLG 126/273.

Home Office and Ministry of Home Security – HO 45/25470; 186/1668; 186/1763; 197/34; 197/46; 197/47; 197/49; 197/48; 199/114; 200/8; 200/9; 205/124; 205/190; 205/191; 205/192; 205/194; 205/195; 205/196; 205/201; 205/202; 205/208; 205/209; 205/226; 205/253; 205/269; 205/284; 205/306; 205/319; 205/364; 206/6; 206/9; 206/15; 207/153; 207/450; 207/451; 207/625; 207/653; 207/656; 207/664; 207/721; 207/731; 207/997; 251/92; 338/37; 338/53; 338/116.

Land Registry – LAR 1/348.

Public Record Office – PRO 1/844; 1/11734; 8/64.

Transport departments – MT 6/2728; 6/2489/11; 114/79; 124/11; 124/12.

Treasury – T 219/866; 867; 219/868; 229/878.

Treasury Solicitor – TS 27/494.

War Office – WO 32/19655; 106/59 11–5919; 199/1034; 205/7; 216/756.

Natural History Museum, Kensington:

Demolition of the War Room – DF 1004/CP/274.

Construction of East Wing for the Department of Palaeontology – DF 1004/143.

(U.S.) Historical Manuscripts Collection:
File 8–3.6A CA.

Selected Internet resources

Many of these websites have superb photographs or valuable text files. Other references can be found using a good Internet search engine.

Belsize Park shelter:
http://fp.coldwar.f9.co.uk/belsize_park.htm

Birmingham Anchor telephone exchange
http://www.subbrit.org.uk/rsg/sites/b/birmingham_anchor_exchange/index.html
http://www.birminghamanchor.co.uk/
http://www.angelfire.com/mac/anchor/index2.html

BBC Broadcasting House:
http://www.miketodd.net/other/bhhistory/index.htm
http://www.roger.beckwith.btinternet.co.uk/bh/bh32/bh32_i.htm

BBC 200 Oxford Street:
http://www.roger.beckwith.btinternet.co.uk/bh/oxfordt/oxfordst.htm

British Museum station: http://www.pendar.macunlimited.net/BritishMuseum.html

Brompton Road station: http://www.subbrit.org.uk/rsg/sites/b/brompton_road/

Cabinet War Rooms:
http://www.iwm.org.uk/cabinet/index.htm
http://www.number-10.gov.uk/

Civil Defence War Room (Exhibition Road)
http://www.subbrit.org.uk/sb-sites/sites/l/london_war_room/index.shtml

COSSAC:
http://www.army.mil/cmh-pg/documents/cossac/cossac.htm

Deep shelters (with link also to bunkers in Berlin):
http://freespace.virgin.net/roy.smith5/deepshelters.htm

Deepdene underground control office
http://www.swanleyl.freeserve.co.uk/military/deepdene.htm

Down Street station:
http://www.starfury.demon.co.uk/uground/downst.html
http://www.geocities.com/losborne.geo/disused/downst.html
http://www.geocities.com/CapeCanaveral/Launchpad/4375/downframe.htm
also
http://www.ltmuseum.co.uk/
and follow link to online tours

Duncan Campbell's unofficial 'Mole Tour' tunnel trip:
http://www.iptvreports.mcmail.com/Tunneltrip.htm

Duke of York's Steps
http://www.subbrit.org.uk/sb-sites/sites/d/duke_yorks_steps/index.shtml

Hidden Bunkers of the Second World War:
http://www.thehistorychannel.co.uk/local/cabinet4.htm

Kingsway exchange:
http://www.subbrit.org.uk/rsg/sites/k/kingsway/

Manchester and Salford deep-level tunnels, Guardian exchange:
http://www.cybertrn.demon.co.uk/guardian/

Paddock:
http://freespace.virgin.net/roy.smith5/paddock.htm

Rotundas:
http://www.subbrit.org.uk/sb-sites/sites/r/rotundas/index24.shtml

Shelters in general:
http://www.holnet.org.uk/learningzone/londonatwar

Sigsaly:
http://www.nsa.gov/wwii/papers/sigsaly.htm

South Kensington civil defence bunker:
http://www.subbrit.org.uk/sb-sites/sites/l/london_war_room/index.shtml

Updates to this book will be posted at
http://www.subbrit.org.uk/LST/

Societies and visits

A few of the sites mentioned in this book – such as the Cabinet War Rooms and King Henry VIII's Wine Cellar – are open to the public. Some others, such as Paddock, can be visited by organised parties or on annual 'open house' days. A few, such as Down Street station and Kingsway telephone exchange, are now completely off-limits for safety or security reasons. Attempting to gain unauthorised access is trespass. Often it is very dangerous too; on at least one of these sites a person has fallen to his death in the process. Anyone attempting to enter a secure site, even an apparently disused one, should expect an unpleasant encounter with its custodians, who may be the military police. It is unwise to pester site owners to gain access; this causes irritation to many of them and makes the work of recognised societies more difficult. A far better idea is joining one of those listed here that arranges organised visits.

Formed in 1974, **Subterranea Britannica** (**Sub Brit**) is a society devoted to the study and investigation of man-made and man-used underground places. A sub-group, called the Research Study Group or RSG, is devoted specifically to the study of structures related to the Cold War period. Membership benefits include publications, conferences and field trips to visit interesting underground sites. Send SAE for further information, to Nick Catford, Membership Secretary, 13 Highcroft Cottage, London Road, Swanley, BR8 8DB or visit the website at
http://www.subbrit.org.uk.

The **Greater London Industrial Archaeology Society** has for several decades carried out the recording of industrial buildings and structures along with a programme of visits, winter lectures and summer walks. Publications include the journal *London's Industrial Archaeology*. Membership details can be had from Sue Hayton, 31 The High Street, Farnborough Village, Orpington, BR6 7BQ.

Founded in 1961, the **London Underground Railway Society** exists to study all aspects of London's underground railways – past, present and future, including the Post Office Railway, the Docklands Light Railway, relevant sections of the national rail network and some long forgotten and bizarre ones in addition to the main system. Visits are organised periodically to places of interest including some less well-known parts of the undertaking. Membership details from LURS, Flat 13, 13 Tavistock Place, London, WC1H 9SH; website at
http://www.lurs.demon.co.uk.

Index

The primary reference is given first.
Entries in italics indicate illustrations.

Tailpiece

London's underground air raid shelters aimed to protect one per cent of people at risk. In Germany a far more elaborate construction programme set out to provide shelter for five per cent of the population in 70 cities, using elaborate above-ground structures of massive proportions. Measured against London's provision, they were both luxurious internally and elegant externally. Many still survive, such as this one in the westerly city of Aachen.